Reading STREET

Grade 5

Pearson Scott Foresman

California Comprehensive Practice Book

PEARSON

Glenview, Illinois • Boston, Massachusetts • Chandler, Arizona • Upper Saddle River, New Jersey

ISBN-13: 978-0-328-64179-6
ISBN-10:   0-328-64179-0
13 14 15 V001 17 16 15 14

Contents

Section 1

California Practice and Review Book

Contents

Contents

Family Times

Summary

Red Kayak

On a cold spring day, 13-year-old Brady Parks helps search for two people who are missing after they went for a canoe ride in a creek near the Corsica River. Brady takes his dog, Tilly, in his father's motorboat to search for the mother and her three-year-old boy. He needs to stay calm and remember what he learned about rescuing people. Lives may depend on him.

Activity

Survival Guide Brady was nervous about rescuing Ben, but he was effective. He knew ahead of time what had to be done. With a family member, prepare for how you should handle different types of emergencies that could happen. Write down these plans in a booklet made out of two or more pieces of paper folded in half.

Family Survival Guide

bottled water
canned food
flashlight
batteries
blankets
radio

Comprehension Skill

Plot and Character

The **plot** is what happens in a story. **Characters** are the people or animals in a story. Characters show you what they are like by what they say and do and how they treat each other.

Activity

Family Stories Make up an adventure story involving yourself or someone you know and tell it to a member of your family. Try to make the story full of action, and make sure to describe the main character with details you know about the person in real life.

Lesson Vocabulary

Words to Know

Knowing the meanings of these words is important to reading *Red Kayak*. Practice using these words.

Vocabulary Words

intentionally on purpose

insistently repeatedly or with persistence

grumbled complained in a low voice

compressions applications of pressure

minute extremely small

neutral a position of gears in which no motion goes from an engine to other working parts

normally usually

Conventions

Four Kinds of Sentences

Sentences can be classified in four different ways. **Declarative** sentences tell something and end with a period. *For example: I forgot to eat breakfast this morning.* **Interrogative** sentences ask something and end in a question mark. *For example: Would you like something to eat?* **Imperative** sentences give a command or make a request and end with a period. *For example: Sit down.* **Exclamatory** sentences express strong feelings and often end with an exclamation mark. *For example: I'm starving!*

Activity

What Did You Say? With a family member, cut up eight strips of paper. Write *I say* on two strips, *I ask* on two strips, *I command* on two strips, and *I believe* on two strips. Put the strips in a hat, and pick one out of the hat. Make up a sentence that goes with the words on the strip of paper you picked. Say it out loud. Take turns picking out strips one at a time. Your sentences can be as funny or as silly as you like.

Practice Tested Spelling Words

_____   _____   _____   _____

_____   _____   _____   _____

_____   _____   _____   _____

_____   _____   _____   _____

_____   _____   _____   _____

Plot and Character

- The **plot** is the pattern of events in a story.
- The person or animal who most affects a story's plot is the **main character.**
- A plot includes (1) a problem or **conflict** the **main character** will experience, (2) **rising action** as the conflict builds, (3) a **climax,** when the main character faces the conflict, and (4) **a resolution,** when the problem or conflict is solved.

Directions Read the following passage. Then complete the diagram by filling in the elements of the story.

Rafael was doing chores in the barn when his radio stopped. He walked into his house and discovered the lights wouldn't turn on. The power was out! Rafael knew all the milk in the refrigerator would spoil if it stayed warm too long. His family's dairy farm couldn't afford to lose that milk.

Then he remembered how his father kept soft drinks cold when they went fishing. Rafael carried 23 gallons of milk to the edge of the stream and placed them in the shallow water almost up to their caps. He knew the cool water would keep the milk chilled until the power came back on.

Main Character
1. _____

⬇

Rising Action
2. _____

⬇

Problem or Conflict
3. _____

⬇

Climax
4. _____

⬇

Resolution
5. _____

Home Activity Your child analyzed the plot of a short passage. Discuss a story with your child identifying characters, the problem or conflict, rising action, and resolution.

R3.3 Contrast the actions, motives (e.g., loyalty, selfishness, conscientiousness), and appearances of characters in a work of fiction and discuss the importance of the contrasts to the plot or theme.

Comprehension 3

Vocabulary

Directions Choose the word from the box that best matches each definition. Write the word on the line shown to the left.

_____ 1. in a way that demands attention

_____ 2. muttered unhappily

_____ 3. extremely small

_____ 4. pushes or presses against something

_____ 5. regularly or usually the case

Directions Choose the word from the box that best completes the sentences below. Write the word on the line shown to the left.

_____ 6. Since the car was in ____, it didn't move when she pressed the gas pedal.

_____ 7. I didn't hurt her feelings ____, but my words were careless.

_____ 8. The workers ____ when the boss told them they had to work faster.

_____ 9. The child tugged at my dress ____, wanting another cookie.

_____ 10. The rescue worker applied fifteen ____ to the man's chest, then breathed into his mouth twice.

Write a Letter of Complaint

Pretend that you have returned from a store where you had a terrible experience. The clerks were so rude that you may never shop there again! On a separate piece of paper, write a letter to the store's manager describing the event. Use as many vocabulary words from this week as you can.

Home Activity Your child identified and used words from the story *The Red Kayak*. Review the definitions of each of the vocabulary words with your child and work together to use the words in sentences.

R1.0 Word Analysis, Fluency, and Systematic Vocabulary Development

Vocabulary · Homographs

- A **homograph** is a word that is spelled the same as one or more other words, has different meanings, and may have a different pronunciation.

- Pairs or groups of homographs often come from different parts of speech.

- When you look up a homograph in a dictionary, read each definition presented. The first definition listed may not be the meaning that matches the way the word is used in the sentence.

bow[1] (bou), *v.* to bend the head in greeting, respect, agreement, or obedience
bow[2] (bō), *n.* a knot made with two or more loops

close[1] (klōz), *v.* to shut
close[2] (klōs), *adj.* without much space between

lead[1] (led), *n.* a soft, bluish-white heavy metallic element
lead[2] (lēd), *adj.* most important

minute[1] (min´it), *n.* the 60th part of an hour of time
minute[2] (mī nüt´), *adj.* very small

present[1] (priz nt´), *v.* to bring before the public
present[2] (prez´nt), *n.* a gift

rose[1] (rōz), *v.* past tense of *rise*
rose[2] (rōz), *n.* a usually prickly, sometimes climbing shrub with colorful flowers

Directions Complete the following sentences using words from the list of homographs above.

1. Practicing for the school play was a lot of work. Our drama club was going to

   _____ the tragedy *Romeo and Juliet* by William Shakespeare.

2. I didn't have the _____ role, but I was nervous!

3. My best friend, Emma, had the part of Juliet. When the show ended, the audience stood and

   applauded for at least a full _____.

4. When Emma took her _____, someone even threw a _____ on
   the stage!

5. We waited for the curtain to _____, and then we went backstage to remove our
   makeup. The play was a success.

R1.3 Understand and explain frequently used synonyms, antonyms, and homographs.

Vocabulary 5

Cause and Effect

Directions Read the following passage. Then answer the questions below.

Jill asked Andy to hold her art project while she ran back to her locker to get an assignment. Andy waited patiently by the door, holding Jill's handmade pottery bowl in both hands. It was really quite pretty, he thought. After about 10 minutes, Andy began to wonder where Jill was. He needed to get home—his family was going out for pizza that night. Andy decided to go back into the school and find Jill.

As he reached out to unlatch the door, it came blasting open, knocking right into Jill's bowl and sending it toward the ground. Andy quickly dove to the cement and caught the bowl.

Andy stood up. He could see a small chip in the lip of the bowl. Jill was standing at the door, her mouth wide open.

"Sorry," he said.

"Sorry?" said Jill. "That was amazing! Thank you for catching it!"

1. Why did Jill ask Andy to hold her pottery bowl?

_____

_____

2. Why did Andy decide to go back into the school?

_____

_____

3. What happened when Andy got to the door?

_____

_____

4. Why do you think Jill was running to the door?

_____

_____

5. What do you think might have happened if Andy had not caught the bowl? Write your answer on a separate sheet of paper.

© Pearson Education, Inc., 5

School + Home **Home Activity** Your child has read a fictional scene and answered questions about cause and effect. Read a story with your child and discuss examples of cause and effect in the story.

G4R2.1 Identify structural patterns found in informational text (e.g., compare and contrast, cause and effect, sequential or chronological order, proposition and support) to strengthen comprehension.

Character and Plot

- A **character** is a person or animal that takes part in the events of a story.
- The **plot** is the pattern of events in a story and includes (1) a problem or **conflict,** (2) **rising action,** as the conflict builds, (3) a **climax,** when the problem or conflict is faced, and (4) a **resolution,** when the problem or conflict is solved.

Directions Read the following passage. Then answer the questions below.

Larry was excited about lunch. For the first time, he had made his own triple-decker sandwich, just the way he liked it. Plus, his mom had added one of his favorite snacks to the bag. Usually Larry just gobbled up his sandwich at lunch and ran out to the playground. But not today—he was going to take his time.

When the lunch bell rang, he grabbed his bag and rushed to the cafeteria. He was so excited he didn't see the backpack someone had left on the floor. SPLAT! Larry tumbled to the floor, landing flat on his lunch bag. When he took his prized sandwich out, it was flat. But Larry didn't mind—he knew it would still be delicious!

1. Why was Larry excited about lunch?

_____

2. How do you think Larry felt about making his own sandwich?

_____

3. Why was Larry in such a hurry to get to the cafeteria?

_____

_____

4. What about Larry's character makes you think Larry didn't mind what happened to his sandwich?

_____

_____

5. On a separate sheet of paper, describe something that you did for yourself for the first time. How was that experience similar to Larry's?

Home Activity Your child analyzed character elements in a passage and answered questions about them. Tell your child a few things that have happened to you recently. Have your child explain how you probably felt about these events.

G4R3.3 Use knowledge of the situation and setting and of a character's traits and motivations to determine the causes for that character's actions.

Comprehension 7

Character and Plot

- A **character** is a person or animal in a story.
- The **plot** is the pattern of events in a story.

Directions Read the following passage. Then complete the diagram by filling in the elements of the story.

Becky sat in front of me in class, and I knew she was cheating. I wanted her to stop. When we passed our homework to the front, she'd quickly copy mine and turn in her paper like it was her work. I knew I should tell the teacher, but I was afraid of being called a snitch. Finally, I got an idea. One night, I wrote two copies of my homework. One version had the correct answers. The other had answers that sounded good, but were wrong.

The next day, I gave my real homework to my friend, Taka, in the front row. "When the homework passes to you, switch mine with this copy," I said. Taka knew about Becky. "Sure, Audrey!" he agreed. The teacher corrected our homework and returned it at the end of class. "Becky," he asked, handing back "her" homework, "were you asleep when you did this work?" Becky stared at the big "zero" at the top of her page in disbelief. She never copied my homework again.

Characters in the Story

1. _____

Problem or Conflict

2. _____

Rising Action

3. _____

Climax

4. _____

Resolution

5. _____

 School + Home

Home Activity Your child identified characters and plot details in a short passage. Discuss the plot of a favorite book or movie with your child, analyzing how its events lead toward the resolution of the problem or conflict established in the beginning of the story

R3.3 Contrast the actions, motives (e.g., loyalty, selfishness, conscientiousness), and appearances of characters in a work of fiction and discuss the importance of the contrasts to the plot or theme.

Dictionary/Glossary

- A **dictionary** lists words in alphabetical order and gives their meanings, pronunciations, and other helpful information.
- A **glossary** is a list of important words and their meanings that are used in a book. Glossaries are located at the back of a book.
- When you see an unfamiliar word, and context clues do not help you figure out its meaning, you can use a dictionary or glossary to learn what it means.

Directions Read the dictionary and glossary entries.

Dictionary Entry

rep•u•ta•tion (rep' ye ta' shen) **1.** *n.* what people think and say the character of someone or something is; character in the opinion of others; name; repute: *This store has an excellent reputation for fair dealing.* **2.** good name; good reputation: *Cheating ruined his reputation.* **3.** fame: *an international reputation.*

Glossary Entry

Ice Age *n.* a cold period in which huge ice sheets spread outward from the polar regions, the last one of which lasted from about 1,600,000 to 10,000 B.C. (p. 107)

W1.3 Use organizational features of printed text (e.g., citations, end notes, bibliographic references) to locate relevant information.

Research and Study Skills 9

Directions Answer the questions below.

1. In the dictionary entry, what does the initial bold entry for the word *reputation* tell you?

_____

2. In the dictionary entry, what does the representation of the word in parentheses tell you?

_____

3. Why do you think the dictionary provides sentence examples in the definition of the word?

_____

4. How many definitions does this dictionary list for *reputation*? Which is the most commonly used definition?

_____

5. What does the italicized *n.* stand for in both entries?

_____

6. What two things do you notice are missing from a glossary entry that you find in the dictionary entry?

_____

7. What is the page number listed at the end of the glossary entry for?

_____

8. What information do you get in both a dictionary and glossary entry?

_____

9. If you were reading a book about life in the desert, would you expect to find *Ice Age* in the glossary? Why or why not?

_____

_____

10. If you were reading a story and came across a word you did not know, where would be the first place you would look for a definition—a glossary or a dictionary?

_____

_____

Home Activity Your child learned how to use a dictionary and a glossary. Make a list of all the possible times you might use a dictionary or glossary.

W1.3 Use organizational features of printed text (e.g., citations, end notes, bibliographic references) to locate relevant information.

Family Times

Summary

Thunder Rose

Thunder Rose is an amazing girl! As a baby she drank milk straight from the cow. Rose constructed a building of iron and wood at age nine, and she could rustle a wild steer with her own hands by twelve. Once, Rose calmed two churning tornadoes with the song her parents sang for her as a baby. All in a day's work for the girl with thunder in her veins.

Activity

The Taller the Better Tall tales use exaggeration to tell the story of impossible events, often because of some superhuman ability of a character. With a family member, make up your own tall tale about someone in your family. Don't hold back—the taller, the better.

Comprehension Skill

Cause and Effect

A **cause** is what makes something happen. An **effect** is what happens as a result of the cause. An effect may have one or more causes. Sometimes authors will use words such as *because* and *so* to show cause and effect.

Activity

The Why of the What Read a story with a family member. After any major event occurs, pause and identify why the event happened. There may be one thing that caused it, or there may be two or more causes.

Lesson Vocabulary

Words to Know

Knowing the meanings of these words is important to reading *Thunder Rose*. Practice using these words.

Vocabulary Words

branded marked by burning the skin with a hot iron

constructed fitted together; built

daintily with delicate beauty; freshly and prettily

devastation waste; destruction

lullaby song for singing to a child

pitch thick, black, sticky substance made from tar or turpentine

resourceful good at thinking of ways to do things

thieving stealing

veins blood vessels that carry blood to the heart from all parts of the body

Grammar

Subjects and Predicates

A complete sentence must have a **subject** and a **predicate.** The subject is the word or group of words that tells whom or what the sentence is about. The predicate is the word or group of words that tell something about the subject. *For example: Michael is supposed to go to bed.* "Michael" is the *subject* and "is supposed to go to bed" is the *predicate*. If a sentence does not have one of each, it is not a sentence but a **sentence fragment.**

Activity

Sentence Junction With a family member, have one of you write down six numbered subjects on a piece of paper. They could be words like "I," "My dog," etc. Have the other person write down six numbered predicates on a separate sheet of paper. These could be phrases like "stared at my homework," "do silly things," etc. Now take turns rolling two numbers on a number cube. Use each pair of numbers to join subjects and predicates from your lists into new sentences. What kinds of inventive sentences can you come up with together?

Practice Tested Spelling Words

© Pearson Education, Inc., 5

Cause and Effect

- A **cause** is what makes something happen. An **effect** is what happens as a result of the cause.
- If there are no clue words, ask yourself, "What made this event happen? What happened as a result of this event?"
- An effect may become the cause of another effect.

Directions Read the following passage and complete the diagram below.

By the third day of non-stop rain, no one on our street could keep the water out of their homes. The homes that had basements were hit hardest. Basements were flooded in spite of efforts to pump the water out. Toys, washing machines, and furniture in basements were soaked through completely.

Our neighbor, Mrs. Chan, was so sad because all her photographs of her grandchildren had been in her basement. Her granddaughter May was my best friend, and I had May's school picture in my wallet. I wrapped it in a plastic bag, put on my raincoat, and ran to Mrs. Chan's house. Just as I handed Mrs. Chan May's picture, a ray of sun peeked out from behind a cloud.

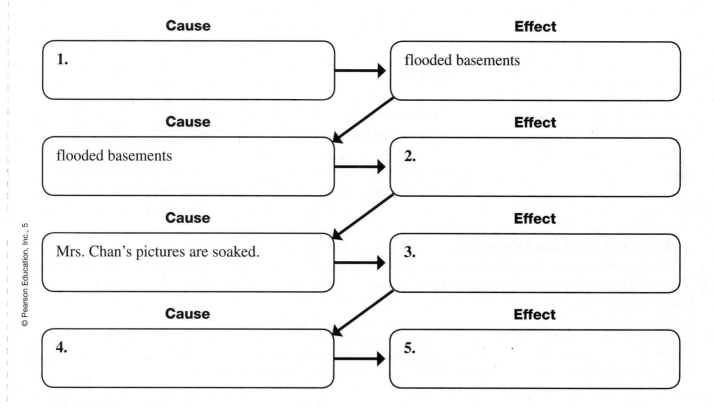

Cause

1.

Effect

flooded basements

Cause

flooded basements

Effect

2.

Cause

Mrs. Chan's pictures are soaked.

Effect

3.

Cause

4.

Effect

5.

Home Activity Your child identified causes and effects in a short passage. While working around the house, have your child explain to you the effects of one of the chores. Then ask your child to figure out if the effect becomes the cause of another effect.

G4R2.2 Use appropriate strategies when reading for different purposes (e.g., full comprehension, location of information, personal enjoyment).

Comprehension 13

Vocabulary

Directions Choose the word from the box that best matches each definition. Write the word on the line.

_____ 1. blood vessels that carry blood to the heart from all parts of the body

_____ 2. song for singing to a child

_____ 3. stealing

_____ 4. a thick, black, sticky substance made from tar or turpentine

_____ 5. fitted together; built

Check the Words You Know
____branded
____constructed
____daintily
____devastation
____lullaby
____pitch
____resourceful
____thieving
____veins

Directions Choose the word from the box that best completes the sentences below. Write the word on the line shown to the left.

_____ 6. The rancher _____ his cattle with the symbol from his ranch so nobody else could claim them.

_____ 7. The cracks in the roof were sealed with _____ .

_____ 8. Grandma and Grandpa danced _____ in time with the music's gentle beat.

_____ 9. When no one else could think of how to solve the school's litter problem, Marisa impressed the principal with her_____ idea.

_____ 10. The tornado caused a lot of _____ when it whipped through town and ripped several homes from their foundations.

Write a Friendly Letter

On a separate sheet of paper, write a friendly letter to someone living out of town about an event that happened where you live. Use as many vocabulary words as you can.

© Pearson Education, Inc., 5

School + Home **Home Activity** Your child identified and used vocabulary words from *Thunder Rose*. Work with your child to learn the words and their definitions. Have your child create colorful flash cards to do so.

R1.0 Word Analysis, Fluency, and Systematic Vocabulary Development

Vocabulary • Multiple-Meaning Words

- **Multiple-meaning words** are words that are spelled the same but have different meanings. These words may be used in ways that are unfamiliar.
- **Context clues,** words and phrases near the multiple-meaning word, may help identify what the word means in a particular context, or situation.

Directions Read the following passage about a hurricane. Then answer the questions below. Look for multiple-meaning words as you read.

As Pedro scaled the ladder to the roof, he felt the blood in his veins pumping through his body. He was the first person to get a look at the destruction the hurricane had created. He looked at the roof and reminded himself to bring up a bucket of pitch next time to repair the new cracks. Looking out over the countryside, he saw that many buildings would need to be constructed again. He started gathering broken branches to pitch down to the ground below. Then he paused and took a deep breath, thinking about what this disaster had done to his community. He knew that none of his neighbors would have to pitch tents and live in their yards while repairs were made to their homes. The people of his town would help each other find shelter, and everyone would be fine.

1. *Vein* can mean "a blood vessel" or "a crack in a rock filled with a mineral deposit." How is it used in the passage? How can you tell?

_____

2. What does *pitch* mean in the third sentence of this passage? What clues help you understand the meaning used in this sentence?

_____

3. What does *pitch* mean in the fifth sentence of this passage? What clues help you understand the meaning used in this sentence?

_____

4. To *scale* something can mean "to climb up something" or "to measure something." How is it used in this passage? How can you tell?

_____

5. What does *pitch* mean in the second-to-last sentence of this passage? What clues help you understand the meaning used in this sentence?

_____

Home Activity Your child read a short passage and identified multiple-meaning words. With your child, make a list of multiple-meaning words that you use every day. Challenge your child to make up a sentence using each meaning.

G3R1.6 Use sentence and word context to find the meaning of unknown words.

Vocabulary 15

Plot and Character

Directions Read the scene. Then answer the questions below.

Alice was rearranging her collection of glass birds. She'd just added a tiny and fragile glass hummingbird to her collection. Just as she finished, her neighbor Jim stopped by with his dog, a nervous and jumpy cocker spaniel. Jim asked, "Can you feed my dog while I'm away tomorrow?" Before she could answer, the phone rang, and Alice left the room to answer it. As she hung up, a crack of thunder pounded through the air. Alice heard Jim's dog barking frantically and then heard a loud crash! Alice didn't dare imagine what devastation the dog had caused. The veins in her head throbbed as she returned to the living room. She saw Jim looking guilty with his dog hiding behind his legs. Jim looked up at Alice and said, "I hope I didn't startle you. I was going to the recycling center after I left here. I dropped my bag of bottles when I heard the thunder." Alice turned to look at the display case with her glass birds. Every bird was in its place. Alice told Jim, "No problem. It was quite a noise. By the way, I'd be happy to feed your dog."

1. What was Alice doing at the beginning of the story?

_____

2. What did Alice think had happened when she heard the crash?

_____

3. How did the writer describe the dog? How does the description of the dog fit with what Alice thought happened?

_____

_____

4. How are Jim and his dog described when Alice returns to the living room? How does their behavior fit with what Alice thought happened?

_____

_____

5. On a separate sheet of paper, write a version of this story in which Jim's dog breaks Alice's collection of birds. Try to use what you know about Alice, Jim, and the dog from this passage to help you figure out how they will react.

Home Activity Your child has read a short passage and answered questions about the characters and the plot. Tell your child a story about a family member and have them identify the plot and the characters.

G3R3.3 Determine what characters are like by what they say or do and by how the author or illustrator portrays them.

© Pearson Education, Inc., 5

Cause and Effect

- A **cause** is what makes something happen. An **effect** is what happens as a result of the cause.
- If there are no clue words, ask yourself, "What made this event happen? What happened as a result of this event?"
- An effect may become the cause of another effect.

Directions Read the following passage. Then answer the questions below.

> Walking home, Arthur could hardly see where he was going. The fierce wind whipped the snow around. At least a foot of snow covered the sidewalks. His socks, shoes, and pant legs were soaked, and his hands felt like ice. He knew his dad would be home from work when he got there. He just hoped that there would be some warm cocoa and popcorn waiting. Finally, he reached his door. As he hurried inside, he could smell cocoa and popcorn. Arthur changed out of his wet clothes and sat down to enjoy his snack with his dad. But the best part of all was the news on television. Because of the bad storm that Arthur had walked through, there would be no school the next day!

1. Why was Arthur unable to see where he was going?

_____

2. What were some of the effects of the snowstorm in the neighborhood?

_____

3. What was an effect of the snowstorm that pleased Arthur?

_____

_____

4. If you had a day off from school because of bad weather, what would you do with it?

_____

_____

5. What was the cause of the last day you had off from school, other than a weekend?

_____

_____

Home Activity Your child read a short passage and answered questions about cause and effect. With your child, write a short story about a hero. Include what caused the person to act heroically and the effects of his or her heroism.

G6R3.3 Analyze the influence of setting on the problem and its resolution.

Comprehension 17

Cause and Effect

- A **cause** is what makes something happen. An **effect** is what happens as a result of the cause.
- If there are no clue words, ask yourself, "What made this event happen? What happened as a result of this event?"
- An effect may become the cause of another effect.

Directions Read the following passage.

Anna wished she hadn't done it. She didn't even like snowball fights. She was just leaving the library with a novel she couldn't wait to read. A bunch of kids from her school came running up the street, laughing and throwing snowballs at one another. Anna knew one of the girls, Lucy, so when Lucy tossed a snowball at Anna, Anna tossed one back. But who knew that Lucy was going to slip on some ice at that exact moment? The snowball flew right over Lucy's head and squarely into Mr. Anderson's nose. Anna rushed over to apologize. Mr. Anderson was about to say something angry. But when he saw the book Anna was carrying, he started to smile. "Do you know," he said, "when I was your age that was my favorite book. I hope you enjoy it as much as I did."

"I'm sure I will," Anna replied with surprise. "I can't wait to read it!"

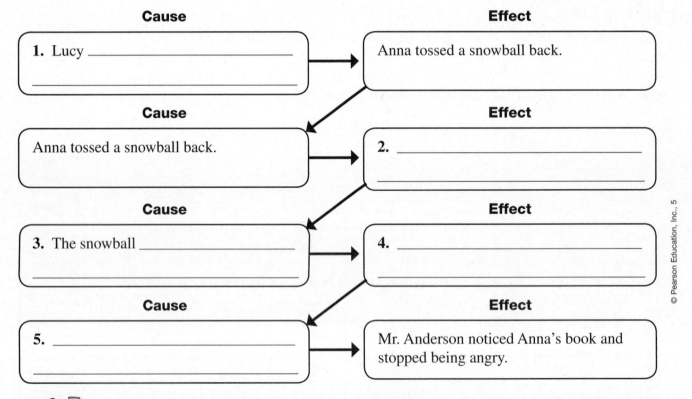

Cause	Effect
1. Lucy _____ _____	Anna tossed a snowball back.

Cause	Effect
Anna tossed a snowball back.	2. _____ _____

Cause	Effect
3. The snowball _____ _____	4. _____ _____

Cause	Effect
5. _____ _____	Mr. Anderson noticed Anna's book and stopped being angry.

 School + Home **Home Activity** Your child read a short passage and identified the causes and effects. Read a short story with your child. Have your child explain to you the effects of one of the story's causes. Then ask your child to figure out if the effect becomes the cause of another effect.

G4R2.2 Use appropriate strategies when reading for different purposes (e.g., full comprehension, location of information, personal enjoyment).

Almanac

An **almanac** is a yearly book that contains calendars, weather information, and dates of holidays. Almanacs also contain charts and tables of current information in subject areas such as populations of cities and nations, and lists of recent prize winners in science, literature, and sports.

Directions Read this almanac entry about the United States Census. Use the information to answer the questions on the next page.

United States Census

Every ten years, the federal government conducts a census, or count, of the number of people who live in the United States. According to the federal Constitution, a census must be completed every ten years to determine the number of representatives each state may send to the U.S. House of Representatives.

The census shows how the populations of cities, regions, and states compare. This data helps government officials decide how and where to spend federal money. Traditionally, a census not only counts the number of citizens, but it also gathers other information, such as:

- the ethnic background of citizens
- the number of adults and children
- the number of employed people and unemployed people
- the income level of citizens and their type of housing

For many decades, the three largest cities have remained New York City, Los Angeles, and Chicago. However, other cities are growing more quickly than any of these three. Many sociologists, economists, and government officials find the growth rates of cities the most interesting information in the census. In recent years, the trend has been for great numbers of people to move from the North to the South—especially to states in the Southwest.

The federal government collects data every year, not just every decade. For instance, the chart below shows data from the 2000 census in one column, but it also includes data collected by the government in 2002. This chart shows the ten fastest growing cities of 100,000 people or more in the United States.

CITY	2000 Population	2002 Population	Numerical Change	Percentage Change
Gilbert, AZ	109,920	135,005	25,085	22.8
North Las Vegas, NV	115,488	135,902	20,414	17.7
Henderson, NV	175,750	206,153	30,403	17.3
Chandler, AZ	176,652	202,016	25,364	14.4
Peoria, AZ	108,685	123,239	14,554	13.4
Irvine, CA	143,072	162,122	19,050	13.3
Rancho Cucamonga, CA	127,743	143,711	15,968	12.5
Chula Vista, CA	173,566	193,919	20,353	11.7
Fontana, CA	128,938	143,607	14,669	11.4
Joliet, IL	106,334	118,423	12,089	11.4

© Pearson Education, Inc. 5

W1.3 Use organizational features of printed text (e.g., citations, end notes, bibliographical references) to locate relevant information.

1. According to the U.S. Constitution, what is the maximum number of years that can pass between federal censuses?

_____

2. What is the purpose of conducting a federal census, according to the U.S. Constitution?

_____

_____

3. In addition to population, what are two examples of other data a census provides?

_____

_____

4. What types of people consult the federal census?

_____

_____

5. What are the three largest cities in the United States?

_____

6. Which state has the most listings among the fastest-growing cities on the 2002 census?

_____

7. Would an almanac be a good place to find information on why nine of ten fastest-growing U.S. cities are located in the Southwest or West? Why or why not?

_____

_____

8. Which city had the highest numerical increase in population between 2000 and 2002?

_____

9. Why is the city with the highest numerical increase in population not listed first in the chart?

_____

_____

10. Between 2000 and 2002, Los Angeles (population 3,503,532) saw a numerical increase in population of 104,239. Why do you think Los Angeles isn't listed on this chart?

_____

_____

Home Activity Your child learned about the contents of almanacs and analyzed data from an almanac. Together, look up information about your town or area of the country in an almanac. Read about population, weather forecast, historical sites, and so on. Discuss how the information in the almanac helps you better understand your own geographical area.

G4W1.8 Understand the organization of almanacs, newspapers, and periodicals and how to use those print materials.

Family Times

Summary

Island of the Blue Dolphins

Karana is an Indian girl stranded alone on an island. While waiting years for a ship to come near and rescue her, she finds inventive ways of living on an island inhabited by wild dogs. She makes a cave house, creates her own tools, finds food, and survives many years on her own.

Activity

Kitchen Foraging With a member of your family, look through your kitchen and try to plan a lunch or dinner for the two of you. But here's the catch: you can't look in the refrigerator, you can only use one utensil, and you're allowed to use only a small amount of water from the sink. *Bon appétit!*

Comprehension Skill

Theme and Setting

The **theme** is the underlying meaning of a story. The **setting** is where and when the story takes place. Setting often helps determine how a story's characters think and behave.

Activity

Far Away Pretend you're stranded on a faraway island with a member of your family. Describe what the island looks like, the animals you encounter, and the trees and plants you see. What's the first thing you would do there: Find food? Build a shelter? Why did you make the choices you made?

Words to Know

Knowing the meanings of these words is important to reading *Island of the Blue Dolphins*. Practice using these words.

Vocabulary Words

gnawed bitten or worn away

headland narrow ridge of high land jutting out into water; promontory

kelp any of various large, tough, brown seaweeds

lair den or resting place of a wild animal

ravine a long, deep, narrow valley eroded by running water

shellfish a water animal with a shell. Oysters, clams, crabs, and lobsters are shellfish.

sinew tendon

Independent and Dependent Clauses

A clause is a group of related words that has a subject and a predicate. If a clause makes sense by itself, it is an **independent clause.** If a clause does not make sense by itself, it is a **dependent clause.** *For example: Tim had a ticket that he bought with his own money.* "Tim had a ticket" is the *independent clause* because it makes sense by itself. However, "that he bought with his own money" is *dependent* because it does not make sense by itself.

Activity

Clause Connection Create a T-chart on a sheet of paper. Cover the right column and have a family member write five independent clauses in it. Now cover the left column and write five dependent clauses. Then uncover the chart and take turns creating new sentences by combining an independent clause from the table with one (or more) dependent clauses.

Practice Tested Spelling Words

_____   _____   _____   _____

_____   _____   _____   _____

_____   _____   _____   _____

_____   _____   _____   _____

Theme and Setting

- The **theme** is the underlying meaning of a story. It is often not stated. You can figure out a theme from events and other evidence in the story.
- The **setting** is where and when the story takes place. Writers use details, such as sights and sounds, to describe it.

Directions Read the following passage. Then complete the diagram with the sights, sounds, smells, or feelings expressed in the passage.

> I love to go to the beach in the summer because a beach can excite the senses. I might hear the roaring waves or the squawk of seagulls. I might feel the gritty warmth of the sand underfoot. Even the mix of odors on the breeze—an airy freshness with a hint of rotting fish—can stay with me long after I've left the water's edge. When I look out toward the vast horizon over the water, I feel as free as the birds darting and diving above my head, and as small as the grains of sand blowing across my toes.

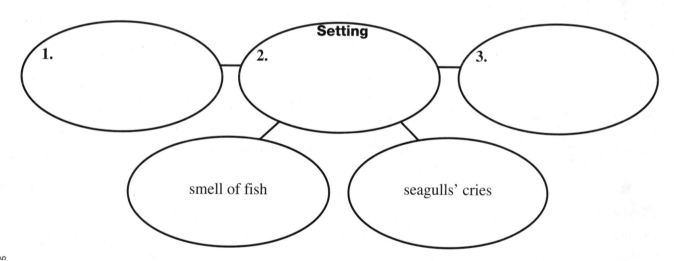

Setting
1.
2.
3.
smell of fish
seagulls' cries

4. What is the theme of the passage?

_____

5. Visualize that you are on a beach. On a separate piece of paper, list a few of the sights, sounds, smells, or feelings you included in your scene.

 School + Home **Home Activity** Your child identified the setting and theme in a fictional passage. Sit with your child in a familiar place and identify its sights, sounds, and smells.

G3R3.4 Determine the underlying theme or author's message in fiction and nonfiction text.

Comprehension 23

Vocabulary

Directions Choose a word from the box that best matches each clue. Write the word on the line.

_____ **1.** This is a good place to build a lighthouse.

_____ **2.** Some call it seaweed, others call it this.

_____ **3.** This could be considered a secret hiding spot.

_____ **4.** This is what the rabbit did to the carrot.

_____ **5.** This works with your muscle to help you move.

Check the Words You Know
___gnawed
___headland
___kelp
___lair
___ravine
___shellfish
___sinew

Directions Choose the word from the box that best completes each sentence. Write the word on the line.

The fox slowly emerged from its **1.** _____. Having **2.** _____ the

last bone from an earlier meal, the fox headed down the hill toward the **3.** _____

in search of more food. While foxes will occasionally eat **4.** _____, they much

prefer the **5.** _____ and muscle of birds or small mammals.

Write a Letter

On a separate sheet of paper, write a letter you might send off in a bottle if you were stranded on an island. Use as many vocabulary words as you can.

Home Activity Your child identified and used vocabulary words from *Island of the Blue Dolphins*. With your child, work together to tell a story incorporating the vocabulary words. Take turns adding sentences to the story until all the words have been used.

R1.0 Word Analysis, Fluency, and Systematic Vocabulary Development

Vocabulary • Synonyms

- Synonyms are words that mean the same or nearly the same as other words.
- Sometimes an author writes a synonym near a difficult word to help readers understand the word. To find synonyms, look for the words *or, such as,* and *like;* or look for a phrase set off by commas.

Directions Read the following passage about food. Then answer the questions below.

British infantry, soldiers in red coats, marched through my village in April of 1777. They didn't come to fight, but to stock up on provisions like supplies of food, gunpowder, and cloth. My family knew the soldiers would take what they wanted without paying us. With most of the grown men gone fighting in the Revolution, we were vulnerable, or quite defenseless against these armed, uniformed bandits.

The soldiers took all our sustenance, such as the food we stored in our pantry and cellar, our chickens for eggs, and our milk cow. Harvest was months away, but we didn't starve. For vegetables, we ate fiddleheads, a type of special fern that is tender and sweet in the spring. We dined on the eggs of wild fowl, early berries, and fish we caught. My family survived the temporary paucity of food until summer arrived.

1. What word in the passage is a synonym for *infantry?* How do you know it is a synonym?

_____

_____

2. What suggests that *provisions* and *supplies* are synonyms?

_____

_____

3. What word in the passage is a synonym for *sustenance?* How do you know it is a synonym?

_____

_____

4. Rewrite the last sentence and give a synonym for the word *paucity.*

_____

_____

_____

Home Activity Your child read a short passage and identified synonyms, different words that mean the same thing. Read a magazine article or a short story with your child and have him or her point out unfamiliar words. Together, look up the words in a dictionary, glossary, or thesaurus.

R1.3 Understand and explain frequently used synonyms, antonyms, and homographs.

Vocabulary 25

Character and Plot

Directions Read the article. Then answer the questions below.

George was lost. He could see the darkening blue sky when he looked up through the dense tree cover. He'd never make it back to base camp in the dark. Darkness was falling fast and the night time sounds of the mountains were growing louder. He knew he'd have to survive out here alone. He had forgotten his emergency kit, too, which only made him angrier at himself. He searched the rocks for a crevice or opening of some kind where he could sleep safely. He had two granola bars in his pack, and he'd been drinking his water sparingly. Every new rustle he heard put him on edge. Bears ruled these mountains, and he didn't want to meet one at night. He found a small opening at the base of a large rock formation. He eased himself into the space slowly, squinting and listening as hard as he could. When he was completely inside, he stood up. Inside the cave, everything seemed quiet and safe.

1. Why does George have to sleep overnight in the mountains?

_____

_____

2. Why is George angry with himself?

_____

3. Why does George look for a safe place to sleep for the night?

_____

4. The night sounds put George on edge. What might he be imagining?

_____

_____

5. On a separate sheet of paper, describe the resolution to George's problem. What do you think will happen next?

 © Pearson Education, Inc., 5

 Home Activity Your child has read a fictional passage and answered questions about the plot and the main character. Have your child summarize this passage to you. Then ask your child to explain how he or she would feel if stuck in the same situation.

R3.2 Identify the main problem or conflict of the plot and explain how it is resolved.

Theme and Setting

- The **theme** is the underlying meaning of a story. It is often not stated. You can figure out a theme from events and other evidence in the story.

- The **setting** is where and when the story takes place. Writers use details, such as sights and sounds, to describe it.

Directions Read the following passage. Then answer the questions below.

Jessica had never seen a real Native American village. Standing in the pueblo, she realized that her books hadn't prepared her for what it would be like. Under the pale spring sunshine, the red clay buildings at the center of the pueblo looked so different than the ones she had read about and seen in books back home. But when she entered one of the shops, it looked very familiar. It had the same kind of display cases, the same food, even the same posters she saw in shops at home.

The lady behind the counter gave Jessica a big smile and said hello. The lady was wearing a t-shirt with the name of the same college Jessica's father attended, the same college Jessica hoped to attend one day. Jessica didn't feel so far away from home anymore.

1. What is the setting of the above passage?

_____

2. Where had Jessica learned about pueblos before her arrival?

_____

3. Why does everything in the store look so familiar to Jessica?

_____

_____

4. What is the underlying theme of this passage?

_____

_____

5. On a separate sheet of paper, write down the visual memories you have of a place you visited for the first time. It could be a new town, someone's home, a new school, etc.

School + Home **Home Activity** Your child answered questions about setting and theme in a fictional passage. Find a family photo that shows a place you have been to and have your child describe the setting in his or her own words. Try to make up a story with your child based on the picture.

G3R3.4 Determine the underlying theme or author's message in fiction and nonfiction text.

Comprehension 27

Theme and Setting

- The **theme** is the underlying meaning of a story. It is often not stated. You can figure out a theme from events and other evidence in the story.
- The **setting** is where and when the story takes place. Writers use details, such as sights and sounds, to describe it.

Directions Read the following passage. Then, complete the graphic below, by filling in the *Setting* circle in the middle, and then writing in some of the sights, sounds, and feelings from the passage.

As a child, living on a tropical island was all Steven knew. He climbed rustling palm trees and ate coconuts. He kept colorful lizards as pets. The sounds of the jungle lulled him to sleep at night. As he got older, he understood how much his parents tried to keep in touch with the world they had left behind. Relatives sent books and magazines from the mainland.

His parents even rigged up an Internet connection using a satellite dish. Visitors often came to the island to learn about his mother's work. Everyone would sit around the rough wooden table and share stories of life back on the mainland. Although he lived far away from the world of airports and subway trains, he understood that another way of life existed.

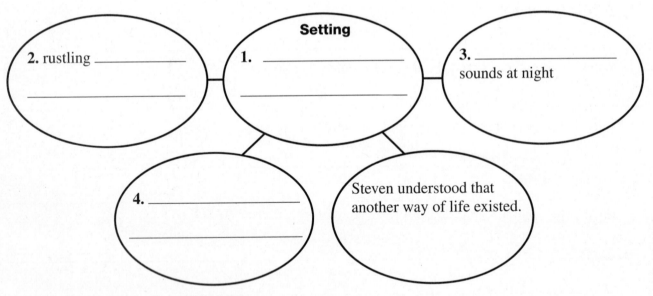

2. rustling _____

Setting

1. _____

3. _____
sounds at night

4. _____

Steven understood that another way of life existed.

5. What is the theme of this passage?

_____

Home Activity Your child identified the setting and theme in a fictional passage. Discuss one of your child's favorite stories with him or her. Have your child describe the story's setting, major characters, and main conflict.

School + Home

© Pearson Education, Inc., 5

G3R3.4 Determine the underlying theme or author's message in fiction and nonfiction text.

SPQ3R

SPQ3R is an acronym for a set of study skills that can help you when you read any text. It is especially helpful when reading nonfiction. Here's what it means: **Survey:** Look at the title, author name, chapter headings, and illustrations to get an idea of what you are about to read. **Predict:** Imagine what the story you're going to read is about. **Question:** Generate questions you want answered when reading the story. **Read:** Read the story, keeping your predictions and questions in mind. **Recite:** Recite or write down what you learned from reading the story. **Review:** Look back at the story, the predictions you made, the questions you posed, the answers you found in the text, and the information you learned from your reading.

Directions Use SPQ3R in reading the passage and answering the questions that follow.

Hawaii: A Remote State

Hawaii is a group of volcanic islands in the central Pacific Ocean some 2,300 miles west of San Francisco, California. Hawaii became the fiftieth state in the United States in 1959. Because of its location in the ocean, it is an important military location of the U.S. Because it is so beautiful, it is also one of the most popular vacation spots for Americans even though the flight to Hawaii is long.

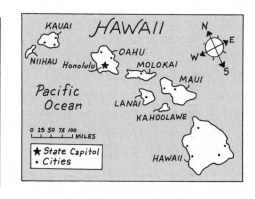

---

1. Before you read this passage, what could you tell about the passage by surveying the map?

_____

2. Before you read this passage, what did you predict the passage would be about?

_____

3. What was a question you wanted the passage to answer before you read it?

_____

4. When did Hawaii become a state? What is one of the things that Hawaii is known for?

_____

5. Write a brief review of what you learned from this passage. In your review, discuss whether your questions were answered and whether your prediction was true.

_____

_____

_____

G4R2.2 Use appropriate strategies when reading for different purposes (e.g., full comprehension, location of information, personal enjoyment).

Research and Study Skills 29

Directions Use SPQ3R in reading the passage and answering the questions that follow.

Assateague Island's Wild Horses

Assateague Island is a 37-mile-long barrier island, a thin strip of land that helps to protect Maryland's shoreline. It has been an outpost for the U.S. Coast Guard for nearly 50 years. But what's most unique about the island is the horses that roam freely on the beaches and marshland. While the origin of the horses is unclear, the popular myth claims the horses jumped from a sinking Spanish ship and swam to reach this island. It is more likely the horses were taken to the island by landowners trying not to pay taxes on livestock, perhaps as long ago as the seventeenth century.

1. Before you read this passage, what could you tell about the passage by surveying the illustration?

_____

2. Before you read this passage, what did you predict the passage would be about?

_____

3. Before you read this passage, what questions did you want the passage to answer?

_____

4. What is most unique about Assateague Island?

_____

5. Write a brief review of what you learned from this passage. In your review, discuss whether your questions were answered and whether your prediction was true.

_____

_____

_____

School + Home **Home Activity** Your child learned about the SPQ3R study skill and applied it to two nonfiction passages. Have your child explain the study skill to you. Then, with your child, apply it to a newspaper or magazine article.

G4R2.2 Use appropriate strategies when reading for different purposes (e.g., full comprehension, location of information, personal enjoyment).

Family Times

Summary

Satchel Paige

Satchel Paige was one of the greatest baseball pitchers that ever lived. Because baseball was segregated, he played in the Negro Leagues. Paige liked traveling the country almost as much as he liked baseball. He could strike out the best hitters with his crazy pitches and long-legged windup. Even when he settled down and started a family, he could not keep away from his first love—baseball.

Activity

Crazy Cards Work with a family member to create baseball-style "trading cards" for members of your family. On one side, draw a picture of a family member that shows a real or imaginary claim to fame—was Grandpa the first person to swim across the Atlantic? Did Aunt Mae eat the most hot dogs in recorded history? On the back, describe your family member and his or her story.

Grandma

Comprehension Skill

Sequence

Sequence is the order that events happen in a story. When you read, think about what comes first, next, and last. Several events can occur at the same time. Words such as *meanwhile* and *during* give clues that two events are happening at the same time.

Activity

Play-by-Play While a member of your family is doing something (cooking, cleaning, playing), try to narrate every action they take as you might hear a sports announcer do it. Try to describe what they do in the exact order they do it.

Lesson Vocabulary

Words to Know

Knowing the meanings of these words is important to reading *Satchel Paige*. Practice using these words.

Vocabulary Words

confidence firm belief in yourself; self-confidence

fastball a pitch thrown at high speed with very little curve

mocking laughing at; making fun of

outfield the three players in the outfield of a baseball field

unique having no like or equal; being the only one of its kind

weakness a weak point; slight fault

windup a swinging movement of the arms while twisting the body just before pitching the ball

Conventions

Compound and Complex Sentences

A **compound sentence** contains two simple sentences joined with a comma and a word such as *and, but*, and *or. For example: I went to the game, but Juan stayed home.* The comma and the word *but* joins two simple sentences into one compound sentence. On the other hand, a **complex sentence** is made up of a simple sentence and another part. The other part has a subject and verb, but it is a dependent clause, which means it doesn't make sense by itself. *For example: After he finished his homework, Juan came and joined me.* "After he finished his homework" does not make sense by itself—it is a dependent clause.

Activity

If, And, or But Work with a family member to create a graphic organizer. Put a simple sentence in a bubble in the center. Take turns adding new bubbles to the main simple sentence to create compound sentences. See who can make the silliest sentence.

Practice Tested Spelling Words

_____ _____ _____ _____

_____ _____ _____ _____

_____ _____ _____ _____

_____ _____ _____ _____

_____ _____ _____ _____

Sequence

- **Sequence** is the order in which events happen in a selection. When you read, think about what comes first, next, and last.

- Several events can occur at the same time. Words such as *meanwhile* and *during* give clues that two events are happening at the same time.

Directions Read the following passage.

Jackie Robinson was the first African American baseball player to play in the modern Major Leagues. He played in the Negro Leagues until 1947 when he was signed to the Brooklyn Dodgers. Despite controversy about Robinson breaking the color barrier, he was an immediate success. During his first season, he led the National League in stolen bases, and after the season ended he was named Rookie of the Year. During his third season, he won the league's batting title and was later named the league's Most Valuable Player.

Directions Fill in the time line below with the events from Jackie Robinson's career. List them in the order in which they happened.

Events in Jackie Robinson's Career

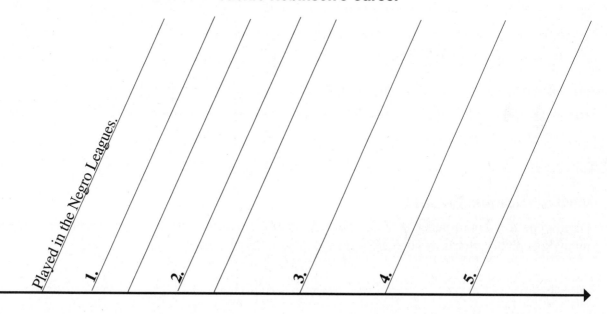

Played in the Negro Leagues.

1.

2.

3.

4.

5.

Home Activity Your child read a short passage and identified its sequence of events using a time line. Read a newspaper article about a current event with your child. Have your child put the events in sequence using a time line.

R2.2 Analyze text that is organized in sequential or chronological order.

Name_____

Vocabulary

Directions Draw a line to match each word on the left with its definition on the right.

1. fastball   firm belief in yourself

2. unique   a pitch thrown at high speed

3. weakness   laughing at; making fun of

4. confidence   having no like or equal

5. mocking   a weak point; slight fault

Check the Words You Know

____confidence
____fastball
____mocking
____outfield
____unique
____weakness
____windup

Directions Choose the word from the box to complete each clue and fill in the crossword puzzle.

DOWN

6. We have full _____ in his hitting.

7. Motions the pitcher makes before throwing the ball is called a _____.

ACROSS

8. If the ball is hit out of the diamond, it's in the _____.

9. A standout hitter like Barry Bonds is _____ among players.

10. Running too slowly is a player's major _____.

Write a News Report

On a separate sheet of paper, write a brief television news report about a baseball game, using as many vocabulary words as you can.

Home Activity Your child identified and used vocabulary words found in the biographical story *Satchel Paige*. Look in the sports pages of a newspaper and read a description of a sporting event with your child. See if you can identify any of the vocabulary words in the article.

R1.0 Word Analysis, Fluency, and Systematic Vocabulary Development

Name_____

Vocabulary • Antonyms

- An **antonym** is a word that means the opposite of another word.
- Words such as *unlike, but,* and *instead* may indicate the presence of antonyms.
- A **thesaurus**, a book that lists words and their antonyms and synonyms (words that mean the same thing), may help bring *clarity,* instead of *confusion,* to your writing and reading.

Directions Read the following passage about an athlete. Then circle the words in the list below that complete antonym pairs.

Although Pete was born without legs, he refused the idea that his disability should slow him down. Unlike people who accepted misfortune as an excuse to give up, Pete tried to live life to the fullest. It was true that his wheelchair sometimes made him feel confined at school. But on the weekends, his favorite sport, rock climbing, made him feel completely free.

Pete always used caution when fastening his ropes and caring for his equipment. Two hundred feet above the rocky bottom of a canyon was no place for recklessness! Starting at the base of a cliff, he would pull his way up to the pinnacle. After straining for hours, he would reach the top, exhausted. Pete didn't feel that school was boring, but it didn't match the exhilarating feeling that came from the physical and mental challenge of rock-climbing.

1. **refused**	disability	excuse	accepted
2. **free**	confined	completely	favorite
3. **caution**	recklessness	rocky	caring
4. **base**	cliff	reach	pinnacle
5. **boring**	mental	feeling	exhilarating

Home Activity Your child read a short passage and identified antonyms, words that mean the opposite of each other. Have your child describe a familiar person, place, or thing using words and their antonyms, using a dictionary, glossary, or thesaurus for help.

R1.3 Understand and explain frequently used synonyms, antonyms, and homographs.

Compare and Contrast

Directions Read the passage. Then answer the questions below.

In 1999, the U.S. Women's Soccer team won the World Cup. Like the men's team in 1998, the women's team had high hopes of winning the international competition. Unlike the men's team from the year before, the U.S. women's team took first place in the contest. Mia Hamm, the leader of the team, was unlike any women's soccer player before. She became known as one of the greatest athletes, male or female, ever to play the game. Her success, however, was not a solo effort. On the American World Cup and Olympic teams, she was surrounded by many great players, and Hamm was always eager to praise her teammates. Like so many figures in women's sports, Hamm appreciates how hard it is to gain recognition. Hamm retired from soccer after leading the U.S. Olympic women's soccer team to a gold medal in 2004. For other women who still play soccer, she remains an inspiration.

1. How was the 1999 U.S. women's soccer team like the 1998 men's team?

_____

2. How was the women's team different than the men's team?

_____

_____

3. How was Mia Hamm different from previous women's soccer players?

_____

4. How is Mia Hamm different from women who play soccer today?

_____

5. On a separate sheet of paper, describe someone who interests you who did great things in his or her field. How was he or she similar to or different from other people who did the same activity?

Home Activity Your child has read a short passage and made comparisons and contrasts about the subject. Talk with your child about two different people in his or her life. Ask your child to compare and contrast these two people.

G4R2.1 Identify structural patterns found in informational text (e.g., compare and contrast, cause and effect, sequential or chronological order, proposition and support) to strengthen comprehension.

Sequence

- **Sequence** is the order in which events happen in a selection. When you read, think about what comes first, next, and last.
- Several events can occur at the same time. Words such as *meanwhile* and *during* give clues that two events are happening at the same time.

Directions Read the following passage. Then answer the questions below.

Alan had to find a way to dunk a basketball through the hoop in the driveway. He just had to! Both of his brothers could, and so could his older sister. Even though he was still only seven, he wanted to know how it felt to slam the ball through the hoop. First, he tried to run as far away as he could and jump to the hoop. Then he set up a box under the net and tried to jump from there to reach the rim. That didn't work, either. Meanwhile, his brothers and sister were watching him as he struggled. Just as Alan was about to give up, they rushed out to him. Before he knew it, he was being lifted up into the air. Then he caught the pass his sister threw. Within a second, the hoop was within reach. He reached out, and *swoosh!* At last, the ball dove through the hoop.

1. What does Alan really want to do as the story begins?

_____

2. What does he try first? What word helps you find what he did first?

_____

3. What does he try next? What word tells you this?

_____

_____

4. What is happening at the same time Alan is trying to dunk the ball? What words tell you this?

_____

_____

5. What is the last thing that happens? How can you tell?

_____

_____

Home Activity Your child read a short passage and answered questions about its sequence of events. Work with your child to develop a sequential solution to a problem he or she is facing.

R2.2 Analyze text that is organized in sequential or chronological order.

Comprehension 37

© Pearson Education, Inc., 5

Sequence

- **Sequence** is the order in which events happen in a selection. When you read, think about what comes first, next, and last.
- Several events can occur at the same time. Words such as *meanwhile* and *during* give clues that two events are happening at the same time.

Directions Read the following passage.

There are many ways you can break in a new baseball mitt, but this is one of the tried-and-true, old-fashioned ways. First, get the mitt wet with warm water. Don't get it too soaked! Without putting the mitt on, spend some time opening and closing it with both hands to loosen up the leather. Next, you want to rub a little bit of oil (not motor oil) into the palm of the mitt where it creases. Put a baseball right in the heart of the mitt and then wrap it tightly with a rubber band. Let it sit that way overnight. The next morning, take the rubber band off the mitt and resume opening and closing it with both hands. You'll need to repeat the overnight process a few times before your mitt really loosens up. But when it does, it'll feel like that mitt was grown on your hand.

Directions Fill in the diagram below with the steps to breaking in a mitt. List them in the order in which they are supposed to be done.

How to Break in a Baseball Mitt

Get the mitt wet with warm water	1. _____	2. Put a ball in the mitt and _____	3. _____	4. Unwrap the mitt and	5. _____

© Pearson Education, Inc., 5

 School + Home **Home Activity** Your child read a short passage and identified the order of steps in a process. With your child, write down the sequence of steps he or she must follow to do something he or she regularly does around the house.

R2.2 Analyze text that is organized in sequential or chronological order.

Newspaper/Newsletter

- A **newspaper** is a daily (or weekly) periodical that contains timely news and information on current events and issues. Daily newspapers generally cover local, regional, national, and international news. Most newspapers organize information from most important to least important. There are three basic kinds of articles found in a newspaper: news stories, editorials (opinions pieces), and feature stories.
- A **newsletter** is a brief publication by a group or organization that contains news of interest to that group's members.

Directions Read the newspaper page and answer the questions below.

HOMETOWN NEWS

JULY 17, 2004   Cloudy, 72°

BARR HITS FOR THE CYCLE–AGAIN

Hometown hero Billy Barr has been having the kind of week baseball players can only dream of. Last night, for the third game in a row, Barr hit for the cycle, which means he hit a single, a double, a triple, and a home run.

"I guess my grandfather was looking out for me tonight," said Barr after the game, referring to his grandfather Alan Barr, one of the first Negro League players to break into Major League baseball in the 1950s. Billy Barr frequently makes reference to his grandfather, who inspired his grandson to play baseball.

The last time a Major League player hit for the cycle in three consecutive games was in 1971, when Sal Bando did it for the Oakland Athletics.

1. Where do you find the date on a newspaper's front page?

_____

2. How does the headline give you a clue to what the article will be about?

_____

3. Most newspapers give the daily weather forecast somewhere on the front page. What is the forecast for this day?

_____

4. Why does the writer mention the last time this event occurred at the very end of the article?

_____

5. Which of the three basic types of articles is this one?

_____

G4W1.8 Understand the organization of almanacs, newspapers, and periodicals and how to use those print materials.

Research and Study Skills 39

Name_____

Directions Read the selection from the newsletter and answer the questions below.

EVANSTON SOCCER NEEDS VOLUNTEERS

Hello Evanston soccer families!

The new season starts soon, and we're busy getting our teams and coaches organized and ready to play. As you can imagine, it's a lot of work. So once again we are asking for volunteers to help us out for the new season. We are an all-volunteer organization. In 2006 we won the Regional Youth Soccer Organization of the year award because of the great support our volunteers gave us. We want to make it two in a row for this year!

Volunteering only requires a few hours of your time each week. Currently, we need about 40 parents to volunteer to be coaches, referees, and board members.

We know how busy everyone's lives are, but our organization can only succeed if everyone pitches in. We hope you'll consider volunteering this year!

---

6. To whom is this newsletter story directed?

_____

7. Who do you think would receive a copy of this newsletter?

_____

_____

8. Name two things this newsletter specifically asks soccer parents to volunteer to do.

_____

9. Based on this newsletter article, who runs this youth soccer organization?

_____

10. If you wanted to find out about a big event happening in your city, where would you go to find out the information—a newspaper or a newsletter? Why?

_____

_____

_____

School + Home **Home Activity** Your child answered questions about newspapers and newsletters. With your child, sketch out the front page of a newspaper based on your family's activities for the day.

G4W1.8 Understand the organization of almanacs, newspapers, and periodicals and how to use those print materials.

Family Times

Summary

Ten Mile Day

On April 28, 1869, 1,400 workers from the Central Pacific Railroad agreed to a challenge. On a bet from Thomas Durant, president of another railroad, the Union Pacific, the workers attempted to lay ten miles of railroad track in one day. Laboring with almost impossible strength, speed, and organization, the workers succeeded.

Activity

Taking Care of Business Very few people alive today know what it's like to carry thousands of pounds of steel by hand over ten miles in one day. Almost everyone, however, has put in a long day's work of one kind or another. With a family member, write a description of hard work that needs to be done in your home. List the skills and traits that can help get the jobs done.

Comprehension Skill

Cause and Effect

The **cause** is what made something happen. The **effect** is what happened as a result of the cause. An effect may have more than one cause, and a cause may have more than one effect. Sometimes authors use clue words such as _because_ and _so_ to show a cause-and-effect relationship.

Activity

One Thing Leads to Another Pick a favorite story about something funny or dramatic that happened to you or one of your relatives in the past. Talk with a family member about the cause (or causes) that made this event occur.

Words to Know

Knowing the meanings of these words is important to reading *Ten Mile Day*. Practice using these words.

Vocabulary Words

barren unable to grow plant life

deafening so loud as to cause a loss of hearing

lurched moved suddenly

previous occurring earlier in time or position

prying moving up, apart, open, or out with force

surveying measuring the size, borders, and shape of (as a plot of land)

Common Nouns, Proper Nouns, and Appositives

A **common noun** names any person, place, or thing. *For example: girl, city, building.* A proper noun names a particular person, place, or thing. Proper nouns include titles of books and movies, as well as many abbreviations. Capital letters are used for the first letter and each important word of a proper name. *For example: Nadine, Mexico City, White House, The Wizard of Oz, U.S.A.* When two nouns refer to each other in the same sentence, they are known as **appositives.** In the sentence: My friend Nadine came over my house to watch a movie, the common noun "friend" and the proper noun "Nadine" are appositives of each other.

Activity

The Proper Way With a family member, make two separate lists of ten common nouns. Exchange your lists and try to change each common noun into a proper noun.

Practice Tested Spelling Words

Cause and Effect

- A **cause** is what makes something happen. An **effect** is what happens as a result of the cause.
- An effect may have more than one cause, and a cause may have more than one effect.

Directions Read the following passage and complete the diagram below.

Colonists came to America seeking opportunities unavailable to them in Europe. England viewed America as a source of revenue and raw materials for its growing economy. As the colonies flourished, laws were enacted forcing them to buy finished products from England rather than allow colonists to make and sell their own. Laws including new taxes on tea, textiles, and sugar, made colonists resent the meddling in their everyday lives, and they felt restrained. When they protested, the king sent troops to enforce the laws and keep order. In response, colonists formed their own government and signed the Declaration of Independence. The king didn't accept this call for self-government, and soon the American Revolution began.

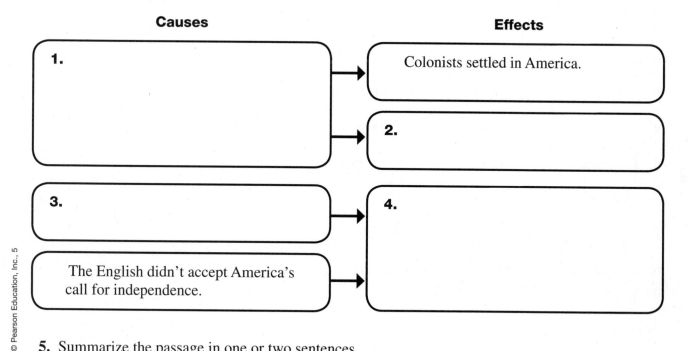

Causes

1.

Effects

Colonists settled in America.

2.

3.

4.

The English didn't accept America's call for independence.

5. Summarize the passage in one or two sentences.

_____

_____

Home Activity Your child read a short passage and identified causes and effects. Look up an event in the U.S. Revolutionary War and discuss causes and effects described in the selection.

G4R2.6 Distinguish between cause and effect and between fact and opinion in expository text.

Name_____

Vocabulary

Directions Choose the word from the box that best completes each sentence. Write the word on the line.

The wagon **1.** _____ forward, almost throwing

me out the back. My father and mother sat on the driver's bench,

2. _____ the foothills of the Sierra Nevada

Mountains below us. Like many immigrant families, we traveled

west over miles of dry, **3.** _____ lands.

Everything we could take from our **4.** _____

life back in Boston was now in our covered wagon. We were headed

to California to try our luck **5.** _____ gold from

the earth to make our fortune.

Directions Circle the word that has the same or nearly the same meaning as the first word in each group.

6. prying	extracting	attempting	bragging
7. surveying	wondering	planning	measuring
8. lurched	fumbled	staggered	belched
9. deafening	loud	empty	dry
10. previous	sinister	related	earlier

Journal Entry

On a separate piece of paper, write a journal entry as if you have just moved to another country. Use as many vocabulary words as you can.

School + Home **Home Activity** Your child identified and used vocabulary words from *Ten Mile Day*. Together with your child, read an article about life in another country. Talk with your child about what it might be like to live in that country.

R1.0 Word Analysis, Fluency, and Systematic Vocabulary Development

Vocabulary · Multiple-Meaning Words

- Some words have more than one meaning. They are called **multiple-meaning words.**
- **Context clues,** words and phrases near the multiple-meaning word, may help identify what a word means in a particular context, or situation.

Directions Read the following passage. Then answer the questions below.

Many things surprised Svetlana when she arrived with her family in America. Mostly, she was surprised at how many cars were on the road. Plenty of people had cars in Bulgaria, of course, but everyone here seemed to enjoy being mobile all the time. The sidewalks were clean and wide, but people would refuse to use them, even on sunny days. She noticed her neighbors getting in their cars just to go a half mile instead of walking.

In Bulgaria, when Svetlana needed to go somewhere a few miles away, she would usually ride her bicycle. Occasionally, she would ride the moped she shared with her whole family. It used little gas, and she could park it anywhere. To what did Svetlana attribute people's addictions to their automobiles? She supposed they believed owning a car was a sign of success. She took pride in the exercise she got walking and bicycling!

1. *Mobile* can mean "capable of motion" or "a hanging sculpture whose parts are moved by air currents." How do you think these two meanings are related to one another?

_____

2. *Refuse* can mean "indicate unwillingness" or "garbage." Which of these definitions is meant in the fourth sentence?

_____

3. *Moped* can mean "acted as if drained of energy by sadness" or "a small two-wheeled vehicle that has both an engine and pedals." Use a dictionary to find out how to pronounce *moped*. Which meaning uses two syllables?

_____

4. *Attribute* can mean "characteristic, quality, or trait" or "explain by suggesting a source or cause." Which definition is meant in the second paragraph?

_____

Home Activity Your child identified words with multiple meanings in a fictional passage. With your child, make a list of words you often use that have different meanings.

G3R1.6 Use sentence and word context to find the meaning of unknown words.

Vocabulary 45

© Pearson Education, Inc., 5

Sequence

Directions Read the passage. Then answer the questions below.

Mike Nee came to America in 1927. He was 21 years old and had spent his entire life on the west coast of Ireland. Once in America, he found work with the local gas company. He was young, strong, and a tireless worker. Within a couple of years, he was able to buy himself a house. Soon after that, he met Ellen, who was also from Ireland. They married in 1932 and hoped to have a large family just like the ones they grew up in. They had many struggles in their first years of marriage. But they were determined to share the good life in their new country with children of their own. After many years, Mike and Ellen welcomed their daughter Mary into the world in 1943. There truly couldn't have been two happier parents.

1. When did Mike Nee come to America?

_____

_____

2. How many years passed after coming to America before Mike and Ellen got married?

_____

_____

3. Which did Mike do first—get married or buy a house?

_____

_____

4. How many years passed between Mike and Ellen's marriage and the birth of their daughter?

_____

_____

5. How old was Mike when he became a father?

_____

_____

Home Activity Your child has read a short passage and answered questions about the sequence of events. Together, read one of your child's favorite stories and discuss the sequence in which events in the story occur.

R2.2 Analyze text that is organized in sequential or chronological order.

Cause and Effect

- A **cause** is what makes something happen. An **effect** is what happens as a result of the cause.
- An effect may have more than one cause, and a cause may have more than one effect.

Directions Read the following passage. Then answer the questions below.

In the early part of the twentieth century, there were a large number of immigrants who came to the United States. Many people came from eastern European countries like Poland, Italy, and Russia. Because large U.S. cities offered an easier transition into American culture, many ethnic neighborhoods developed in major cities. These cities offered jobs and public transportation was widespread. Immigrants were able to be near other relatives who'd moved to the U.S., and a community of familiar languages and customs was welcoming to newcomers. These areas where immigrants settled helped define the neighborhoods that became a part of big cities like Chicago, New York, and Boston.

1. What were the nationalities of many immigrants in the early twentieth century?

_____

2. What features of big cities appealed to immigrants?

_____

_____

3. What do you think happened to the population in big cities during this time? What do you think was the cause of this effect?

_____

_____

4. How were the immigrants' cultural backgrounds preserved in the new country?

_____

5. Write a summary of the passage in one or two sentences.

_____

_____

_____

Home Activity Your child read a short passage and answered questions about cause and effect. Read an article about your city or a neighborhood where you live. See if you can identify some of the reasons why your city or neighborhood is the way that it is.

G4R2.6 Distinguish between cause and effect and between fact and opinion in expository text.

Comprehension 47

Cause and Effect

- A **cause** is what makes something happen. An **effect** is what happens as a result of the cause.
- An effect may have more than one cause, and a cause may have more than one effect.

Directions Read the following passage and complete the diagram below.

> When Abraham Lincoln was elected President in 1860, most Americans didn't even vote for him. Four men ran for President that year, and no one won more than 50% of the vote. Lincoln won because he got enough electoral votes to win. Without a majority, however, his presidency was difficult from the very start. Many Southern states wanted their own separate country in which slavery would continue to be legal. But Lincoln promised to end slavery.
>
> Some people were so opposed to Lincoln's goals that they threatened his life. He had to be brought to Washington, D.C., secretly in the dark of night. In spite of the threats, Lincoln did not change his mind about his goals. Unfortunately, the Southern states did not want to change either, and the Civil War started.

Causes		**Effects**
Four men ran for President in 1860.	→	**1.** Most Americans _____ _____
	→	**2.** Lincoln got enough _____ _____
Lincoln's goal was to keep the country united.	→	**4.** A terrible _____ _____ _____
3. The Southern states _____ _____	→	

5. Write a summary of the passage.

_____

_____

© Pearson Education, Inc., 5

Home Activity Your child read a short passage and identified causes and effects. Read an article about a government officeholder and talk about how he or she has caused things to happen in your community.

G4R2.6 Distinguish between cause and effect and between fact and opinion in expository text.

Electronic Encyclopedia

An **encyclopedia** gives general information about many different subjects. An electronic encyclopedia can be found on a CD-ROM or on the Internet. They often have interactive graphics and maps, as well as audio files. They are organized alphabetically by **entries,** which are the topics. You can locate topics by using **keyword searches.** Keyword searches give you a list of topics to choose from. Cross-referencing is represented by hotlinks, which are underlined words.

Directions Read the entry from an online encyclopedia and answer the questions below.

Online Student Encyclopedia ⌂ home

Keyword Search [_____]

Print Article   E-Mail Article to Friend   Bookmark Article

Ellis Island

Ellis Island is located in New York Harbor. It was named after its owner in the 1770s, Samuel Ellis. Sixteen million immigrants to the United States passed through Ellis Island between 1892 and 1954. In 1965 the island became part of the Statue of Liberty National Monument. The immigration processing center is no longer used; however, it was made into a museum in 1990. The museum houses 400 years' worth of documents and artifacts about American immigration.

See also **Immigration**.

Back to top

---

1. How would you search for information about Samuel Ellis in this online encyclopedia?

_____

_____

2. Can you e-mail this article to a friend? Why do you think e-mailing an article would be useful?

_____

_____

3. Why do you think you would bookmark this page?

_____

_____

4. When was Ellis Island made into a museum?

_____

5. What is a simple way you could learn more about immigration?

_____

G4W1.7 Use various reference materials (e.g., dictionary, thesaurus, card catalog, encyclopedia, online information) as an aid to writing.

Research and Study Skills 49

Directions Read the entry from an online encyclopedia and answer the questions below.

Online Student Encyclopedia   🏠 home

Keyword Search [   ]

Print Article   E-Mail Article to Friend   Bookmark Article

Ethnic Diversity

Most contemporary societies are, to some extent, ethnically diverse. History has played a part in making societies more diverse. Conquerors brought people from different societies to live under their rule. Sometimes people were brought to a new society as slaves. When they are not forced to move, people are often motivated to move to new societies to pursue economic improvement or to flee political and religious persecution. See also ethnicity, immigration.

Assimilation occurs when a newly arrived group takes on some (or all) of the customs and values of the dominant group. Assimilation can occur voluntarily or it can be forced by the dominant group.

Back to top

---

6. This selection is part of a larger topic entitled *Ethnic Groups*. What keywords would you use if you wanted to learn about how the Irish moved to America?

_____

7. If you wanted to learn about people who moved to flee religious persecution, what words would you use in the keyword search?

_____

8. How would you print this article?

_____

_____

9. According to the entry, what are three reasons people leave their native lands?

_____

_____

10. What is the difference between a dictionary and an encyclopedia?

_____

_____

Home Activity Your child answered questions about electronic encyclopedias. With your child, search an encyclopedia for information about your family's ancestors and their native land or lands.

G4W1.7 Use various reference materials (e.g., dictionary, thesaurus, card catalog, encyclopedia, online information) as an aid to writing.

Family Times

Selection Summaries

Week 1 *The Red Kayak*

A boating accident forces a teenager to courageously meet challenges.

Week 2 *Thunder Rose*

Rose is an amazing cowgirl with thunder in her veins and a powerful lullaby in her heart.

Week 3 *Island of the Blue Dolphins*

Karana must be resourceful to survive when she is left all alone on an island.

Week 4 *Satchel Paige*

A great pitcher overcomes challenges in the early days of major league baseball.

Week 5 *Ten Mile Day*

Teams of builders of the Transcontinental Railroad try to set a record for laying the most rails in one day.

Activity

Tell a member of your family more about each of the five stories. Be sure to remember characters, plot, theme, and setting. Then choose your favorite and write three reasons why you like it the best.

Comprehension Skills Review

In Unit 1, you learned and used many skills while reading the stories and selections.

- The **plot** is what happens in a story.
- **Characters** are the people who experience the events of a story.
- The **cause** is why an event happens and the **effect** is what happens.
- The **setting** is where and when the story takes place.
- **Theme** is the "big idea" that holds the entire story together.
- **Sequence** refers to the order in which the events happen. In nonfiction, it means the steps in a process.

Activity

Ask a member of your family to tell you a story about something that happened to him or her when he or she was your age. Try to identify the setting, conflict, and resolution together. Discuss why you think it happened. Then discuss what you learned about the people in the story by the things they did and said and how they reacted to each other. Ask the family member what lesson he or she learned from these events. Finally, retell the story to another family member in the exact order in which the real events happened.

Unit Vocabulary Skills

Homographs

Homographs are words that are spelled the same as other words but have different meanings and sometimes have different pronunciations.

Activity With a family member, take turns brainstorming words that are homographs. Use a dictionary to check your answers.

Multiple-Meaning Words

Multiple-meaning words are words that have more than one meaning.

Activity Read a newspaper, magazine, or book looking for multiple-meaning words. Make a list of the ones you find. Use context clues to figure out which meaning of word is being used.

Synonyms

Synonyms are words that mean the same or almost the same as other words.

Activity Jot down verbs and adjectives you find in the selections. Use a thesaurus to find synonyms for those words.

Antonyms

Antonyms are words that mean the opposite of other words.

Activity Take the list of synonyms you created and this time use a thesaurus to find the opposites of those words.

Unit Spelling Rules

Short Vowel VCCV, VCV

When a syllable ends with a single vowel and a single consonant, the vowel stands for its short sound. VCCV: *butter* VCV: *regular*

Long Vowel VCV When a single vowel appears at the end of a word or syllable, the vowel usually stands for its long sound. VCV: *silent*

Long Vowel Digraphs If a word has two vowels in a row, the first vowel is usually long, and the second vowel is silent. For example: *faint*.

Adding -ed, -ing Remember the following three things when adding *-ed* and *-ing*:

- the final consonant is doubled before adding the ending
- in words that end in *y*, the *y* is changed to *i* before adding *-ed*: *horrified*
- in words that end in *y*, keep the *y* when adding *-ing*: *horrifying*

Contractions Remember that in contractions, an apostrophe takes the place of letters that are left out. For example, *were not* becomes *weren't*.

Activity With a family member, identify as many words in books, magazines, or newspapers that follow this Unit Spelling Rules. Make a list of these words.

⊙ Homographs

The cornstalks grew in rows.

The girl uses oars whenever she rows her boat.

The children have many rows over the bicycle.

Which word in each sentence is a homograph? Say the word as it is pronounced in each sentence.

A **homograph** is a word that is spelled the same as another word or words but has a different meaning and may have a different pronunciation. Which Words to Know word is a homograph?

Words To Know

compressions
grumbled
insistently
intentionally
minute
neutral
normally

Practice

Read the following sentences. Fill in the blanks with one of the Words to Know. Then circle the letter of the correct meaning of the homograph that is underlined in each sentence. Use a dictionary to check your answers.

1. The _____ the sky _____ the way it did, Ernesto could <u>project</u> that a dangerous storm was near.

   a. to make a prediction   b. a special assignment

2. Rather than remaining _____ during the rescue, Ernesto _____ took the <u>lead</u>.

   a. a soft metallic element   b. command

3. Ernesto _____ moved to the <u>bow</u> of the boat where he _____ kept the first-aid kit.

   a. a weapon for shooting arrows   b. the forward part of a vessel

4. Ernesto knew he had to <u>close</u> open cuts and apply _____ to stop bleeding.

   a. block   b. near

On Your Own

As you read "The Big Game," look for one of the homographs above. Pronounce the word as it is used in the story.

School + Home

Home Activity Your child reviewed how to use a dictionary to check the meaning of homographs. With your child, look for homographs in newspapers, magazines, or ads.

R1.3 Understand and explain frequently used synonyms, antonyms, and homographs.

Vocabulary   53

⊙ Character and Plot

A **character** is a person or an animal that takes part in the events of a story.

The **plot** is the sequence of events in a selection. The plot starts with a *problem* or *conflict*, continues with *rising action* as the conflict builds, and reaches a *climax* when the problem or conflict is faced. The plot ends with a *resolution* or *outcome*.

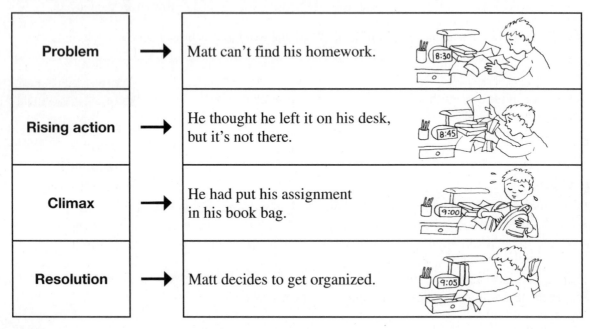

Problem →	Matt can't find his homework.
Rising action →	He thought he left it on his desk, but it's not there.
Climax →	He had put his assignment in his book bag.
Resolution →	Matt decides to get organized.

Practice

Now answer the following questions.

1. Who is the main character in the story on the chart above?

_____

2. What is Matt's problem?

_____

3. What is the climax of the story?

_____

4. What is the resolution?

_____

On Your Own

Use what you know about character and plot as you read "The Big Game."

School + Home

Home Activity Your child reviewed using the skills character and plot. Retell one of your favorite stories or movies. Discuss who the characters are. Have your child explain the problem, rising caution, climax, and resolution of the story or movie.

R3.3 Contrast the actions, motives, (e.g., loyalty, selfishness, conscientiousness), and appearances of characters in a work of fiction and discuss the importance of the contrasts to the plot or theme.

⊙ Multiple-Meaning Words

A **multiple-meaning word** is a word that has more than one meaning. Context clues can help you figure out which meaning of a multiple-meaning word is being used. Circle the two Words to Know that are multiple-meaning words. Use a dictionary to check your answers.

Practice

Read the following sentences. Fill in the blanks using the Words to Know. Then use context clues to choose the definition that best matches the underlined multiple-meaning word.

> **Words To Know**
>
> branded
> constructed
> daintily
> devastation
> lullaby
> pitch
> resourceful
> thieving
> veins

1. After the _____ of the dust storm, the
   rancher _____ a new roof on her <u>place</u> using
   _____.
   a. dwelling or property   b. rank
   c. seat

2. She even had a <u>chance</u> to have her cattle _____ to help
   prevent _____.
   a. luck   b. opportunity
   c. accidental

3. The rancher _____ hummed a sweet _____ as she thought <u>back</u>
   to how far she had come since the dust storm.
   a. first one way then another   b. part of a person's body
   c. behind in space or time

4. She had been _____ and one could <u>point</u> out that she was physically
   strong by the way her _____ showed against her muscle.
   a. a sharp end   b. direct attention to
   c. a unit of scoring

On Your Own

As you read "The Big Game," look for multiple-meaning words. Use context clues to determine how these multiple-meaning words are used in the story.

Home Activity Your child used context clues to determine the correct meaning of multiple-meaning words. With your child, make a list of as many multiple-meaning words as you can. Use each word in a sentence and have your child tell you the correct meaning of the word as it is used in your sentence.

G3R1.6 Use sentence and word context to find the meaning of unknown words.

Vocabulary 55

⊙ Cause and Effect

A **cause** is why something happens.

An **effect** is what happens.

Because the room was disorganized,

Matt couldn't find his homework.

- Clue words such as *because, so,* and *since* may signal causes and effects.
- Ask yourself "What happened?" and "Why did it happen?" to determine causes and effects.

Practice

In the boxes below, write the words that identify the cause and effect in each sentence. If there is a clue word, circle it.

1. Matt's homework wasn't on his desk so he searched his book bag.

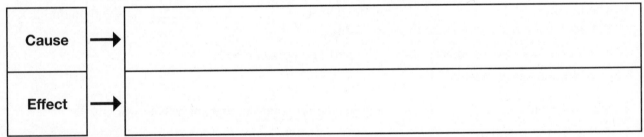

Cause	
Effect	

2. He was tired because it was almost bedtime.

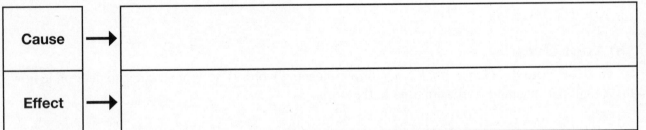

Cause	
Effect	

On Your Own

Use what you know about cause and effect as you read "A Real Winner."

School + Home

Home Activity Your child reviewed how to determine causes and effects. Think of a cause, and have your child supply the effect. For example, say "Because it was raining outside…" and have your child finish the sentence.

© Pearson Education, Inc., 5

⊙ Synonyms

A **synonym** is a word that means the same or almost the same as another word. A thesaurus is a useful tool for finding synonyms. Sometimes synonyms can help you understand the meanings of unknown words.

Words To Know

- gnawed
- headland
- kelp
- lair
- ravine
- shellfish
- sinew

Practice

Write the Word to Know that goes with each numbered item on the lines below. Then use a thesaurus to help you find other words.

1. Which word means the same or almost the same as *cliff*? _____

2. Which word means the same or almost the same as *nibbled*? _____

3. Which word means the same or almost the same as *valley*? _____

4. Which word means the same or almost the same as *mollusk*? _____

5. Which word means the same or almost the same as *muscle*? _____

6. Which word means the same or almost the same as *den*? _____

7. Which word means the same or almost the same as *algae*? _____

8. What type of shellfish is in the drawing above? _____

On Your Own

As you read "The Big Game," look for the words *fresh, great, raced, wild,* and *slow*. Use a thesaurus to find words similar to these that would make sense in the story.

School + Home

Home Activity Your child reviewed using a thesaurus to find synonyms of words. With your child, read a passage from a favorite book. Select a word from each sentence and identify a synonym for that word.

R1.3 Understand and explain frequently used synonyms, antonyms, and homographs.

⊙ Theme and Setting

The **theme** is the "big idea" of a story. The reader determines theme from the events and characters in a story.

The **setting** is the time and place in which a story takes place.

Practice

Think about Matt's story from this week. Look at the picture. Answer the questions.

1. What is the theme of Matt's story?

_____

2. Writers use details such as sights and sounds to describe the setting. List what you would see and hear if you were in Matt's room.

_____

_____

_____

3. Imagine if the setting were Matt's dining room at dinner. What might the sights and sounds be?

_____

_____

4. If Matt were an organized person, what might his room look like?

_____

_____

On Your Own

Use what you know about theme and setting as you read "The Big Game." Write a statement of what the theme and setting are in the passage.

Home Activity Your child reviewed theme and setting. Name the title of a favorite book or movie. Have your child explain the theme and identify the setting of it.

R3.4 Understand that *theme* refers to the meaning or moral of a selection and recognize themes (whether implied or stated directly) in sample works.

© Pearson Education, Inc., 5

⊙ Antonyms

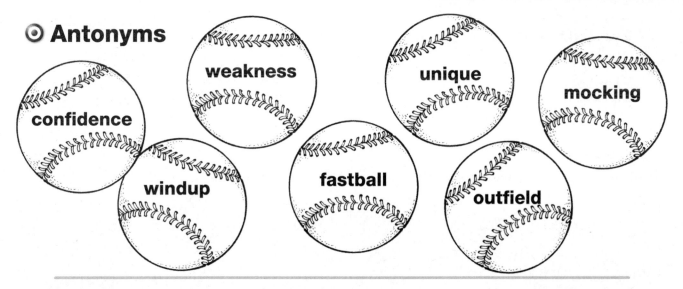

An **antonym** is a word that has the opposite meaning of another word. A thesaurus helps identify antonyms of words. Often context clues such as *unlike, while, on the other hand,* and *even though* also help.

Practice

Fill the blanks with the Words to Know that correctly complete each sentence. Circle the two words in each sentence that are antonyms. Use a thesaurus to help you determine the antonyms. Then underline the context clues that show a contrast.

Words To Know
confidence
fastball
mocking
outfield
unique
weakness
windup

1. His greatest _____, on the other hand, can also be his greatest strength.

2. A _____ can be _____ even though it is common to baseball.

3. He displays a lot of _____ in his _____ when he pitches, unlike his timidity when at bat.

4. Some spectators took to _____ the players in the _____, while others were cheering them on.

On Your Own

As you read "A Real Winner," look for the words *win, created, best, rough,* and *easy.* Use a thesaurus to list some antonyms for each. Read the context in which the words are used in the selection for any clue words that can help determine their opposites.

Home Activity Your child reviewed using a thesaurus to determine the meanings of antonyms, words that have the opposite meanings of other words. Take turns saying a word and having the other person name an antonym.

R1.3 Understand and explain frequently used synonyms, antonyms, and homographs.

Vocabulary 59

Name_____

⊙ Sequence

Sequence refers to the order of events, or the steps in a process. Clue words, such as *first, next,* and *then* can help you follow the sequence of events. Dates are also clues as to when events happened.

Practice

Directions: Look at the pictures and read the captions. Then answer the questions.

First, immigrants would settle in one of the cities along the Atlantic Ocean.

In 1825, the Erie Canal was completed. Settlers moving west sailed up the Hudson River from New York City to reach the canal.

Next, settlers would use flatboats to navigate the Ohio and Mississippi Rivers to St. Louis, Missouri.

Finally, settlers would travel in overland wagons on trails leading to California.

1. Circle the sequence clue words in each caption. List them.

_____

2. In what year was the Erie Canal completed?

_____

3. Would settlers moving west travel on the Ohio and Mississippi Rivers before or after using the Erie Canal?

_____

4. What was the final destination for settlers heading west?

_____

On Your Own

Use what you know about sequence as you read "A Real Winner."

Home Activity Your child reviewed using clue words to determine a sequence of events. With your child, list the sequence of events for getting ready for school.

© Pearson Education, Inc., 5

R2.2 Analyze text that is organized in sequential or chronological order.

⊙ Multiple-Meaning Words

A **multiple-meaning word** has more than one meaning. Context clues can help determine the meaning that is intended for a multiple-meaning word.

Practice

Read the following sentences. Fill in the blanks using one of the Words to Know. Then use context clues to determine which definition of the underlined multiple-meaning word is being used in each sentence. Circle the letter of the correct definition.

Words To Know
barren
deafening
lurched
previous
prying
surveying

1. Workers grabbed hold of each <u>side</u> of the crate and began

   _____ it open to reach their supplies.

   a. a surface that is not the front, back, top, or bottom of an object

   b. position or point of view

2. They began _____ the _____ land before laying a single

   railroad <u>track</u>.

   a. footprint

   b. metal rail

3. The continuous hammering sounds of stakes being struck were the cause of <u>major</u> ear

   _____.

   a. greater

   b. military rank

4. A <u>team</u> of iron men that at a _____ time stood still, now _____

   forward to move the crates.

   a. group

   b. partner

On Your Own

As you read "A Real Winner," look for multiple-meaning words. Use context clues to determine how these multiple-meaning words are used in the selection.

Home Activity Your child reviewed using context clues to determine the meanings of multiple-meaning words. Choose a passage from a favorite book and list all of the multiple-meaning words you find.

G3R1.6 Use sentence and word context to find the meaning of unknown words.

Vocabulary 61

⊙ Cause and Effect

- A **cause** is why something happens, and an effect is what happens. Sometimes an effect may have more than one cause, and a cause may have more than one effect.

Practice

Matt had a baseball game late in the afternoon.

Matt and his family usually eat dinner at 6:00 in the evening.

Matt finished his homework late in the evening.

Matt always makes sure he has his homework finished before going to bed.

Matt is usually in bed by 9:00.

1. What caused Matt's family to eat dinner later than usual?

_____

_____

2. What two events caused Matt to finish his homework later in the evening?

_____

_____

3. What was the effect of Matt finishing his homework later in the evening?

_____

_____

4. What were two effects of Matt's family eating dinner later than usual?

_____

_____

On Your Own

Use what you know about cause and effect as you read "A Real Winner." What do you think were the effects in the story? What caused such effects?

Home Activity Your child reviewed identifying multiple causes and effects. Discuss how a situation might have many effects or how a situation might have many causes.

© Pearson Education, Inc., 5

The Big Game

Marisol strolled innocently into the Middlebrook school gym and inhaled the fresh pine scent that sprang from the sparkling clean floors of the basketball court. *The gym is like an icebox this early in the morning*, she thought. *I'll probably spend the entire game freezing on the sidelines.* She zipped up her Middlebrook Stingrays sweatshirt and took her regular place on the bench. She had no idea of the devastation to come.

Today was the Stingrays' big game against the Prairie View Lions. The Stingrays were guaranteed to win since Berta was on the team. Marisol glanced at the court and saw Berta skillfully dribbling the ball. As usual, the group of players who worshipped Berta surrounded her.

"Watch this, I can dribble the ball through my legs," Berta boasted. The obedient group was impressed.

I wish I could play like that, Marisol grumbled.

The referee's whistle brought Marisol back to reality. Both teams took their positions on the court. Marisol stayed on the bench. The scoreboard blasted its horn, and the crowd cheered for the Stingrays. The ball echoed as it slapped against the wood floors, and the athletes' shoes squeaked with every sudden move. The gym buzzed with the intensity of a swarming beehive.

Berta was definitely the star of the show, sinking one ball after another. With two minutes left in the fourth quarter, the score was close: Berta: 29 Lions: 28. Suddenly, Marisol heard a horrified gasp from the crowd. Marisol was stunned to see Berta on the floor clutching her ankle in pain.

"Marisol! Looks like you'll finally have the chance to get acquainted with the court. You're going in for Berta," the coach said. "Do you see Number 6? Cover her like peanut butter on jelly."

Wow, thanks for the great advice, Marisol thought sarcastically. She felt her stomach drop, and she willed herself to walk onto the court. For a moment she thought she might faint. The two guards for the Lions quickly dribbled the ball down the court, and the *thump* pounded in Marisol's ears. *Just follow Number 6. Just follow Number 6,* she repeated to herself.

The ball whizzed back and forth. Number 6 faked left and then right. Marisol jumped right and then left. The point guard threw the ball over Marisol's head. Number 6 caught it, pivoted toward the basket, and shot. The ball bounced off the rim and flew straight toward Marisol.

"Rebound!" the crowd screamed.

⊙ **DAY 3** Setting
Underline the words in the first paragraph that help you visualize how the setting looks, smells, and feels.

⊙ **DAY 1** Character
Circle words and phrases that show Berta's personality.

⊙ **DAY 1**
Homographs What does *close* mean as it's used in paragraph 6?

_____

_____

Name a homograph of *close* and define it.

_____

_____

_____

⊙ **DAY 2** Cause and Effect What causes Marisol to play in the game?

_____

_____

_____

⊙ **DAY 2** Multiple-Meaning Words
What does *crowd* mean as it's used in the story?

_____

_____

© Pearson Education, Inc., 5

R2.0 Students read and understand grade-level appropriate material.

"The Big Game" 63

What is another meaning of *crowd*?

_____

_____

_____

⊙ **DAY 2** Cause and Effect What is the effect of Marisol's shot?

_____

_____

⊙ **DAY 1** Plot Draw a box around the climax of the story.

⊙ **DAY 3** Synonyms What is a synonym for *silent?*

_____

⊙ **DAY 3** Theme What is the theme of the the story?

_____

_____

_____

_____

_____

Without thinking, Marisol stuck her hands out and caught the ball. Her mind raced. *What do I do now?* Behind the sound of her heartbeat, she could hear the crowd cheering her on. Number 6 was moving toward her. Marisol turned toward the basket and set up her shot. The crowd went wild. *What are they saying?* Marisol thought. *Go? Go?* Marisol threw the ball and watched with amazement as it swished through the basket. *I made it! I made my first basket!* Marisol was overjoyed.

The sound of the buzzer ended the game, and the crowd grew strangely silent. Marisol heard the slow *thump* of the ball as it bounded away on its own. Then the Lions formed a circle and chanted, "We're number one!" All at once, it hit Marisol. She had scored two points for the Lions. Her team had lost the game because of her.

Marisol left the gym quickly. Her embarrassment and disappointment gnawed at her and she mumbled, "How could I have done something like that?"

"Hey, Marisol, wait up!" Berta limped over. "What an awesome shot! You know that was an impossible angle to shoot from."

"Really? It would have been better if I'd shot it in the right basket," Marisol said dryly.

"Well, if I hadn't been so busy showing off, I might not have hurt myself and could have stayed in the game. Or if we'd made all of our free throws, we might still have won by a point."

"I hadn't thought of it that way."

"Hey, want to practice with me?" asked Berta. "The angle you shot from is my weakness."

"Sure, that would be great," Marisol answered. *I guess it takes a whole team to win or lose a game,* she thought as she skipped home.

Home Activity Your child read a selection and used comprehension and vocabulary skills from Unit 1. Have your child retell the selection, identifying the characters and plot of the selection.

R2.0 Students read and understand grade-level appropriate material.

A Real Winner

Jack Roosevelt Robinson faced challenges all his life. They started soon after he was born in rural Georgia in 1919. The Robinson family moved to Pasadena, California, in 1920, but circumstances didn't make them feel welcome. Many businesses, schools, and even professional sports teams kept white people apart from black people. This was called *segregation*.

Jack, better known as "Jackie," was a natural athlete and team leader. Through high school and junior college Jackie excelled at football, basketball, track, and baseball. In 1939 he won a scholarship to the University of California in Los Angeles, where he was the first student to win a letter in all four sports.

In the spring of 1941 Jackie left college to get a job. In December of that year, Pearl Harbor in Hawaii was attacked, and the United States entered World War II. Jackie enlisted in the army in 1942 and went to Fort Riley, Kansas. He wanted to become an officer, but African American soldiers weren't allowed to be officers at the time. However, he met Sgt. Joe Lewis. Joe Lewis was the world heavyweight boxing champion. Sgt. Lewis spoke up, and Jackie and several other black servicemen were admitted to Officers' Candidate School.

Later Jackie was sent to Fort Hood, Texas. Though military regulations said that any soldier could sit anywhere on a military bus, one day Jackie was told by a higher-level officer to move to the back. Because he refused and stood his ground, he was sent to military court. He was found innocent in 1944 and then asked for, and received, an honorable discharge.

In April 1945 Jackie was hired to play shortstop with the Kansas City Monarchs, a team in the Negro Leagues. Black baseball players who were not allowed to play in white major league ball clubs had created this league. The low pay and terrible conditions he faced in the league discouraged Jackie, but this did not get him down. Soon his reputation as a star player caught the attention of major league baseball scouts.

Branch Rickey, general manager of the Brooklyn Dodgers, had sent scouts to observe Jackie in action. Mr. Rickey wanted to build the best team he could. Rickey was told of the talent and confidence of Jackie Robinson. When the two men met in August of 1945, Rickey told Jackie he was looking for a unique player "with guts enough not to fight back" against the attacks of bullies. Jackie accepted his assignment. Rickey advised him to marry his college sweetheart, Rachel Isum, so that he would have someone by his side during rough times.

⊙ **DAY 4** Sequence
Was Pearl Harbor attacked before or after Jackie left college?

_____
_____

Circle the clue words that tell you.

⊙ **DAY 5** Cause and Effect Underline the cause of Jackie going to military court.

⊙ **DAY 5** Multiple-Meaning Words
What does *scout* mean as it's used in the story?

_____
_____

What is another definition of *scout*?

_____
_____

⊙ **DAY 4** Antonyms
What is an antonym for *terrible*?

_____
_____

© Pearson Education, Inc., 5

R2.0 Students read and understand grade-level appropriate material.

"A Real Winner" 65

⊙ **DAY 4** Sequence
Which position did
Jackie play first for
the Dodgers?

_____

What sequence word
tells you this?

_____

⊙ **DAY 5** Cause
and Effect What is
the effect of Jackie
Robinson's number
being retired?

_____

_____

_____

_____

_____

In 1946, Jackie played with the Montreal Royals, the Dodgers'
minor-league "farm" team. In many U.S. cities, the newcomer to a baseball
team was jeered and called terrible names. The sound of the crowd was
sometimes deafening. He and his wife got hate mail and threats. But with
Jackie on the team, the Royals won the minor league pennant.

In 1947 the Dodgers announced that Jackie would play first base for
them as Number 42. He later played second and third base and even the
outfield. He was a powerful hitter and set records for stealing bases. He was
named National League Rookie of the Year the first year on the team. But it
wasn't easy. Some of his own teammates wrote a petition to get rid of him.
Branch Rickey stood his ground and kept Jackie on the team.

In 1949 Jackie was named Most Valuable Player. In his ten years with
the Dodgers, the team won the National League pennant six times and also
the 1955 World Series.

When Jackie retired in 1956, he won the Spingarn Medal for his work
with black youth. In 1962 he was the first African American named to the
Baseball Hall of Fame. He worked hard for the civil rights of all Americans
until his death in 1972.

Jackie Robinson is still honored for opening most professional sports
to all athletes. In 1997, Number 42 was retired forever. From this point
forward, no one entering the league will wear that number.

School + Home **Home Activity** Your child read a selection and used comprehension and vocabulary skills from Unit 1. Have
your child summarize the selection, using sequence words and identifying causes and effects.

R2.0 Students read and understand grade-level appropriate
material.

Connect Text to Text

Reading Across Texts

Think about the selections "A Real Winner" and "The Big Game." Complete the Venn diagram below with details that show similarities and differences between the two texts.

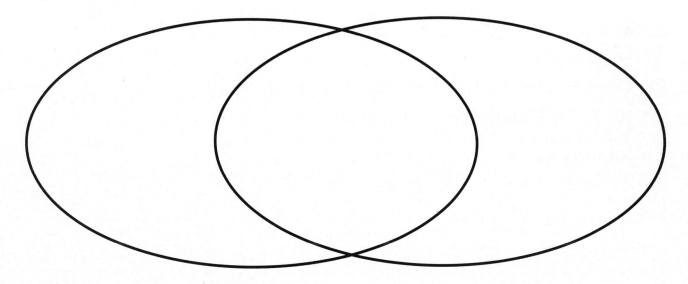

Writing Across Texts

Imagine you are Jackie Robinson from "A Real Winner" or Marisol from "The Big Game." What advice would you give someone facing a challenge?

_____

_____

_____

_____

_____

_____

_____

_____

_____

Home Activity Your child read two selections this week. Have your child explain to you how they were alike and how they were different.

Summarize Your Learning

> ### What kinds of challenges do people face and how do they meet them?
>
> • *The Red Kayak*   • *Thunder Rose*   • *Island of the Blue Dolphins*
> • *Satchel Paige*   • *Ten Mile Day*

Think About It!

Think about the selections you read in this unit.

- How were they alike? How were they different?
- Were the selections you read this week similar to others you have read this week?
- What did you learn?

Write three big ideas about challenges that you learned about in this unit.

- _____
- _____
- _____

Question It!

Write three questions about your big ideas. Put a star by your favorite question.

- _____
- _____
- _____

Talk About It!

Discuss your favorite question with a partner.

- Did your partner give the same answer you had? What was the same?
  What was different?
- Did your partner learn the same things that you learned? What was the same?
  What was different?
- What did you not understand that you want to know more about?
  Where will you look for information?

© Pearson Education, Inc., 5

Home Activity Your child reviewed and discussed the selections from Unit 1. Have your child describe to you the big ideas about challenges from this unit.

Family Times

Summary

At the Beach

On a regular day at the beach, Fernando leads three other children on an adventure he knows they shouldn't take. Little Javi unexpectedly gets hurt by a sea urchin. Fernando lies to his parents at first. He eventually confesses, and his mother praises him for telling the truth.

Activity

To Tell or Not to Tell Imagine that you did something you shouldn't have. Would you lie if you thought you could get away with it? Talk over this problem with members of your family. List your reasons for telling the truth.

Comprehension Skill

Compare and Contrast

When writers **compare** and **contrast** things, they tell how things are alike or different. Words such as *same*, *also*, *before*, *although*, and *however* are clues that things are being compared or contrasted.

Activity

Yours and Mine With a family member, find two pairs of shoes from different people in your house and put them side by side. Compare and contrast the size, color, style, and how much wear they show. Try comparing and contrasting other household items by using a Venn Diagram.

Lesson Vocabulary

Words to Know

Knowing the meanings of these words is important to reading *At the Beach*. Practice using these words.

Vocabulary Words

algae a group of related living things, mostly living in water

concealed put out of sight; hidden

driftwood wood carried along by water or washed ashore from the water

hammocks hanging beds or couches made of canvas, cord, etc.

lamented felt or showed grief for

sea urchins small, round sea animals with spiny shells

sternly strictly, firmly

tweezers small pincers for picking up small objects

Conventions

Modifiers

Remember to use **modifiers** correctly. To avoid confusion, keep your modifiers close to the words they modify. Sometimes using modifiers incorrectly changes the meaning of a sentence. For example, *Only Ken visits* has a different meaning from *Ken only visits*. Prepositional phrases should be kept close to the words they modify too. For example, *The gift from France is on the table* has a different meaning from *The gift is on the table from France*.

Activity

Mixed-Up Modifiers With a family member, make a list of seven words or phrases you can use as modifiers. Then pick a sentence out of a newspaper, magazine, or book. Each of you should make a new sentence by inserting as many modifiers as you can from your list into the sentence you chose. How are the meanings of the new sentences similar to the meanings of the original sentences? How are they different?

Practice Tested Spelling Words

Compare and Contrast

- To **compare** and **contrast** two or more things is to show how things are alike and different.
- Some clue words are: *as, like, but,* and *however.*
- Sometimes writers do not use clue words when they compare and contrast things.

Directions Read the following passage. Fill in the columns below based on Alex's observations about the differences between the ocean and the lake back home.

Alex had never been to the ocean before, so he was excited when Joel invited him to go with Joel's family to Rhode Island. As they walked across the sand, Joel asked Alex if he knew anything about a "riptide," a strong flow of water near the shore. Afraid to admit he knew nothing about the sea, Alex told Joel he knew all about riptides. As he swam, Alex noticed several differences between lakes and oceans. Both were cold. Salty ocean water, however, seemed to allow him to float more easily. Ocean waves were also much larger than freshwater ones.

In the lake Alex remembered that small fish swam around his feet. In the ocean, crabs crawled over them. Suddenly, Alex and Joel heard a whistle blow. A lifeguard was ordering swimmers out of the water. Alex heard the lifeguard explain to a man that the riptides had become too strong and had pulled a young girl hundreds of feet from shore. She had almost drowned. Alex gulped. He knew he had put himself in danger by not being honest about his ignorance.

Lake	Ocean
fresh water	1.
2.	3.
4.	5.

Home Activity Your child compared and contrasted details from a short passage. Discuss with your child two places that you have gone for enjoyment. Ask your child to make a list of the similarities and differences.

R3.3 Contrast the actions, motives (e.g., loyalty, selfishness, conscientiousness), and appearances of characters in a work of fiction and discuss the importance of the contrasts to the plot or theme.

Vocabulary

Directions Choose the word from the box that best matches each definition. Write the word on the line.

_____ 1. handheld, usually small tool used for pinching or grasping

_____ 2. put out of sight; hidden

_____ 3. harsh, firm, or strict

_____ 4. wood floating in a body of water or washed upon the shore of one

_____ 5. any of a group of aquatic organisms ranging in size from microscopic to hundreds of feet

Directions Choose the word from the box that best completes each sentence. Write the word on the line.

_____ 6. The underwater divers harvested dozens of the spiny _____ at the ocean floor to sell to a local restaurant featuring Japanese specialties.

_____ 7. The brother and sister swung lazily in _____, side by side under a tree, discussing how to spend the last summer day before school started.

_____ 8. He _____ his glee at winning the match, trying at least to appear to have a sense of good sportsmanship.

_____ 9. The puppy's ears drooped and her tail stopped wagging as I _____ lectured her about not chewing on the furniture.

_____ 10. The pop music star _____ the loss of his youth and fame, sadly wondering if another fan letter would ever arrive in the mail.

Write a Description

On a separate sheet of paper, write a description of what life might be like as a dolphin, living in the ocean. Use as many of the vocabulary words as you can.

Home Activity Your child identified and used vocabulary words from *At the Beach*. With your child, write a story about making the choice to be honest with someone.

R1.0 Word Analysis, Fluency, and Systematic Vocabulary Development

© Pearson Education, Inc., 5

Vocabulary • Unfamiliar Words

- **Dictionaries** provide alphabetical lists of words and their meanings.
- Sometimes looking at the words around an unfamiliar word can't help you figure out the word's meaning. If this happens, use a dictionary to find the meaning.

Directions Read the following passage. Look for unfamiliar words and nearby clues as to their meaning. Use a dictionary to look up words you do not know. Then answer the questions below.

The smell of brine was heavy in the air as Dr. Jansen dipped the glass vial into the brackish water of the salt marsh. She was collecting the samples from the grassy place by the shoreline to test for pollution. Many species of animals depended on the ecosystem of the marsh to remain healthy.

She held up the last vial and peered through the grass as she screwed the plastic cap on the top. She smiled, knowing that even though the water seemed to be absent of life, tiny organisms swam through the cloudy, muddy water. Glancing out over the waves in the distance, Dr. Jansen smiled. The seagulls whirling above the sand, swooping and diving in circles, always seemed to act as if there might be bread crumbs in Dr. Jansen's laboratory bag.

1. Smell can travel a long way in the air. What does *brine* smell like? How do you know?

_____

2. Find a word in the passage whose meaning cannot be guessed by context clues nearby. Look up the word in a dictionary and provide the definition.

_____

3. What might the word *vial* mean, based on the context clues in the paragraph? Use a dictionary to check your answer.

_____

4. What might the word *whirling* mean, based on the context clues in the paragraph? Use a dictionary to check your answer.

_____

5. The word *organism* is not easily guessed by context clues in the passage. Look the word up in a dictionary and provide its definition.

_____

Home Activity Your child identified unfamiliar words that could be defined using a dictionary or glossary. Work with your child to identify unfamiliar words in a newspaper or magazine article. Ask your child if he or she needs to use a dictionary to find the meaning of the words. If so, ask your child to look up at least one definition in a dictionary or glossary.

G3R1.6 Use sentence and word context to find the meaning of unknown words.

Vocabulary 73

Author's Purpose

Directions Read the following passage. Then answer the questions below.

The sun was high in the sky as it shone down on the men in the pirate ship. Diego tried to untie his wrists before Captain Flemming turned around. "You're a terrible pirate!" Diego shouted at Flemming. "What's that, lad?" Flemming asked. "A pirate? And how exactly would you describe yourself?" Flemming had a good point. Diego was a pirate too. But Diego considered himself an honest one.

"You'd better hope I don't escape this island, Flemming!" Diego warned bitterly. Flemming smiled a wicked grin. "Well, if you ever do, don't forget to bring me my treasure. You buried it! Har, har, har!" Diego had his own reason to be happy. He'd recently spied a small boat hidden in the weeds just beyond the beach. Flemming hadn't noticed the boat. It was just a matter of time before Diego would be free.

1. What is the purpose the author has for writing this passage?

_____

2. How can you tell what the author's purpose is?

_____

_____

3. What type of passage is this?

_____

4. Who is Diego?

_____

5. Does the author succeed at his or her purpose?

_____

_____

Home Activity Your child answered questions about the author's purpose for writing a short passage. Read a newspaper article with your child and discuss what the author's purpose might be.

R3.7 Evaluate the author's use of various techniques (e.g., appeal of characters in a picture book, logic and credibility of plots and settings, use of figurative language) to influence readers' perspectives.

© Pearson Education, Inc., 5

Name_____

Compare and Contrast

- When you **compare** and **contrast** two or more things, you show how they are alike and different.
- Clue words, such as *like* or *as* show comparisons. Words such as *but* or *however* show contrast.
- Sometimes, writers do not use clue words when they compare and contrast things.

Directions Read the following passage. Then answer the questions below.

Plagiarism, taking another writer's work and presenting it as one's own, is becoming a big problem in schools. Even though students have a very good chance at getting caught, they still plagiarize. In elementary and secondary schools, students are typically punished by a failing grade, being kicked off teams, or being suspended from school. At the college level, however, the penalties can become more serious. Students are often expelled from the college after only one instance of plagiarism. Teachers and professors usually know, or have a strong suspicion, that a student is plagiarizing.

The student who does his or her own work typically shows improvement slowly over time. A student who copies someone else's work may turn in one assignment that is of poor quality, and then the next week hand in writing that could win prizes. Internet sites that sell or give away finished writing assignments tempt many students who cheat. Like these students, teachers have started using the Internet. Web sites are now available where teachers can upload a student's paper and find out if it has been written by anyone else anywhere in the world.

1. How is plagiarism usually dealt with in elementary and secondary schools?

_____

2. How is plagiarism usually dealt with at the college level?

_____

3. What is the difference between the work of students who do and don't plagiarize?

_____

_____

4. How has the Internet made it possible for students to cheat?

_____

5. How has the Internet made it possible for teachers to catch plagiarism?

_____

Home Activity Your child answered compare and contrast questions about plagiarism. Have your child think about other ways that students are tempted to cheat. Have your child list possible consequences for these offenses.

G4R2.5 Compare and contrast information on the same topic after reading several passages or articles.

Comprehension 75

Compare and Contrast

- When you **compare** and **contrast** two or more things, you show how they are alike and different.
- Clue words such as *but* or *however* show contrasts. The clue words *like* and *as* show comparisons.
- Sometimes, writers do not use clue words when they compare and contrast things.

Directions Read the following passage. Fill in the columns below based on Jorge and Ed's friendship before and after the tornado touched down.

> Jorge and Ed grew up on opposite ends of the same street. They went to the same school, and they were sometimes in the same classroom. They were always friendly to each other, but Jorge and Ed didn't really know each other very well.
>
> On the night the tornado touched down, things changed between Jorge and Ed. The roof of Ed's house was blown off. Jorge and his parents were the first people there to help Ed's family. They worked together all night to help clean up Ed's house. That night, Jorge and Ed began to know each other a lot better. They became good friends.

Before	**After**
1. They lived _____ _____ _____	**2.** They worked _____ _____ _____
3. They were sometimes _____ _____	**4.** They became _____ _____ _____

5. On a separate sheet of paper, compare and contrast one of your friendships now with what it was like at the beginning. How has it changed? How has it remained the same?

Home Activity Your child compared and contrasted *before* and *after* details from a short passage. Read a favorite story with your child. Identify an important event in the story and compare and contrast what happened before and after that event.

G4R2.1 Identify structural patterns found in informational text (e.g., compare and contrast, cause and effect, sequential or chronological order, proposition and support) to strengthen comprehension.

Reference Book

A **reference book** is a type of **manual.** Manuals usually contain instructions, either for immediate use or for reference. A grammar reference book is a manual for using language. Like other manuals, it usually has a table of contents, an index, sections, illustrations, and explanations. Be sure to consult a grammar reference book whenever you have questions about grammar.

Directions Use the following selection from a grammar book to answer the questions below.

The Apostrophe

Use an apostrophe

1. to show possession

John's dad collects bottle caps.

2. with *s* to show the plural of letters

b's   j's   t's

3. to show the omission of a letter, letters, or numbers

We'll   class of '05   won't

Study the following contractions and notice the letter or letters that have been omitted to form the contraction.

they're — they are	*she'll — she will*
we've — we have	*let's — let us*
o'clock — of the clock	*aren't — are not*

---

1. How many ways is an apostrophe used?

_____

2. Which of the ways the apostrophe is used would apply if you were describing ownership of something?

_____

3. How would you use an apostrophe to contract the words *must* and *not*?

_____

4. What numbers are omitted in the recent class of *'05*?

_____

5. Insert apostrophes where needed in the following sentence: *Ill take my moms casserole over to the neighbors house at 6 oclock.*

_____

_____

G4W1.7 Use various reference materials (e.g., dictionary, thesaurus, card catalog, encyclopedia, online information) as an aid to writing.

Research and Study Skills 77

Directions Use the following table of contents from a grammar book to answer the questions below.

6. Which chapter would you look in for a usage question about the word *theirs*?

_____

7. Why do you think grammar books are organized by individual parts of speech?

_____

_____

8. What kind of words might you find in the section on "Personal Pronouns"?

_____

9. If you were having trouble writing a word that showed ownership, in which section of the grammar book would you look?

_____

10. Why might the short essays at the end of each chapter be included in a grammar book?

_____

_____

Home Activity Your child answered questions about grammar reference books and manuals. With your child, find a manual to an item in your house (computer, refrigerator, television, phone, etc.) and read through the table of contents to see how it is organized. Does it make sense? Could you easily find an answer to a question or a problem by using the manual?

G4W1.6 Locate information in reference texts by using organizational features (e.g., prefaces, appendixes).

Family Times

Summary

Passage to Freedom

The family of a Japanese diplomat living in Lithuania in 1940 is confronted by Jewish refugees asking for Japanese visas to escape the German Nazis. Without his country's permission, the diplomat issues thousands of the visas. Even today, years after his death, Japanese and Jewish families alike honor Mr. Sugihara for his bravery.

Activity

Adventure Visa With a family member, make your own passport from a few sheets of folded paper. Design an official-looking seal on the cover, and then draw a variety of colorful visas in your passport that represent all the countries you have visited on an imagined adventure.

Comprehension Skill

Author's Purpose

An **author's purpose** is the reason why the author writes a story. Authors may write to persuade, inform, entertain, or express ideas or feelings.

Activity

Tag-Team Story With a family member, take turns making up a story about your family. You start it, then the other person continues it for a while, and so on. When the story is finished, try to figure out the authors' purpose in your story. Is there more than one? How do you know?

Lesson Vocabulary

Words to Know

Knowing the meanings of these words is important to reading *Passage to Freedom*. Practice using these words.

Vocabulary Words

agreement harmony in feeling or opinion

cable a message sent through wires, also called a telegram

diplomat person who manages relations between nations

issue to distribute officially to a person or persons

refugees people who flee to another country for safety

representatives people appointed or elected to act or speak for others

superiors people who are higher in rank or position

visa an official signature or endorsement upon a passport or document, showing it has been examined and approved

Conventions

Possessive Nouns

A **possessive noun** shows ownership. Possessive nouns can be either singular or plural. Singular nouns form singular possessives. *For example: shoe/shoe's, Ron/Ron's.* Plural nouns form plural possessives. *For example: women/women's, girls/girls'.* To form a noun's possessive form, you usually add –'s to it. If the noun is a plural noun that ends in *s*, add only an apostrophe. *For example: table/table's, bus/bus's, men/men's, toes/toes'.*

Activity

Whose Favorite? With a family member, try to list the favorite foods of every member of your family you can think of. Identify each family member's favorite food using a complete sentence: "Yin's favorite food is tacos."

Practice Tested Spelling Words

_____   _____   _____   _____

_____   _____   _____   _____

_____   _____   _____   _____

_____   _____   _____   _____

Author's Purpose

- The **author's purpose** is the reason or reasons the author has for writing.
- An author may write to persuade, to inform, to entertain, or to express himself or herself.

Directions Read the following passage.

Levi Coffin was an abolitionist. He helped people who had been enslaved head north to find freedom. Levi was part of the Underground Railroad for many years. A few thousand enslaved people passed through his home in Indiana on their way to Canada. Levi was able to give them supplies for their journey. Eventually, people called Levi the "President of the Underground Railroad." Since it was illegal at the time to help people escape slavery, Levi took a risk to do what he knew was right.

Directions Complete the chart by answering the questions about the author's purpose.

Questions	Answers
What information is the author providing you with?	1.
For what purpose did the author write this passage?	2.
How do you know?	3.
Why did the author not use "I" in the passage?	4.
What idea is the author trying to convey in the last sentence?	5.

© Pearson Education, Inc., 5

 Home Activity Your child analyzed the author's purpose in a nonfiction passage. Look at an article in a newspaper or magazine. Read the article with your child and discuss what you each think is the author's purpose.

R3.7 Evaluate the author's use of various techniques (e.g., appeal of characters in a picture book, logic and credibility of plots and settings, use of figurative language) to influence readers' perspectives.

Name_____

Vocabulary

Directions Choose the word from the box that best matches each definition. Write the word on the line shown to the left.

_____ 1. people who flee to another country for safety

_____ 2. to distribute officially

_____ 3. official signature or endorsement on a passport or document

_____ 4. people appointed or elected to act or speak for others

_____ 5. harmony in feeling or opinion

Directions Choose the word from the box that best matches the clue.

6. These people are in a higher position or rank.

__ __ __ __ __ __ __ __ __

7. You might need this to travel to another country.

__ __ __ __

8. Today we might use e-mail instead of this to send a message.

__ __ __ __ __

9. A person who manages the relationship between countries

__ __ __ __ __ __ __ __

10. This is the opposite of *conflict*.

__ __ __ __ __ __ __ __ __ __

Write a Newspaper Article

On a separate sheet of paper write an imaginary newspaper article about people helping refugees come to a new country. Use as many vocabulary words as you can.

Home Activity Your child identified and used vocabulary words from *Passage to Freedom*. With your child, discuss the meaning of each word from the vocabulary list. Help your child use each word in a sentence.

© Pearson Education, Inc., 5

R1.0 Word Analysis, Fluency, and Systematic Vocabulary Development

Vocabulary • Unfamiliar Words

- As you read, you may find **unfamiliar words,** or words you do not understand. You can use a dictionary or glossary to look up the word.
- **Dictionaries** and **glossaries** provide alphabetical lists of words and their meanings.
- A dictionary is a book of words and their meanings, and a glossary is a short dictionary at the back of some books.
- An **entry** shows the spelling of a word and comes before the definition.

Directions Read the following passage. Then answer the questions below using a dictionary or your glossary.

Ayako's father is a diplomat, sent to our country by his homeland. Last week I went home with Ayako after school and her mother was crying. Ayako translated what her mother was saying so I could understand. Her father's superiors had called and told them that it was not safe to return to their homeland. Now Ayako and her family are refugees. Her father is not sure what job he can get. Ayako's little brother asks every day when they will be able to see their friends and relatives back home, but nobody knows the answer. Her family has made an agreement that they will try to be brave and to wait patiently for things to change. Someday, they will go home again.

1. What is the definition of *diplomat?* Put it in your own words.

_____

2. What entry do you have to look at in the dictionary to find the meaning for *translated?* What does *translated* mean?

_____

3. What does *superiors* mean? What part of speech is it?

_____

4. What is the meaning of *agreement?* Use it in an original sentence.

_____

_____

5. Explain why a dictionary would give more complete information for an entry than a glossary.

_____

_____

Home Activity Your child used a dictionary to find out the meanings of unfamiliar words. Choose a few words that your child does not know. Have your child use a dictionary to find their meanings.

Sequence

Directions Read the passage. Then answer the questions below.

Anne Frank wrote a famous diary about what it was like to live in hiding during World War II. Anne was born in Germany in 1929. After a few years, Anne's father moved her family to the Netherlands. Later, when Nazi soldiers took over the Netherlands, Anne's family hid above a warehouse in the hopes that the Nazis would not find them there. While they were in hiding, friends brought them things they needed.

Anne wrote in her diary about her days in hiding. They were long and boring for her, and she missed going to school. In 1944, the Germans found out where Anne's family was hiding. They took them to concentration camps. Anne, her sister, and her mother all died at the camps. Anne's father survived and went on to publish Anne's diary.

1. What clues in the passage help you understand the sequence of events?

_____

2. What clue words tell you when Anne moved to the Netherlands?

_____

3. When did friends help the Frank family?

_____

4. Why is it important that the events of the passage are placed in order?

_____

_____

5. Create a numbered list of nine events of the passage in their proper order.

_____

_____

_____

_____

_____

Home Activity Your child has read a biographical scene and placed its details in the order in which they occurred. With your child, read a short story. Have your child explain whether or not the sequence of events in the story affected the story's outcome.

 R2.2 Analyze text that is organized in sequential or chronological order.

Author's Purpose

- The **author's purpose** is the reason or reasons the author has for writing.
- An author may write to persuade, to inform, to entertain, or to express himself or herself.

Directions Read the following passage. Then answer the questions below.

> Tom stood outside the school office, not knowing what to do. He should have been excited about the class pizza party. He loved pizza. But he wasn't excited. Tom's class won the pizza party when three of his classmates entered the best guess for the number of marbles it took to fill up a jar. The problem was, Tom knew that his classmates had cheated. They had found the principal's notes, which told exactly how many marbles had been used, and had copied the number down. A group of third-graders had come within fifteen marbles all by themselves, just by estimating. Even though he loved pizza, Tom didn't think it was fair to enjoy the party that the third-graders had earned. If he did nothing, Tom would feel dishonest. He took a deep breath and went into the office to talk to the principal.

1. Why do you think the author wrote this passage?

_____

_____

_____

2. Do you think the author met his or her purpose for writing? Why or why not?

_____

3. Why do you think the author wrote the passage from Tom's point of view?

_____

_____

4. Why does the author tell a story instead of simply writing an essay about why cheating is wrong?

_____

5. Did you need to change your normal reading pace to understand it? Why or why not?

_____

_____

_____

Home Activity Your child analyzed the author's purpose in a passage, and monitored his or her understanding of it. Read a persuasive piece such as a newspaper editorial with your child and discuss how the author persuades the reader.

R3.7 Evaluate the author's use of various techniques (e.g., appeal of characters in a picture book, logic and credibility of plots and settings, use of figurative language) to influence readers' perspectives.

Comprehension 85

Author's Purpose

- The **author's purpose** is the reason or reasons the author has for writing.
- An author may write to persuade, to inform, to entertain, or to express himself or herself.

Directions Read the following passage. Then complete the chart by finishing the statements.

In 1940 Varian Fry went to France to help people flee from the Nazi powers who had come there. He made up documents that would let people leave the country. He also came up with routes they could take to find safety. Varian stayed in France for thirteen months before he was forced to leave. He rescued many people. Some of them were famous artists, writers, and musicians. It was not until many years later that he was finally honored for his work in France.

Questions	Answers
What is the author telling you about?	**1.** The author tells us about how Varian Fry
For what purpose did the author write this passage?	**2.** The author wants to
How do you know?	**3.** The author uses
Why do you think the author told you that Varian was forced to leave France?	**4.** To tell us that Varian would have
What idea is the author trying to tell us in the last sentence?	**5.** To tell us that sometimes

© Pearson Education, Inc., 5

Home Activity Your child analyzed the author's purpose in a nonfiction passage. Read a nonfiction passage with your child and work together to determine the author's purpose. Discuss whether this purpose means a reader can expect to read the passage relatively quickly or slowly.

R3.7 Evaluate the author's use of various techniques (e.g., appeal of characters in a picture book, logic and credibility of plots and settings, use of figurative language) to influence readers' perspectives.

Parts of a Book

The **parts of a book** include its **cover, title page, copyright page, table of contents, chapter titles, captions, section heads, glossary,** and **index.** Examining the parts of a book can give you clues about a book and assist you in learning as much as you can from it.

Directions Read the following copyright page and answer the questions below.

Rising Sun Setting: Japanese in America During World War II

Copyright © 1988 Daniel Kwong
All rights reserved.

No part of this publication may be reproduced or transmitted in any form or by any means, electronic or mechanical, including photocopying, recording or any information storage and retrieval system now known or to be invented, without permission in writing from the publisher.

Published by World History Books, Inc.
4 Park Avenue, New York, N.Y. 10010
Library of Congress Cataloging in Publication Data

Kwong, Daniel J.,
Rising Sun Setting: Japanese in America During World War II
I. Title.   954.67   ISBN: 0-569-12900-K

PRINTED IN THE UNITED STATES OF AMERICA

---

1. What is the purpose of the copyright page in a book?

_____

_____

2. The owner of the copyright is listed after the symbol © and the year of publication. Who owns the copyright to this book?

_____

3. What do you think it means to own the copyright to a book?

_____

4. Why do you think there is a message about reproducing this book?

_____

5. Who published this book? When was the book published?

_____

© Pearson Education, Inc., 5

W1.3 Use organizational features of printed text (e.g., citations, end notes, bibliographic references) to locate relevant information.

Research and Study Skills   87

Directions Study the following table of contents page. Then answer the questions below.

CONTENTS

Forming a Government
for the United States of America

6. What does the title tell you this book will be about?

_____

_____

7. What do the numbers on the right side of the page represent? Where would you find a chapter about checks and balances?

_____

_____

8. What can you learn about a book by studying its table of contents before you read?

_____

9. What is the purpose of the chapter titles?

_____

10. What other sections can you find in this book besides chapters?

_____

Home Activity Your child learned about the parts of a book. Pick out several kinds of books around your home (nonfiction, a reference book, a work of fiction) and examine the parts of the different books together.

W1.3 Use organizational features of printed text (e.g., citations, end notes, bibliographic references) to locate relevant information.

© Pearson Education, Inc., 5

Family Times

Summary

The Ch'i-lin Purse

Hsiang-ling was a spoiled young girl, but on her wedding day, she gave a purse full of riches from her mother to a less fortunate bride getting married on the same day. Later, Hsiang-ling was separated from her husband and son after a horrible storm. She found work taking care of a spoiled young boy in a wealthy home. The boy's mother turned out to be the poor bride Hsiang-ling had helped so long ago. The mother was so grateful that she split her family's fortune with Hsiang-ling and helped her find her husband and son.

Activity

A Gift of Kindness Do something nice for a family member today. Help them finish a chore or task they don't like doing, or offer to take care of something for them to free up a little of their time. You'll be surprised how much small deeds like this are appreciated.

Comprehension Skill

Compare and Contrast

When writers **compare** and **contrast** things, they tell how those things are alike or different. Words such as *same, also, before, although,* and *however* are clues that things are being compared or contrasted.

Activity

On Your Street With a family member, go outside and look at the houses and buildings on your street. Can you guess which ones might have been built by the same company? Do you see similarities? What are some of the differences? Compare and contrast the buildings and houses as you walk down the street.

Lesson Vocabulary

Words to Know

Knowing the meanings of these words is important to reading *The Ch'i-lin Purse*. Practice using these words.

Vocabulary Words

astonished surprised greatly; amazed

behavior manner of behaving; way of acting

benefactor person who has given money or kindly help

distribution the act of giving some to each, of dividing and giving out in shares

gratitude kindly feeling because of a favor received; desire to do a favor in return; thankfulness

procession something that moves forward; persons marching or riding

recommend to speak in favor of; suggest favorably

sacred worthy of reverence; not to be violated or disregarded

traditions customs or beliefs handed down from generation to generation

Conventions

Action and Linking Verbs

Action verbs tell what the subject of a sentence does. *For example: I smiled at the old woman.* "Smiled" is an *action verb*. **Linking verbs** link, or join, the subject to a word or words in the predicate. They tell what the subject of a sentence is like. *For example: Wai's painting looked amazing. Looked* is a *linking verb*. Common linking verbs include *am, is, are, was, were, will be, seem, feel,* and *look*.

Activity

Can You Do It? With a family member, play this fill-in-the-blank word game. Write down a handful of sentences that include an action verb— but leave a blank space where the action verb would normally be. Next, both of you should write ten action verbs on strips of paper. Write the present and past-tense forms of each verb on the strip. Finally, take turns picking a verb strip out of a hat or bowl and using it to fill in a blank in one of your sentences. Make the sentences as silly as you can.

Practice Tested Spelling Words

Family Times

Summary

Jane Goodall's 10 Ways to Help Save Wildlife

Internationally known scientist and conservationist Jane Goodall offers ten suggestions for ways we can all help save wildlife. From thinking of animals as individuals to recycling paper and getting involved with animal-rights organizations, Goodall suggests simple steps everyone can take.

Activity

Name Game Jane Goodall suggests we name animals and insects to make them seem more like individuals. With your family, make it a point to name the bugs and animals you encounter in everyday life for a week. Maybe Larry the spider won't seem so scary.

Comprehension Skill

Fact and Opinion

A **statement of fact** can be proved true or false. A **statement of opinion** tells what someone thinks or feels, and cannot be proven true or false. Opinions often include words that make judgments, such as *interesting*, *beautiful*, or *I believe*.

Activity

A Simple Answer With a family member, take turns making statements about your family. Have the other person guess whether each statement is true or false. If you're the person making the statements, remember to have a mix of true ones and false ones.

Lesson Vocabulary

Words to Know

Knowing the meanings of these words is important to reading *Jane Goodall's 10 Ways to Help Save Wildlife*. Practice using these words.

Vocabulary Words

conservation preservation from harm or decay; protection from loss or from being used up

contribute to help bring about

enthusiastic full of enthusiasm; eagerly interested

environment condition of the air, water, soil, etc.

investigation a careful search; detailed or careful examination

Conventions

Main and Helping Verbs

Main verbs show the action in a sentence. Main verbs are always the last word in a verb phrase. **Helping verbs** clarify the meaning of the main verb. For instance, they may indicate when the action takes place. They come before the main verb in a sentence. *Have, has, had, will, is, am, are, was,* and *were* can be helping verbs. *For example: Bob is building an airplane. Is* is the *linking verb* and *building* is the *main verb.*

Activity

Say It, Do It With a family member, take turns making statements and have the other person act out the action verb. For example, if someone says "I'm flying over the trees," the other person would act out "flying."

Practice Tested Spelling Words

_____   _____   _____   _____

_____   _____   _____   _____

_____   _____   _____   _____

_____   _____   _____   _____

_____   _____   _____   _____

Fact and Opinion

- A **statement of fact** can be proved true or false. A **statement of opinion** tells what someone thinks or feels.
- Statements of opinion often contain words that make judgments, such as *interesting* or *beautiful*.
- A single sentence might contain both a statement of fact and a statement of opinion.

Directions Read the following passage.

Dirty beaches are disgusting. I hate to see the shore of a lake or ocean dotted with candy wrappers, soda bottles, or other bits of garbage. Garbage on beaches is more than an eyesore. It also kills wildlife. Animals such as fish and turtles may eat drifting garbage they find in the water. If they do, they may choke. The plastic six-pack yokes from soda cans are dangerous to birds. Birds often become tangled in the plastic and die. To help keep beaches clean, you can volunteer on clean-up days. People who clean beaches help protect the environment and deserve the best places to sit when they visit the shore.

Directions Fill in the diagram below based on the passage.

Statement	Can it be proved true or false?	Fact? Opinion? Or both?
Dirty beaches are disgusting.	1.	2.
The plastic six-pack yokes from soda cans are dangerous to birds.	3.	4.
5.	The first part can be proved true or false, but not the second part.	contains both fact and opinion

Home Activity Your child identified statements of fact and opinion in a nonfiction passage. Tell your child a series of statements about your family and have your child determine whether they are fact or opinion. For each fact, ask your child how the statements can be proved true or false.

R2.5 Distinguish facts, supported inferences, and opinions in text.

Vocabulary

Directions Choose a word from the box that best matches each clue. Write the word on the line.

_____ **1.** preservation from harm

_____ **2.** surroundings

_____ **3.** full of eager interest

_____ **4.** give money, help, or time

_____ **5.** detailed, thorough examination

Check the Words You Know

___conservation
___contribute
___enthusiastic
___environment
___investigation

Directions Choose the word from the box that best completes each sentence. Write the word on the line.

Migrating birds, like the Canada goose, travel twice each year to a new

6. _____ . Scientists who study these annual moves are interested in

7. _____ of bird habitats. These **8.** _____

scientists **9.** _____ greatly to the safety of birds. Through

10. _____, research, and observation, environmental scientists serve

an important role in preserving nature.

Write an Opinion

On a separate sheet of paper, write your opinion on what people should do to help endangered animals. Explain why you feel the way you do. Use as many vocabulary words as you can.

Home Activity Your child identified and used vocabulary words from *Jane Goodall's 10 Ways to Help Save Wildlife*. With your child, find out information on endangered plants or animals in your area. Use the vocabulary words to discuss them.

R1.0 Word Analysis, Fluency, and Systematic Vocabulary Development

© Pearson Education, Inc., 5

Vocabulary • Context Clues

As you read, you will find unfamiliar words. You can use context clues to figure out the meaning of a new word. **Context clues** are found in the words and sentences around an unfamiliar word.

Directions Read the following passage. Then answer the questions below. Look for context clues around unfamiliar words to determine their meanings.

The U.S. Fish and Wildlife Service (USFWS) is one of our country's most enthusiastic protectors of endangered species. When the environment, or home, of one of our nation's species is threatened, the USFWS tries to protect it as best they can. They will begin with an investigation of the threat, and when they discover what is causing it they will act to repair the damage. Conservation of wetlands, prairies, and other geographically sensitive areas is an important part of the preservation goals of the USFWS. We can all help save endangered species by being responsible citizens and making sure we don't litter or contribute to the destruction of these sensitive lands.

1. What does the word *enthusiastic* mean?

_____

2. What context clues can help you understand the meaning of the word *environment*?

_____

3. Look at the sentence before the word *conservation*. How does this sentence give a clue to the meaning of *conservation*?

_____

_____

4. What does *contribute* mean as it is used in this passage?

_____

5. What is the meaning of *investigation*? How do you know?

_____

_____

_____

Home Activity Your child answered questions about unfamiliar words in a nonfiction passage by using context clues. Explain a process to your child, like making a complicated meal, using unfamiliar words, and help your child figure out what the new words mean by their context.

G3R1.6 Use sentence and word context to find the meaning of unknown words.

Compare and Contrast

Directions Read the article. Then answer the questions below.

The vast majority of frogs eat a diet of insects and worms. A frog's long tongue can strike out at a passing fly in a split second, scooping up its prey and pulling it back into its mouth faster than the human eye can see. This diet partly explains why so many species of frogs live near water. There are always plenty of insects to be found in and around a water source.

But some frogs eat more than insects and worms. Some frogs eat other frogs, mice, snakes, and even turtles! This is only seen among very large frogs, such as the North American bullfrog. They still use their lightning-fast, sticky tongues to grab their prey. However, the bullfrog's large size gives it the power to capture and eat such large meals.

1. What do the majority of frogs eat?

_____

_____

2. What does a North American bullfrog sometimes eat that most frogs do not?

_____

_____

3. Why do you think a North American bullfrog would need to eat a mouse?

_____

_____

4. What do both small and large frogs use to catch their prey?

_____

_____

5. On a separate sheet of paper, compare what you eat during a meal to what an older relative eats. What is the same and what is different?

Home Activity Your child has compared and contrasted information about frogs in a nonfiction passage. Discuss with your child the differences and similarities of two kinds of animals; such as birds and fish. How are they alike? How are they different?

G3R2.1 Identify structural patterns found in informational text (e.g., compare and contrast, cause and effect, sequential or chronological order, proposition and support) to strengthen comprehension.

© Pearson Education, Inc., 5

Fact and Opinion

- A **statement of fact** can be proved true or false. A **statement of opinion** tells what someone thinks or feels.
- Statements of opinion often contain words that make judgments, such as *interesting* or *beautiful*.
- A single sentence might contain both a statement of fact and a statement of opinion.

Directions Read the following passage. Then answer the questions below.

> Some people prefer cats to dogs as house pets. Fans of cats say they are just as friendly as dogs and that they are equally loving. We know from studies that cats sleep a bit more than dogs; a majority of a cat's day is spent napping. We also know that cats are preferable in pet-therapy situations because they are smaller and easier to handle for elderly or handicapped persons. For the past few years, polls have found that more people have cats as pets than dogs. But cats are hunters, and if let outside, a house cat will hunt birds, mice, and other small mammals. Some people say they are more frightened of cats than dogs. For some reason, they say, dogs seem friendlier.

1. What takes up most of a cat's day?

_____

2. Give one example of a statement of opinion found in the passage.

_____

_____

3. How do you know that your example is a statement of opinion?

_____

_____

4. Give one example of a statement of fact in the passage.

_____

_____

5. On a separate sheet of paper, give your opinion of cats and dogs. Which would you prefer to have as a pet?

Home Activity Your child answered questions about facts and opinions based on a passage. Read a newspaper or magazine article with your child and discuss which parts are statements of fact and which ones are statements of opinion.

R2.5 Distinguish facts, supported inferences, and opinions in text.

Fact and Opinion

- A **statement of fact** can be proved true or false. A **statement of opinion** tells what someone thinks or feels.
- Statements of opinion often contain words that make judgments, such as *interesting* or *beautiful*.
- A single sentence might contain both a statement of fact and a statement of opinion.

Directions Read the following passage about penguins. Fill in the chart below.

Molting is a process during which an animal sheds an outer layer of protection and grows a new one. When humans do this, it involves tiny amounts of skin or hair at a time. We should feel sorry for molting penguins, though, because molting is a difficult time for them. While penguins molt each year, they cannot go into the water. Penguins eat fish and other sea life, so while a penguin is molting, it cannot eat. A molting penguin also looks strange. Molting penguins migrate to a communal molting site, usually in a sheltered area. Depending on the size of the penguin, molting can take anywhere from two weeks to a full month! Maybe penguins think of molting as a way to diet.

Statement	Can it be proved true or false?	Fact? Opinion? Or both?
When an animal sheds an outer layer, it is called molting.	1.	2.
We should feel sorry for molting penguins, though, because molting is a difficult time for them.	The first part cannot be proved true or false, but the second part can.	3.
4. A molting penguin also	5.	Opinion

Home Activity Your child answered questions about facts and opinions in a nonfiction passage. Read a magazine article with your child and ask him or her to identify facts and opinions in the text.

R2.5 Distinguish facts, supported inferences, and opinions in text.

Electronic Media

- There are two types of **electronic media**—computer and non-computer. Computer sources include computer software, CD-ROMs, and the Internet. Non-computer sources include audiotapes, videotapes, films, filmstrips, television, and radio.

- To find information on the Internet, use a search engine and type in your keywords. Be specific. It's a good idea to use two or more keywords as well as typing "AND" between keywords. To go to a Web page that's listed in your search results, click on the underlined link.

Directions Use the following list of electronic media to answer the questions below.

- *Monkey-ing Around* (Public Television documentary about captive monkey behavior)
- *Monkey Project* (Internet site for an international primate organization)
- *Field Recordings: Monkeys of Gambia* (CD of natural monkey sounds recorded in Gambia in 1998)
- "Jane Goodall's Quest" (Taped interview with Jane Goodall)
- *World Wildlife Fund's Annual Report 2003* (CD-ROM with annual assessment of endangered species and habitats)
- *One World* (Internet site about wild animal habitats that are endangered)

1. Which source would be most helpful in writing a report on Jane Goodall?

_____

2. How would you access information from the *World Wildlife Fund's Annual Report 2003*?

_____

3. If you were doing an Internet search, what keywords would you type into the search engine to find the Web site *One World?*

_____

_____

4. Which source would be most helpful if you wanted to learn about the sounds monkeys make?

_____

5. Which source would you start with if you were investigating primates in your local zoo?

_____

_____

G4W1.7 Use various reference materials (e.g., dictionary, thesaurus, card catalog, encyclopedia, online information) as an aid to writing.

Research and Study Skills   **107**

Directions Use the following Internet search results found on a search engine to answer the questions below.

Search Results

Prairie Shores
     State of Illinois' official site for prairie habitat information. Northern Illinois prairies adjacent to Lake Michigan. Flora, fauna, ecosystems, wildlife habitats.

Federally Protected Ecosystems
     U.S. Department of the Interior. Based on annual assessment, site lists all federally protected ecosystems by state, region, ecosystem type, EPA ranking, etc.

Our Backyard
     Waukegan community organization site to protect Amber Prairie. Updates on preservation effort, fundraising efforts, state and federal decision deadlines.

Habitat and Ecosystem Interdependence
     University of Northern Illinois three-year study on development impact on Amber Prairie and its ecosystems, habitats, and indigenous species.

---

6. What does the information below the underlined links tell you?

_____

7. What keywords might have been used to get these search results?

_____

8. Which sites are the official government sources regarding this prairie?

_____

9. Which site would be the least reliable if you were doing a report for school?

_____

10. Why might the *Habitat and Ecosystem Interdependence* site be valuable if you were doing a report?

_____

_____

 Home Activity Your child answered questions about electronic media. With your child, look around your house and see how many different types of electronic media you have on hand. Talk with your son or daughter about how each of the various electronic media sources could be valuable in his or her studies.

G4W1.7 Use various reference materials (e.g., dictionary, thesaurus, card catalog, encyclopedia, online information) as an aid to writing.

Family Times

Summary

The Midnight Ride of Paul Revere

Revolutionary war hero Paul Revere warned the colonists of an advancing attack by the British army. Revere rode his horse through the night warning every village and town. The colonists, prepared by Revere's warning, defeated the British forces.

Activity

Household Poetics With a family member, write a short poem describing something you do every day, like eating lunch or walking to school. Try to make the poem as exciting as possible.

Comprehension Skill

Sequence

The **sequence** of events is the order in which they take place. Clue words such as *first*, *next*, and *then* may show sequence in a story.

Activity

Recipe for the Day Write out the order of events that have happened today, from when you woke up to when you started this activity. Try to be as detailed as possible. Then, using what you wrote as a guide, tell a family member about what you have done with your day. Pay attention to the words you use to indicate sequence.

Lesson Vocabulary

Words to Know

Knowing the meanings of these words is important to reading *The Midnight Ride of Paul Revere*. Practice using these words.

Vocabulary Words

fate what becomes of someone or something

fearless without fear; afraid of nothing; brave; daring

glimmer a faint, unsteady light

lingers stays on; goes slowly, as if unwilling to leave

magnified caused something to look larger than it actually is

somber having deep shadows; dark; gloomy

steed a horse, especially a riding horse

Grammar

Subject-Verb Agreement

Subject-verb agreement occurs when the correct singular or plural verb is used to match the singular or plural noun or pronoun in the subject. Singular nouns and pronouns take singular verbs. Plural nouns and pronouns take plural verbs. *For example: Jenny wants to go to Philadelphia. Her parents want to go to Boston instead.* "Jenny" is *singular,* so it takes the singular "wants," but "her parents" is *plural,* so it takes the plural "want."

Activity

Mix 'n' Match With a family member, take a piece of paper and divide it into twelve squares. On six of the squares, write six different subjects (nouns). Make some plural, like *cats*, and some singular, like *dog*. On the other six squares, write six different verbs that agree with the nouns. Then mix up the squares, and match the subjects and verbs in different combinations so they all agree.

Practice Tested Spelling Words

© Pearson Education, Inc., 5

Sequence

- The **sequence** of events is the order in which they take place, from first to last.
- Clue words such as *first, next,* and *then* may show sequence in a story or article, but not always. Other clues are dates and times of day.
- Sometimes two events happen at the same time. Clue words that show this are *meanwhile* and *in that same year.*

Directions Read the following passage and complete the time line below.

The Reverend Martin Luther King Jr. is one of the heroes of freedom in America. In 1948, at the age of 19, King became a minister. That same year, he graduated from Morehouse College. He is best known, however, for his role in the civil rights movement. In 1955, he helped organize the Montgomery Bus Boycott. In 1963, he led the Freedom March on Washington, D.C. Because of his frequent participation in civil rights protests, he was arrested 30 times. In 1964, he was awarded the Nobel Peace Prize. Dr. King was assassinated in 1968.

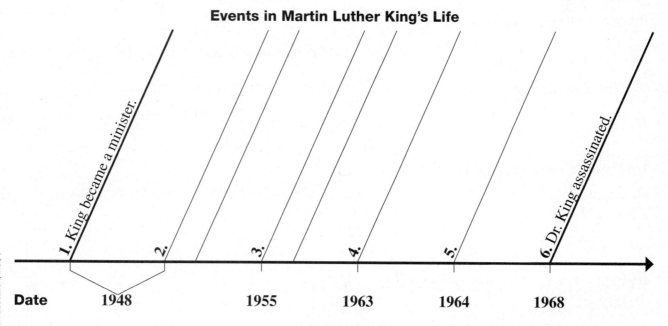

Events in Martin Luther King's Life

1. King became a minister.
2.
3.
4.
5.
6. Dr. King assassinated.

| Date | 1948 | 1955 | 1963 | 1964 | 1968 |

5. Which two events happened at nearly the same time? How can you tell?

_____

_____

Home Activity Your child read a short passage and made a time line of key events in the life of Dr. Martin Luther King Jr. Talk with your child about some of the important events in your own life. Create a time line to show the sequence of those events.

© Pearson Education, Inc., 5

R2.2 Analyze text that is organized in sequential or chronological order.

Vocabulary

Directions Choose the word from the box that best completes each sentence. Write the word on the line.

_____ 1. a high-spirited horse

_____ 2. made something look larger

_____ 3. not afraid

_____ 4. a faint, unsteady light

_____ 5. dark or gloomy

Check the Words You Know

___fate
___fearless
___glimmer
___lingers
___magnified
___somber
___steed

Directions Choose a word from the box that best matches each clue. Write the word on the line.

Some have fought for freedom in a **6.** _____ and inspiring way.

The founding fathers **7.** _____ this kind of commitment when they

fought against the British and, some would say, **8.** _____ itself.

The **9.** _____ of hope they felt eventually became reality when

they defeated the English king's forces. That dedication to the fight for freedom

10. _____ in all Americans to this day.

Write a Conversation

On a separate sheet of paper, write a short conversation between two members of the colonial army in 1775. Use as many vocabulary words as you can.

Home Activity Your child identified and used vocabulary words from the poem *The Midnight Ride of Paul Revere.* With your child, look up information about Paul Revere and his activities as a colonist in the 1700s. Discuss the information, using as many vocabulary words as possible.

R1.0 Word Analysis, Fluency, and Systematic Vocabulary Development

Vocabulary • Antonyms

- An antonym is a word that means the opposite of another word.
- Words such as *unlike, but,* and *instead* may indicate the presence of antonyms.
- A thesaurus is a book that lists words and their antonyms and synonyms.

Directions Read the following passage about the colonists. Then circle the words in the list below that are antonyms.

Sometimes your life may seem complicated, but in fact it may be simple compared to a colonist's life. For example, in the 1700s the car had not been invented. Instead of depending on cars for swift travel, people rode horses to get where they needed to go—a very slow method of transportation. The pace was more leisurely than driving a car, but it was still faster than walking.

Walking outside the settlement left a person open to such dangers as wolves and certain Native American tribes. Most tribes were peaceful, but some were hostile in response to the early colonists' behavior. Since there were no sidewalks or streetlights outside of town, it was best not to linger but to come home quickly. Horses gave colonists an extra measure of safety.

1. **complicated**	hard	long	boring	simple
2. **swift**	slow	fancy	costly	speedy
3. **leisurely**	respectable	tiring	fast	cheap
4. **hostile**	peaceful	grateful	shy	helpful
5. **linger**	stay	talk	rush	sleep
6. **danger**	pleasure	safety	flight	strength

Directions Use a thesaurus to find antonyms for the following words.

7. depend _____   8. danger _____

9. best _____   10. extra _____

Home Activity Your child read a short passage and identified antonyms, words that mean the opposite of each other. Have your child describe a familiar person, place, or thing using words and their antonyms, using a dictionary, glossary, or thesaurus for help.

R1.3 Understand and explain frequently used synonyms, antonyms, and homographs.

Name_____

Literary Elements · Setting and Theme

Directions Read the article. Then answer the questions below.

Patrick Henry was one of the many interesting characters in the American Revolution. He provided us with one of the great sayings in American history As a young man, he tried and failed at being a farmer and shopkeeper. He eventually educated himself and became a lawyer. Patrick Henry became a famous activist in the fight against British control of the colonies. He spoke out against English rule early and often. He urged fellow colonists to revolt. He challenged the British over their restrictions upon American liberty. In 1775, at a meeting of colonial leaders, he spoke his most famous line: "I know not what course others may take, but as for me, give me liberty or give me death." This was the theme of his adult life.

1. When and where did Patrick Henry live?

_____

_____

2. How do you know Patrick Henry was outspoken?

_____

_____

3. How did Patrick Henry feel about British rule of the colonies?

_____

_____

4. Why do you think Patrick Henry said, "Give me liberty or give me death"?

_____

_____

5. On a separate sheet of paper, describe something you feel so strongly about that you would say something like what Patrick Henry said.

School + Home **Home Activity** Your child read a short passage and answered questions about setting and theme. Discuss the setting of one of your child's favorite places. Ask your child: What does it look like? What do you see there?

R3.4 Understand that theme refers to the meaning or moral of a selection and recognize themes (whether implied or stated directly) in sample works.

© Pearson Education, Inc., 5

Sequence

- The **sequence** of events is the order in which they take place, from first to last.
- Clue words such as *first, next,* and *then* may show sequence in a story or article, but not always. Other clues are dates and times of day.
- Sometimes two events happen at the same time. Clue words that show this are *meanwhile* and *in that same year.*

Directions Read the following passage. Then answer the questions below.

> In 1773, American colonists in Boston raided three British ships in Boston Harbor. They dumped more than 300 crates of British tea into the water. They were protesting England's taxes on the American colonies. Eight months earlier, the British government had created a tax on all tea shipped from England to America. The colonists were furious. On the night of December 16, 1773, Samuel Adams led approximately 100 colonists and stormed the British ships waiting to unload their tea. By dumping all the tea into the harbor, the colonists let the King know that they would not stand for his high taxation.

1. What did the British do that angered the American colonists? What year did they do it?

_____

2. How long did it take for the colonists to take action?

_____

3. Why did the colonists dump the tea into Boston Harbor?

_____

_____

4. Why is knowing that the colonists were angry at the British important to the sequence of events?

_____

_____

5. Imagine that you have been asked to give a history presentation on the Boston Tea Party. On a separate sheet of paper, list at least five questions you might try to answer in your presentation.

© Pearson Education, Inc., 5

 Home Activity Your child read a short passage and answered questions about the sequence of events described in it. Read a newspaper or magazine article with your child and discuss the sequence of events it describes.

R2.2 Analyze text that is organized in sequential or chronological order.

Sequence

- The **sequence** of events is the order in which they take place, from first to last.
- Clue words such as *first, next,* and *then* may show sequence in a story or article, but not always. Other clues are dates and times of day.
- Sometimes two events happen at the same time. Clue words that can show this are *meanwhile* and *in that same year.*

Directions Read the following passage and complete the time line below.

Thomas Jefferson was the third President of the United States. After a close election, he took office in 1801. In 1803, Jefferson proposed an expedition to explore the West. This became the Lewis and Clark expedition. Meanwhile, he made an agreement with France called the Lousiana Purchase.

Jefferson's re-election in 1804 was different from his first. This time he won every state except three. Lewis and Clark returned in 1806. They had traveled all the way to present-day Oregon. Jefferson was asked to run for President for a third term. He refused because he did not want the President to become like a king. In 1809, Jefferson returned to his much-loved home, Monticello.

Thomas Jefferson's Presidency

1801	1803		1804	1806	1809
Jefferson is elected President.	1. Jefferson proposes	2.	3. Jefferson is elected	4.	Jefferson returns home to Monticello.

5. Which two events happened at nearly the same time? How can you tell?

_____

_____

 Home Activity Your child read a short passage and identified the sequence of events in it. Read a historical story or article with your child and chart the sequence of events in the article.

R2.2 Analyze text that is organized in sequential or chronological order.

Name_____

Illustration/Caption

- **Illustrations** or **pictures** can convey information about characters and events in a story. They can help establish mood, dramatize action, reinforce the author's imagery or symbolism, or help explain the text.
- A **caption** is the text explaining the illustration or picture. It usually appears below or to the side of the image.

Directions Look at the illustration and read the caption. Then answer the questions below.

This illustration shows Benjamin Franklin flying a kite in an experiment to relate lightning and electricity.

1. Based on the illustration, in what kind of weather did Franklin fly his kite?

_____

_____

2. Look at the picture. How did Franklin's experiment work?

_____

_____

3. What do the clothes of the people in the illustration tell you?

_____

_____

4. Why do Ben Franklin and his companion look pleased?

_____

_____

5. Can you tell where the event took place by looking at the illustration?

_____

R2.1 Understand how text features (e.g., format, graphics, sequence, diagrams, illustrations, charts, maps) make information accessible and usable.

Directions Look at the illustration and read the caption. Then answer the question below.

This illustration shows the Illinois state quarter, whose design was inspired by the artwork of Thom Cicchelli of Chicago.

6. Look at the illustration of the quarter. Who is pictured on the quarter?

_____

_____

7. Based on the illustration, in what year was Illinois admitted to the United States?

_____

8. What do the tall buildings show?

_____

9. What does the caption tell you that is not reflected in the image?

_____

10. What do you think the 21 stars signify?

_____

_____

Home Activity Your child learned how illustrations and captions can help convey information about a story. Look at one of your child's favorite books and discuss how the illustrations in it help your child learn more about the story.

R2.1 Understand how text features (e.g., format, graphics, sequence, diagrams, illustrations, charts, maps) make information accessible and usable.

© Pearson Education, Inc., 5

Name

Family Times

Selection Summaries

Week 1 *At the Beach*

When a boy gets hurt while following Fernando on a forbidden adventure, Fernando lies about what happened.

Week 2 *Passage to Freedom*

A Japanese diplomat helps Jewish refugees escape German Nazis.

Week 3 *The Ch'i-lin Purse*

A bride's kindness is repaid years later.

Week 4 *Jane Goodall's 10 Ways to Help Save Wildlife*

The famous scientist gives suggestions that everyone can do to help wild animals.

Week 5 *The Midnight Ride of Paul Revere*

After spreading word of a British invasion, Paul Revere became a hero.

Activity

Tell a member of your family more about each of the five stories. Be sure to remember characters, plot, theme, and setting. Then write three reasons why you like one the best.

Comprehension Skills Review

In Unit 2, you learned and used many skills while reading the stories and selections.

- When you **compare** and **contrast,** you tell how things are alike and different.
- The **author's purpose** is the reason the author writes a story.
- A **fact** can be proved true. An **opinion** is what someone thinks or believes.
- **Sequence** refers to the order in which the events happen.

Activity

Doing the right thing isn't always easy. Sometimes we're afraid to do the right thing because we might get into trouble. Talk with a family member about a time when he or she did the right thing, even though it was difficult. Then tell about a time when you did the right thing. How were your experiences alike? How were they different?

Unit Vocabulary Skills

Unfamiliar Words

When you find an **unfamiliar word** while reading, you can look up its meaning in a dictionary.

Activity Make a list of unfamiliar words that you encounter while reading, and put them in alphabetical order.

Greek and Latin Roots

Many English words have **Greek and Latin roots.** You can use a dictionary to find out a word's roots.

Activity As you read, look for words that seem similar, and check their roots in a dictionary. Do they come from the same root word?

Unfamiliar Words

When you find an **unfamiliar word** while reading, you can try to determine its meaning by looking at the words and sentences around it.

Activity Write each unfamiliar word on an index card. Write the definition you infer on the other side.

Antonyms

Antonyms are words that mean the opposite of other words.

Activity Take the list of words similar to each other you created and this time use a thesaurus to find the opposites of those words.

Unit Spelling Rules

Digraphs *th, sh, ch, ph*

Consonant digraphs are two consonants together that stand for one new sound.

Irregular Plurals

Regular plurals follow the rules. Irregular plurals often have base word changes. Some irregular plurals are the same as the singular form.

Vowel sounds with *r*

Vowels and vowel sounds have a slightly different sound when they are followed by *r*. Vowels followed by *r* are called *r*-controlled vowels.

Final syllables *en, an, el, le, il*

Vowels in unaccented syllables often stand for the same sound, /ə/.

Final syllables *er, ar, or*

Final syllables *er, ar,* and *or* often sound alike even when they are spelled differently. Some sounds can be spelled in different ways.

Activity With a family member, identify as many words as possible in books, magazines, or newspapers that follow the Unit Spelling Rules. Make a list of these words.

⊙ Unfamiliar Words

Unfamiliar Words As you read, you will come across words that are new to you. You can check the meanings of words that you don't know in a dictionary.

Practice

Guide words appear on the top of each dictionary page to show the first and the last word on each page. For each Word to Know, circle the correct set of guide words.

1. driftwood

   a. document – donkey   b. dried – drink

2. algae

   a. aluminum – amalgam   b. aleph – alphabet

3. sternly

   a. stepson – sticker   b. steam – steed

4. hammocks

   a. hardly – harrowing   b. hamburger – Hamptons

5. concealed

   a. conjure – contrite   b. collect – concentrate

6. sea urchins

   a. seatmate – secret   b. secret agent – sedative

7. tweezers

   a. turnabout – turtle   b. turtledove – twilled

8. lamented

   a. landmass – lap   b. lame – landmark

On Your Own

As you read "Augie's Present," look for words that are unfamiliar to you. Find their definitions in a dictionary.

© Pearson Education, Inc., 5

School + Home **Home Activity** Your child reviewed how to use a dictionary to check the meanings of unfamiliar words. With your child, look for unfamiliar words in a newspaper or magazine. Look up the words together, using guidewords when necessary, and discuss their meanings.

Name_____

⊙ Compare and Contrast

When you **compare and contrast,** you tell how things are similar to and different from each other.

Read the following passage. Then answer the questions below.

Mariska had always loved swimming in the calm waters of the lake near her house. Today, however, she was at the ocean for the first time! She shivered as the brisk wind came off the water. The great stretch of sandy beach astonished her. The lake near her house was much smaller. It didn't have waves like these, either.

Mariska laughed at the little sea birds as they ran away from the oncoming water. Her lake had birds, too, but they were bigger ones like ducks and loons. Mariska gasped as she felt the sand being washed away from under her feet. "This place is amazing!" she said. "Especially at high tide!"

Practice

1. What is going on in the passage?

_____

2. What does Mariska notice about the ocean that is different from the lake she is used to?

_____

_____

3. What does Mariska notice that is the same?

_____

4. Did Mariska prefer the beach or the lake?

_____

_____

On Your Own

Use what you know about drawing conclusions as you read "Augie's Present."

© Pearson Education, Inc., 5

Home Activity Your child reviewed the skill of drawing conclusions. Share a magazine article and work together to draw conclusions from what you read.

Name_____

⊙ Unfamiliar Words

Remember that **unfamiliar words** are words you have not seen before or do not know. When you run across an unfamiliar word in your reading, you can look up its meaning in a dictionary or a glossary.

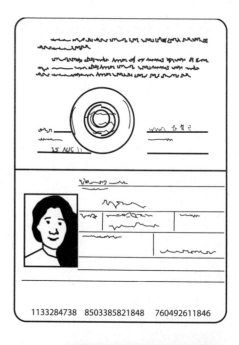

1133284738 8503385821848 760492611846

Practice

Read the following passage. Fill in the blanks with the correct Word to Know from the list.

The _____ needed more help than just

shelter and blankets. Each needed a _____

that would allow safe passage from their war-torn country.

The _____ sent a _____ to

his _____ asking them to deal with the

important _____. The government's

_____ were in _____, and

the documents were provided quickly. The refugees were saved.

Words To Know

- agreement
- cable
- diplomat
- issue
- refugees
- representatives
- superiors
- visa

On Your Own

As you read "Franklin Delano Roosevelt," look up unfamiliar words in the dictionary. Make a list of the words you find.

School + Home

Home Activity With your child, read a newspaper or magazine feature article. As you read, pause to look up unfamiliar words in a dictionary.

🐻 **G3R1.7** Use a dictionary to learn the meaning and other features of unknown words.

⊙ Author's Purpose

Authors write for many
different reasons.

The **author's purpose** is the reason the author wrote the text.
Authors write to entertain, to inform, to persuade, and to express
their feelings and ideas.

Draw a line from the kind of writing to the author's purpose for
writing it.

Newspaper editorial   to inform

Poem   to express himself or herself

User's guide   to entertain

Novel   to persuade

Practice

Read the sentence or sentences after each number below. On the lines below, write what the author's
purpose is, and tell how you know.

1. The dog growled at Stacy. She shuddered. Then, to her amazement, the dog said, "Hey, what are
you so scared of?"

_____

2. If you use this brand of shampoo, you will have the most beautiful hair.

_____

3. The firefighters responded to the report of a fire at 822 North Street at 6:30 P.M.

_____

4. I just want to thank you for the gift—it was such a nice surprise!

_____

On Your Own

Use what you know about cause and effect as you read "Franklin Delano Roosevelt." List one cause
you find in the selection and two effects of that cause.

School + Home **Home Activity** Your child reviewed the purposes authors have for writing. Flip through a newspaper and
discuss the purposes of the people who wrote letters to the editor, the articles, and the columns.

Name_____

⊙ Greek and Latin Roots

Greek and Latin Roots are used in many English words. When you find a word you don't know, being familiar with its Greek or Latin root may help you understand what the word means.

Practice

Read the following sentences and fill in the blanks with the Words to Know. Then circle the correct meaning of each underlined word.

Words To Know
astonished
behavior
benefactor
distribution
gratitude
procession
recommend
sacred
traditions

1. My family is Chinese-American, and we <u>benefit</u> from

   having many interesting Chinese _____.
   For example, we burn paper money to show

   _____ to our ancestors.

   a. get something good from   b. get nothing good from

2. I left a big <u>gratuity</u>, or tip, for the waiter in the restaurant. My

   family was _____ until I explained that he had
   done a great job and that I wanted

   to thank him for his considerate _____.

   a. money that someone gives   b. money that someone has to pay
      to show they are pleased   even if they don't want to

3. The villagers made a long _____ through their town to check on the

   _____ of food to everyone. All the families who were hungry felt <u>grateful</u> for
   this kindness.

   a. helpful   b. thankful

4. In some parts of the world, cows are considered <u>beneficial</u> and _____, so people
   will not kill or eat them.

   a. something that needs help   b. something that is good for all

5. You have been such a generous _____ to my family and me. Can you

   _____ a way for us to pay you back and show our <u>gratefulness</u>?

   a. a feeling of being pleased   b. a feeling of needing
      or thankful   help from someone

On Your Own

As you read "Augie's Present," look for words that have Greek or Latin roots. Make a list of the words you find.

Home Activity Your child reviewed Greek and Latin roots, which are often parts of English words. Discuss with your child the roots he or she learned about and look for words with similar roots in magazines and newspapers.

R1.4 Know abstract, derived roots and affixes from Greek and Latin and use this knowledge to analyze the meaning of complex words (e.g., *controversial*).

Vocabulary 125

© Pearson Education, Inc., 5

Name_____

⊙ Compare and Contrast

When you **compare** two things, you tell the ways in which they are similar. When you **contrast** two things, you tell the ways they are different.

This is Amy and her dog. When she takes her dog for a walk, her dog holds his head up as Amy holds the leash tight.

This is Ann and her dog. When Ann takes her dog for a walk, her dog walks with his head down.

Practice

Amy and Ann are sisters. Compare their pictures. How are Amy and Ann alike?

_____

_____

_____

Now, contrast Amy and Ann. How are they different?

_____

_____

_____

On Your Own

Use what you know about comparing and contrasting as you read "Augie's Present."

Home Activity Your child reviewed comparing (telling how things are alike) and contrasting (telling how things are different). Discuss two favorite games or books with your child, and ask him or her to compare and contrast them.

🐻 **G4R2.1** Identify structural patterns found in informational text (e.g., compare and contrast, cause and effect, sequential or chronological order, proposition and support) to strengthen comprehension.

© Pearson Education, Inc., 5

Name_____

⊙ Unfamiliar Words

Unfamiliar Words Use context clues to help you figure out **unfamiliar words**. Context clues are the words and sentences around the unfamiliar words.

Practice

Read each sentence. Complete the sentences with the correct Words to Know. Then circle the letter of the definition for each underlined unfamiliar word. Use context clues to help you.

> **Words To Know**
>
> **conservation**
> **contribute**
> **enthusiastic**
> **environment**
> **investigation**

1. The scientists conducted the _____ to find out where the <u>exotic</u> butterflies had gone.

   a. unusual   b. difficult

2. They first went to the <u>isolated</u> land far from the city, where the butterflies had lived, to see if their _____ had changed.

   a. not close   b. not easy

3. When they found that the landowner had removed plants the butterflies fed on, they explained to him how <u>replacing</u> the plants would _____ to restoring the butterflies.

   a. putting something away   b. putting something back

4. Excited to play a part, the landowner was _____ about helping the butterflies and thanked the scientists <u>vigorously</u>.

   a. with not much feeling   b. with lots of feeling

5. Together, the scientists and the landowner restored the habitat and created a _____ success story. Their work was <u>renowned</u> for years to come.

   a. secret and hidden   b. celebrated and praised

On Your Own

As you read "Franklin Delano Roosevelt," read the context in which any unfamiliar words appear for any clues that can help you determine their meanings. List the unfamiliar words and clues you find.

Home Activity Your child reviewed using context clues to determine the meanings of unfamiliar words. Practice this skill with your child while reading a newspaper or magazine.

R1.3 Understand and explain frequently used synonyms, antonyms, and homographs.

⊙ Fact and Opinion

A **fact** is something that can be proved. An **opinion** is something that is a belief, thought, or feeling, and cannot be proved. Opinions often include words that make judgments, such as *best, beautiful,* or *interesting.*

Fact: Sharks are fish.

Opinion: Sharks are scary.

Practice

In the passage below, underline statements of fact and circle statements of opinion.

> The great white is one of the largest species of shark. With their huge mouths full of razor-sharp teeth, these large, powerful fish are truly one of nature's most frightening creations. Great whites feed mostly on seals and sea lions. These sharks have been seen attacking seals from below and rocketing high out of the water. The great white is an awesome creature that deserves our respect.

1. Write three facts about great white sharks.

_____

_____

_____

2. Write three opinions about great white sharks.

_____

_____

_____

On Your Own

Use what you know about fact and opinion as you read "Franklin Delano Roosevelt."

School + Home

Home Activity Your child reviewed fact and opinion. Invite your child to share his or her opinions on a topic.

R2.5 Distinguish facts, supported inferences, and opinions in text.

Name_____

⊙ Antonyms

Antonym An **antonym** is a word that means the opposite of another word. The thesaurus lists antonyms for a word in its entry.

Words To Know	
fate	magnified
fearless	somber
glimmer	steed
lingers	

Practice

Read the passage. Write the antonym of the underlined word on the lines below. Use the Words to Know box.

"I am so (**1.**) joyous today," sighed the king, "as I must give all of my kingdom to the evil knight, Sir Spector, who has laid siege to my castle."

"But King Horace, as long as the Silver Knight still lives, there is a (**2.**) big bright light of hope," said the king's servant.

"Not even the Silver Knight is (**3.**) frightened enough to challenge Sir Spector," said the king. "I fear it is (**4.**) our choice that he shall rule the kingdom forever."

Just then, hoofbeats rang out, (**5.**) made smaller by the loud echoes of the stone castle walls. A voice called, "Surrender to me, Sir Spector! I am the Silver Knight! How dare you attempt to steal the crown from the rightful king!"

The Silver Knight's steed reared up. Knight and horse made a dazzling sight. Sir Spector screamed and ran away. The Silver Knight took off her helmet and her long hair shone in the sunlight. "Thank you, Lady Gwen!" said the king. "I hope you will join us for a feast to celebrate your victory. After all, a hero always (**6.**) flees after she has saved the day!"

1. _____ 2. _____ 3. _____

4. _____ 5. _____ 6. _____

7. A **steed** is a kind of _____.

On Your Own

As you read "Franklin Delano Roosevelt," look for antonyms and how they are used in the story.

Home Activity Your child reviewed antonyms. Have a contest with your child and see who can list the most pairs of antonyms. A thesaurus will help resolve any questions.

R1.3 Understand and explain frequently used synonyms, antonyms, and homographs.

Name_____

Sequence

___

Sequence is the order in which events happen.

___

| Jesse gets up every day at 7. | After getting dressed and brushing his teeth, he eats breakfast. | Jesse walks six blocks to school, through the town square. | School starts at 9 in the morning. |

Practice

1. What time does Jesse get up on school days?

_____

2. What does Jesse do before having breakfast?

_____

_____

3. What does Jesse do after breakfast?

_____

4. What time does Jesse have to be at school?

_____

_____

On Your Own

Use what you know about sequence as you read "Franklin Delano Roosevelt."

Home Activity Your child reviewed sequences of events. Discuss the sequence of events that your family follows when doing a regular activity, such as making dinner.

130 Comprehension

Practice Book Unit 2 Cumulative Review

Franklin Delano Roosevelt

"The only thing we have to fear is fear itself." So said one of our country's most brilliant and well-spoken Presidents, Franklin Delano Roosevelt. This brave leader was President of the United States from 1933 to 1945. He was elected to serve an extraordinary four terms in office when no other President had served more than two. Millions of Americans listened to Roosevelt's radio broadcasts, known as "fireside chats." His voice carried across the darkness, traveling through the radio to people who were hungry, afraid, and poor. Americans listened to their President and heard a voice that would lead them to a brighter future.

From the moment he was born, Franklin Delano Roosevelt was given wealth and privileges. His rich parents educated him at home until the age of 14. He then went to Groton, a private school in Massachusetts, and then went to college at Harvard University. Franklin was accustomed to having money, but he was also taught to be generous to others. While at Harvard, he became inspired by his fifth cousin, President Theodore Roosevelt. It was Theodore who first turned Franklin's attention to politics and economics.

Franklin later met Theodore's niece, Eleanor. Eleanor and Franklin were soon engaged, and the young couple married in 1905. Eleanor, who worked with the poor in New York City, opened Franklin's eyes to the problems of hunger and poverty in America.

Franklin Delano Roosevelt went into politics and was elected to the New York Senate in 1910. He was reelected in 1912, and later became Assistant Secretary of the Navy in 1913. During World War I, Roosevelt proved he was a capable leader who strengthened and organized the navy.

Then disaster hit. While vacationing at Campobello Island in Canada, the healthy young Roosevelt was struck down with polio, a dangerous disease that causes paralysis. At the time, no cure or vaccine for polio existed. Roosevelt would have to spend the rest of his life in a wheelchair or leg braces.

Despite these intense difficulties, Franklin was able to continue his political career, thanks in part to the help of Eleanor and others. In 1928, he was elected as New York governor, and he went on to serve several years in that position. As governor, Franklin worked to provide tax relief, cheaper utilities, employment, and help to those in need. His achievements as governor paved the way for his election to the presidency in 1932.

⊙ **DAY 2** Author's Purpose What do you think is the author's purpose in this passage?

_____

_____

_____

⊙ **DAY 4** Fact and Opinion Look at the very first sentence. Is it a fact, or is it Roosevelt's opinion?

_____

⊙ **DAY 5** Antonyms What is an antonym for *generous*?

_____

⊙ **DAY 2** Unfamiliar Words Circle the words in the paragraph that help you to understand the meaning of *paralysis*.

⊙ **DAY 5** Sequence When was Roosevelt first elected as governor?

_____

© Pearson Education, Inc., 5

R2.0 Students read and understand grade-level appropriate material.

Name _____

⊙ **DAY 5** Sequence
What event happened
before Roosevelt
declared war?

_____

_____

⊙ **DAY 4** Unfamiliar
Words What
words help you
to understand the
meaning of *neutrality*?

_____

_____

⊙ **DAY 4** Fact and
Opinion Look at the
last sentence of the
selection. Circle the
words that provide a
fact and underline the
words that provide an
opinion.

⊙ **DAY 2** Author's
Purpose Do you think
the author achieved
her purpose?

_____

_____

_____

_____

_____

When Franklin was elected President in 1932, the United States in deep trouble. A time of poverty and hardship called the Great Depression was ravaging the country. People were out of work, farmers couldn't earn a living, and banks were closing. For many, food was scarce and money was tight. Americans were in desperate need of a good leader.

As his first order of business, President Roosevelt started the New Deal, a series of programs and policies that helped farmers and the unemployed. Roosevelt stabilized the banks, created more jobs, and provided aid to those in need. When it was time for reelection in 1936, Roosevelt won by a landslide.

The Great Depression left many Americans focused only on their problems at home. But in Europe and Asia, more troubles were brewing. Roosevelt became increasingly worried about the political environment in Germany, Italy, and Japan. Then in 1939, World War II erupted in Europe. Americans hoped to distance themselves from the violence overseas, but Roosevelt knew this would be difficult. He offered as much assistance to the Allied Forces as he could, short of officially entering the war.

With the world in turmoil, Roosevelt was elected in 1940 to a third term in office. Then on December 7, 1941, Japan bombed Pearl Harbor, a naval base on Honolulu, Hawaii. More than 2,500 people died in the bombing. That was the end of the United States's neutrality. The very next day, President Roosevelt declared war.

During the war, Roosevelt worked hard to strengthen his relationships with the representatives of Britain and the Soviet Union. He was elected to his final term as President in 1944. Roosevelt worked constantly to bring an end to the war, but his health was beginning to fail. He died on April 12, 1945, leaving behind a country that would mourn the loss of its beloved and fearless leader.

School + Home **Home Activity** Your child read a selection and used comprehension and vocabulary skills from Unit 2. Have your child summarize the selection using sequence words and identifying facts and opinions.

R2.0 Students read and understand grade-level appropriate material.

Augie's Present

The year was 1942. I looked through my dirty window at the even dirtier gray sky beyond it. Nothing felt right anymore, not since my brother Augie had joined the army and left for Europe nearly three months ago. His birthday was coming up soon. I hoped he'd have a chance to celebrate somehow.

On the street down below, cars and people were beginning to stir. *Stay safe today, Augie,* I thought to myself.

The smell of porridge curled through the air, and Ma was soon knocking on my bedroom door. "Get up, Susan," she told me. "Breakfast will be ready soon, and you need to get to school."

I sighed and pulled myself out of bed. That was Ma—practical to a fault. Nothing worried or scared her.

By the time I was ready to leave, Ma was halfway through cleaning our small apartment. She was always bustling through life, working hard to make ends meet. We didn't have much, but we had enough to get by.

"Out you go," Ma told me, kissing me on the cheek. "And don't you forget—learning is a privilege and a luxury. I won't have you missing school and moping about just because you're thinking of your brave brother overseas. He did the right thing by leaving."

I nodded quietly. "His birthday's coming up soon, Ma," I said. "We have to find a way to make it special."

"I know, honey," she told me. "We will." Then she shooed me out the door.

The school day went by quickly. Mrs. Heaton passed out some arithmetic homework and gave us a reading assignment. Then at recess, my friends and I gossiped about the war. It was all anyone ever talked about. After a few more hours of writing and geography, it was time to head back home.

I wandered slowly toward our apartment, thinking all the while about Augie. Ma and I had received a brief letter from him last week. *All's well,* he had written. *Surely sister Susie's staying sweet.* It was something Augie often wrote—a tongue twister with extra meaning. Both my brother and I had a terrible sweet tooth.

I was walking past a bakery when an idea began to form inside my head. I peered into the window at a large case full of pastries and cookies. I was sure they cost more than we could afford, but perhaps I could find a way to earn them.

○ **DAY 1** Compare and Contrast How does Augie's being in Europe affect the way Susan behaves? How does this compare to the way Ma behaves?

_____

_____

_____

_____

_____

○ **DAY 1** Unfamiliar Words Circle the word that helps you to understand the meaning of *luxury*.

○ **DAY 3** Compare and Contrast What do Augie and Susan have in common?

_____

_____

_____

R2.0 Students read and understand grade-level appropriate material.

"Augie's Present" 133

DAY 3 Greek and Latin Roots The Latin root *gratus* means "pleasing." What word in this story has this root?

_____

DAY 3 Compare and Contrast
Compare and contrast how Susan feels at the beginning of the story to how she feels at the end.

_____

_____

_____

_____

_____

_____

_____

_____

A large man inside was sweeping up the dust and flour off the floor. He coughed and grumbled to himself, obviously annoyed by his work. When he saw me standing at the window of his shop, he frowned and continued sweeping. I'm sure he could tell just by looking at me that I hadn't a spare cent to buy anything. But I wasn't going to let that stop me. I took a deep breath and entered the store. The doorbell rang softly above my head.

I cleared my throat and watched the man keep sweeping. "Excuse me, sir," I said to him.

Finally, he looked up. "What is it?" His broom continued to kick clouds of flour dust into the air.

"Could you use some help?" I paused, seeing his unsmiling face, then kept talking. "I could sweep for you, if you like."

"I'm quite capable of doing it myself, young lady," he said sternly, emptying a dustpan.

"Oh, I'm sure you are," I told him. "But you'd probably like to be doing other things…like baking, or…" My voice trailed off. This wasn't working. The baker stopped sweeping for a moment to look at me. He narrowed his eyes and waited. "I'd work for cookies," I said.

The man looked me up and down. Then he tossed me the broom. "I guess you could use a few cookies, kid," he said. "You're awfully skinny. Tell you what. You sweep for me every day this week, and by Friday, you'll have yourself a big box of cookies to take home."

With gratitude, I began sweeping what was left of the mess.

Later when I got home, Ma eyed me suspiciously. "You're late," she told me. "What happened?"

My eyes twinkled. "I found a present for Augie. Something absolutely delicious."

Ma looked at me, astonished. "Well, young lady, just how do you think we'll afford that?"

I told her about my brand-new job. She smiled and patted me on the shoulder. "Your brother will love his present," she told me. I nodded happily. Soon Augie would have his cookies and a birthday message to keep him company all the way across the ocean.

© Pearson Education, Inc., 5

School + Home **Home Activity** Your child read a selection and used comprehension and vocabulary skills from Unit 2. Have your child retell the selection, comparing and contrasting the characters.

R2.0 Students read and understand grade-level appropriate material.

Connect Text to Text

Reading Across Texts

Think about the selections "Franklin Delano Roosevelt" and "Augie's Present." Complete the Venn diagram below with details that show similarities and differences between the two texts.

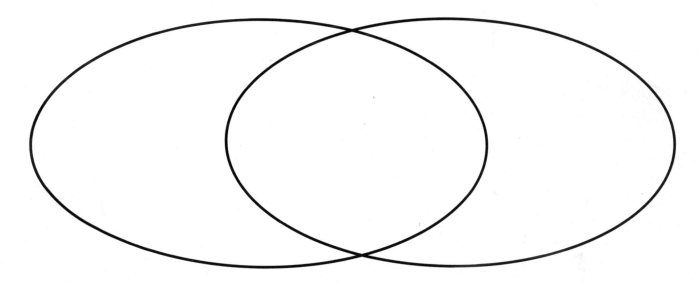

Writing Across Texts

Think about how President Roosevelt from "Franklin Delano Roosevelt" and Susan from "Augie's Present" helped people in need. Now imagine that you have the power to do something good for someone else. What would you do for him or her, and why would you do it?

_____

_____

_____

_____

_____

_____

_____

_____

_____

_____

Home Activity Your child read two selections this week. Have your child explain to you how they were alike and how they were different.

Summarize Your Learning

> ### What makes people want to do the right thing?
>
> - *At the Beach*   - *Passage to Freedom*
> - *The Ch'l-Lin Purse*   - *Jane Goodall's 10 Ways to Help Save Wildlife*
> - *The Midnight Ride of Paul Revere*

Think About It!

Think about the selections you read in this unit.

- How were they alike? How were they different?
- Were the selections you read this week similar to others you have read?
- What did you learn?

Why do you think it is sometimes hard for people to do the right thing? Write three reasons.

- _____
- _____
- _____

Question It!

What makes people want to do the right thing? Write three questions that you would ask someone who has helped another person or made an important contribution to the world.

- _____
- _____
- _____

Talk About It!

Discuss your questions with a partner.

- What questions did your partner have? Were they similar to yours? Were they different from yours?
- What things did you and your partner want to know?
- What did you discover?

Home Activity Your child reviewed and discussed the selections from Unit 2. Have your child describe to you the big ideas from this unit, focusing on why people want to do the right thing.

Family Times

Summary

The Fabulous Perpetual Motion Machine

The Pérez Twins, Carla and Carlos, are determined to win this year's science fair. Because they are fabulous, they definitely don't want to do anything boring. What could be less boring than a machine that needs no power and *never stops?* Gathered together with parents, a reporter, and their friends Larry and Effie, they give their perpetual motion machine a test run to make sure it works. The machine does seem to run forever, but with one small problem—everything in the house that runs on electricity stops working! The fabulous twins lose no time looking for another fabulous project to enter in the science fair.

Activity

People throughout history have come up with ideas for inventions that aren't possible. Think of a crazy invention that would help you and your family if only you could make it work. The more fantastic it is, the better! Either draw a diagram of your machine with labels for the different parts, or write a description about what it does and how it works.

Comprehension Skill

Author's Purpose

The **author's purpose** is the main reason or reasons an author has for writing. An author may write to persuade you, to inform you, to entertain you, or to express ideas or feelings. The kinds of ideas the author uses and the way he or she states them help you to see the author's purpose.

Activity

The Art of Persuasion With the purpose of persuasion in mind, write an advertisement you might hear on the radio for a product you have created. Think about the kinds of words people use when they want to sell something. Have your family help you perform the radio ad.

Lesson Vocabulary

Words to Know

Knowing the meanings of these words is important to reading *The Fabulous Perpetual Motion Machine*. Practice using these words.

Vocabulary Words

applauds shows approval by clapping hands, shouting, etc.

browsing looking here and there

fabulous wonderful; exciting

inspecting looking over carefully; examining

project a special assignment planned and carried out by a student or group of students

Conventions

Past, Present, and Future Tenses

Present tense verbs show action that is happening now. *For example: walk, bounce, talk.* **Past tense** verbs show action that happened in the past. Most past tense verbs are formed by adding *-ed* to the present tense. *For example: walked, bounced, talked.* **Future tense** verbs show action that will happen in the future. Future tense verbs are formed by adding the word *will* or a form of *is going to* to the present tense. *For example: will walk, will bounce, is going to talk.* Some verbs, however, do not follow the usual past tense rules. These verbs are called **irregular verbs,** and their past tense forms must be memorized. *For example: fly/flew; eat/ate; write/wrote.*

Activity

Verb Verse Work with a family member to write a poem using the past tense, present tense, and future tense of the same verbs. Be as creative and clever as possible. Perform the poem for other family members.

Practice Tested Spelling Words

Name_____

Author's Viewpoint/Bias

- A **viewpoint** is how an author looks at a subject from past experience or knowledge.
- A **bias** is an author's feelings or preferences for or against something.
- Examining the author's beliefs may help you understand the author's viewpoint.
- A bias in an author's writing may be revealed by the types of evidence the author uses to support his or her viewpoint.

Directions Read the passage. Then answer the questions below.

Almost two centuries ago, Robert Stirling invented an engine that may change the world of tomorrow. Now known as the Stirling engine, his design may be the closest thing to a perpetual motion machine. Today, most electricity is created by burning oil or coal, which pollutes the environment with filthy exhaust. Energy is created with Stirling engines just by heating the air inside. Because hot air expands, Stirling knew that he could force it through a tube.

If a plunger is placed inside the tube, the hot air pushes it through. The plunger is attached to a bar, which is attached to a gear. When the plunger moves, the bar moves, turning the gear. By the time the plunger reached the end of the tube, the air behind it has cooled. The air shrinks and pulls the plunger back. The cycle starts again. In Stirling's day, people attached the gear to other machines to power them. Today, we can attach the gears to generators, turning motion into electricity. The Stirling Engine only needs heat, which can come from the sun. Scientists are studying how this historical idea can help create clean energy and protect the environment at the same time.

1. What does the author suggest is good about the Stirling Engine?

_____

2. What hint is given about the author's viewpoint by the use of the word *environment*?

_____

3. The author has a bias about how energy should be created. What is the author for or against?

_____

4. What evidence does the author use that explains her or his bias about oil and coal?

_____

5. How does knowing the author's bias affect your opinion of the information in the passage?

_____

Home Activity Your child identified the author's viewpoint and bias in a passage. Review with your child the information that helped him or her decide on the viewpoint and bias.

R3.7 Evaluate the author's use of various techniques (e.g., appeal of characters in a picture book, logic and credibility of plots and settings, use of figurative language) to influence readers' perspectives.

Comprehension 143

Name_____

Author's Viewpoint/Bias

- A **viewpoint** is how an author looks at a subject from past experience or knowledge.
- A **bias** is an author's feelings or preferences for or against something.
- Examining the author's beliefs may help you understand the author's viewpoint.
- A bias in an author's writing may be revealed by the types of evidence the author uses to support his or her viewpoint.

Directions Read the following passage. Then complete the diagram below.

The "Space Elevator" is the most exciting invention in the history of space travel. Imagine a ski lift, or even a clothesline. That's pretty much how the elevator will work. There will be one huge pulley on the ground and another one up in space. The cable that runs between them will be attached to cars as big as buses. Earth's gravity and rotation will turn the pulleys around and around—forever. It will be like a perpetual motion space train!

When this elevator is built, space travel will be clean, safe, and affordable to everyone. No fuel will be used, so there will be no pollution from emissions. The safest astronauts today still have to worry about terrible accidents. The space elevator will be much safer, because it won't have to be launched or landed. When a "Space Elevator" car reaches the ground, it will pause and people will just hop on. Because no fuel has to be purchased, the trip will be inexpensive. The elevator will carry passengers swiftly to a space station and as easily as skiers are carried to the peak of a mountain. From there, who knows where they might go?

Author's Viewpoint How does the author look at space travel? 1.	**Evidence** 2. 3. 4.	**Author's Bias** What is the author for or against?

© Pearson Education, Inc., 5

Home Activity Your child used a graphic organizer to identify the author's viewpoint and bias in a short passage. Have your child write a short paragraph about something that he or she really likes about your home or neighborhood. Talk with your child about how his or her viewpoint affects the bias in favor of the subject of the paragraph.

R3.7 Evaluate the author's use of various techniques (e.g., appeal of characters in a picture book, logic and credibility of plots and settings, use of figurative language) to influence readers' perspectives.

Advertisement

- An **advertisement** is meant to sell a product or service. Written advertisements may appear in newspapers or on the Internet. Advertisers use many techniques to persuade the reader.
- **Loaded words** affect the reader by creating emotions or making value judgments.
- A **slogan** is a short phrase that is easily remembered.
- A **generality** is vague. It lacks specific details and supporting evidence and facts.
- **Getting on the bandwagon** is another way of saying "everyone else does it."
- A **sweeping generalization** has inadequate evidence and speaks for a large group.

Directions Read this advertisement for a car dealership and answer the questions.

Best Deals Ever on Pre-Loved Cars!

If you've ever wanted a luxury sports car with all the extras, now's the time to buy. **Carz-for-U Sales** is having its biggest sale ever on many of its top-of-the-line sports cars. Most cars come equipped with many of the latest luxury features! Choose from the exciting new fluorescent colors that everyone's buying. These are orange, white, green, or pink. Have you had credit card problems? Don't worry. We always find a way for you to buy your dream car with a just small down payment. **Carz-for-U Sales**—the best deals on wheels!

---

1. Which technique is the advertisement's headline an example of? Why do you think the advertiser calls the cars "pre-loved" instead of "pre-owned" or "used"?

_____

_____

2. Which technique is being used in the third sentence?

_____

3. Which sentence in the ad uses the getting-on-the-bandwagon technique?

_____

_____

4. The advertiser says that at Carz-for-U Sales, "We always find a way for you to buy your dream car with just a small down payment." What kind of technique is being used? What doesn't the advertiser tell the reader?

_____

_____

5. What technique is used in the last sentence? Do you think it is effective? Explain.

_____

_____

G4R2.2 Use appropriate strategies when reading for different purposes (e.g., full comprehension, location of information, personal enjoyment).

Research and Study Skills 145

Directions Read this advertisement for a credit card and answer the questions.

ACT NOW!

Diamond Classic Plus

New, Promotional 5.9% APR! *

- No annual fee
- Online account and bill payment
- **FREE additional cards**
- Special **cardmember privileges**

Your Credit Limit: Up to $15,000

Reply within 10 days

Can you believe it? The holidays are just around the corner. Impress your friends with your new **Diamond Classic Plus Card** with no annual fee.

Save hundreds of dollars with free coupons to your favorite stores and restaurants—as part of your **cardmember privileges.** All you have to do is sign up before December 1. Pay your bill online and save with our special online **Shopping Mall.** Need cash? You can use your new card to receive cash within seconds.*

How can you benefit from this offer? It's easy. Just fill out the Application below and mail it today!

*See details on reverse.

---

6. List two statements the advertiser uses to convince the reader to take immediate action.

_____

7. Identify three examples of loaded words used in the advertisement.

_____

8. The advertiser uses an asterisk twice to refer to the note at the bottom of the page. Why do you think the advertiser refers the reader to the other side of the letter?

_____

9. List three services or extras the advertiser offers beyond being able to buy now and pay later.

_____

10. Would you fill out the application? Why or why not?

_____

Home Activity Your child learned about advertisements. Write an advertisement for an imaginary product or service with your child using some of the advertising techniques your child has learned about. Discuss how the advertisement tries to persuade the reader.

G4R2.2 Use appropriate strategies when reading for different purposes (e.g., full comprehension, location of information, personal enjoyment).

Name

Family Times

Summary

The Dinosaurs of Waterhouse Hawkins

The year is 1853. The place is London. Waterhouse Hawkins has created the first-ever dinosaur models in his workshop. Afterward, he holds a great party to celebrate with guests like Queen Victoria and Prince Albert. No one has ever seen a model of a dinosaur, and they are all astonished.

Activity

Artist's Workshop Find books about dinosaurs and look through them. Compare illustrations of the various dinosaurs. Select one that you and a family member like and draw your own versions of it.

Comprehension Skill

Fact and Opinion

You can prove a **statement of fact** true or false. A **statement of opinion** cannot be proved true or false. Statements of opinion express somebody's thoughts or feelings.

Activity

Can you prove it? State a fact about something you know. *For example: Our dog is a golden retriever.* Have others suggest how that fact could be stated as an opinion. *For example: Our retriever is the best dog ever!* Then turn it around and start with an opinion.

Words to Know

Knowing the meanings of these words is important to reading *The Dinosaurs of Waterhouse Hawkins.* Practice using these words.

Vocabulary Words

erected put up; built

foundations parts on which the other parts rest for support; bases

mold a hollow shape in which anything is formed, cast, or solidified

occasion a special event

proportion a proper relation among parts

tidy to put in order

workshop space or building where work is done

Conventions

Principle Parts of Irregular Verbs

An **irregular verb** is one that does not add *–ed* to form the past tense. Most irregular verbs have different spellings for the past and the past participle. For example, for the verb *buy*, *bought* is the past tense, and *has*, *have*, or *had bought* is the past participle.

Activity

Irregular Verb Charts Work with a family member to make a graphic organizer of irregular verbs. Write an irregular verb in a central square, the past tense and the past participles in the circles around the square, and then write a sentence using each form of the verb in a rectangle next to each circle. Create more charts using new irregular verbs such as *write* and *know*.

Practice Tested Spelling Words

_____   _____   _____   _____

_____   _____   _____   _____

_____   _____   _____   _____

_____   _____   _____   _____

_____   _____   _____   _____

Fact and Opinion

- You can prove a **statement of fact** true or false. You can do this by using your own knowledge, asking an expert, or checking a reference source such as an encyclopedia or a nonfiction text.
- A **statement of opinion** gives ideas or feelings, not facts. It cannot be proved true or false.
- A sentence may contain both a statement of fact and a statement of opinion.

Directions Read the following passage. Then complete the diagram below by following its instructions, and answer the questions.

In 1861, the fossil remains of an *Archaeopteryx* (Ahr-key-OP-ter-iks) were discovered in Germany. They are about 150 million years old. Many scientists believe *Archaeopteryx* is the earliest known bird. When I saw it in a museum, I thought it looked like it was part dinosaur and part bird. It had feathers and wings like birds. It also had teeth and three claws on each wing. According to many scientists, *Archaeopteryx* could fly, but I'm not so sure. I think it might have flapped its wings, but I can't imagine it ever got off the ground.

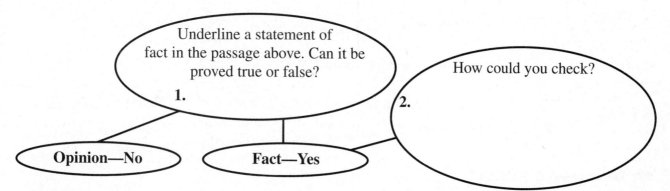

Underline a statement of fact in the passage above. Can it be proved true or false?

1.

How could you check?

2.

Opinion—No

Fact—Yes

3. Write a statement of opinion from the passage. How do you know it is a statement of opinion?

_____

_____

4. Which sentence contains both a fact and an opinion?

_____

_____

5. In the last sentence, the author expresses an opinion that *Archaeopteryx* couldn't have flown. What kind of details would support this opinion?

_____

School + Home **Home Activity** Your child read a short passage and identified facts and opinions. Read an article together. Ask your child to identify statements of fact and ask how they can be proven.

R2.5 Distinguish facts, supported inferences, and opinions in text.

Vocabulary

Directions Draw a line to connect each word on the left to the matching definition on the right.

1. proportion   a special event

2. foundations   put up; built

3. erected   space or building where work is done

4. workshop   a proper relation among parts

5. occasion   parts on which other parts rest for support

**Check the Words
You Know**

____erected
____foundations
____mold
____occasion
____proportion
____tidy
____workshop

Directions Choose the word from the box that best completes each sentence. Write the word on the line to the left.

_____ 6. Julia poured plaster into a _____ shaped like a bird.

_____ 7. She was creating a statue for a special _____.

_____ 8. We have _____ a statue in front of the new library.

_____ 9. When she finished making the bird, her _____ was a mess.

_____ 10. She likes to wipe up the dust made by the plaster and _____ her workbench before she goes home.

Write a News Report

On a separate sheet of paper, write a news report about an important discovery, like the discovery of the *Archaeopteryx* fossil remains. Use as many vocabulary words as you can.

School + Home **Home Activity** Your child identified and used vocabulary words from *The Dinosaurs of Waterhouse Hawkins*. Read a story or nonfiction article with your child about dinosaurs or animals. Have him or her describe the dinosaur or animal and then explain whether the description is a statement of fact or of opinion.

R1.0 Word Analysis, Fluency, and Systematic Vocabulary Development

Vocabulary • Multiple-Meaning Words

- **Multiple-meaning words** are words that are spelled the same but have different meanings.
- When you read a word you know, but whose meaning does not make sense in the sentence, **context clues,** the words and ideas around it, may help you understand the meaning.
- Use a dictionary to help you find the meanings of unfamiliar words.

Directions Read the following passage. Then answer the questions below.

Fossil collectors know that they are not allowed to remove fossils from most places. It is against the law to remove fossils from someone else's property and from public lands. In order to collect fossils, collectors meet at a "fossil fair" to buy fossils from other collectors. It's also possible they might add to their collection by keeping a file with photographs and drawings of fossils. Sometimes collectors make copies of fossils by pouring plaster into a mold. They can look very realistic.

1. *Fair* can mean "not favoring one more than others" or "a gathering of buyers or sellers." How is it used in the passage? How can you tell?

_____

2. *Might* can mean "possibly would" or "great power." How is it used in the passage? How can you tell?

_____

3. *File* can mean "a container, drawer, or folder for keeping papers in order" or "a steel tool used to smooth rough surfaces." How is it used in the passage? How can you tell?

_____

_____

4. *Mold* can mean "a furry, fungus growth" or "a shape in which anything is formed or cast." How is it used in the passage? How can you tell?

_____

_____

5. Write a sentence using the meaning of *mold* not used in the passage.

_____

_____

Home Activity Your child read a short passage and used context clues to understand new multiple-meaning words in a passage. Read an article with your child. Identify multiple-meaning words in that article. Write sentences that use each meaning of the multiple-meaning words.

G6R1.2 Identify and interpret figurative language and words with multiple meanings.

Vocabulary 161

Name_____

Main Idea and Details

Directions Read the following passage. Then answer the questions below.

As a young girl, Mary Nicol was interested in prehistory and fossils. When she was a child, she had a difficult time in school. But as soon as she was old enough, she began attending classes about prehistory at the University of London. She was a talented illustrator and soon had a chance to illustrate a book by a famous researcher, Louis Leakey. They married, and she changed her name to Mary Leakey. The Leakeys went to Africa to find fossils in 1935.

While in Africa, Mary made several important discoveries that changed how scientists thought about early humans. In 1948, she found the first skull of a fossil ape. It was twenty million years old. In 1959, she found a two-million-year-old fossilized skull of an early human. In 1978 she uncovered a footprint trail. It was left in volcanic ash nearly 2.3 million years ago. This proved that there were humanlike beings in those days that walked upright on two feet.

1. What is the topic of the passage?

_____

2. What is the passage's main idea?

_____

_____

3. Give an example of a supporting detail.

_____

_____

4. Give another example of a supporting detail.

_____

_____

5. Summarize the passage in a few sentences.

_____

_____

_____

Home Activity Your child has read a short passage and answered questions about its main ideas and details. Read a nonfiction story with your child. Ask him or her to identify the main idea of a paragraph and the supporting details.

R2.3 Discern main ideas and concepts presented in texts, identifying and assessing evidence that supports those ideas.

Fact and Opinion

- You can prove a **statement of fact** true or false. You can do this by using your own knowledge, asking an expert, or checking a reference source such as an encyclopedia or a nonfiction text.
- A **statement of opinion** gives ideas or feelings, not facts. It cannot be proved true or false.
- A sentence may contain both a statement of fact and a statement of opinion.

Directions Read the following passage.

> Dinosaurs are really interesting. I wanted to find out what happened to them so I went to the library to read some articles and books. This is what I found out: About 65 million years ago, dinosaurs became extinct. They had lived on Earth for about 165 million years. That's much longer than humans have been around! Suddenly, they all began to die off. No one knows for sure why this happened.
>
> According to many scientists, an asteroid believed to be about 4.9 miles wide crashed to Earth and caused the extinction. When it crashed it might have scattered dust into the atmosphere, created tidal waves, and caused huge fires. This could have caused sunlight to be blocked for months and for the temperature to drop. Living things on Earth would have had difficulty surviving.

1. Give an example of an opinion from the passage.

_____

2. How can you tell this is an opinion?

_____

3. Give an example of a fact from the passage.

_____

4. How would you prove that this is a fact?

_____

_____

5. Select one statement of fact from the passage. On a separate piece of paper, list as many ways as you can think of to verify it.

Home Activity Your child read a short passage and identified facts and opinions. Together, read an editorial from a newspaper or magazine. Identify facts and opinions in the editorial. Ask your child how he or she can tell the difference between the facts and opinions.

R2.5 Distinguish facts, supported inferences, and opinions in text.

Fact and Opinion

- You can prove a **statement of fact** true or false. You can do this by using your own knowledge, asking an expert, or checking a reference source such as an encyclopedia or a nonfiction text.
- A **statement of opinion** gives ideas or feelings, not facts. It cannot be proved true or false.
- A sentence may contain both a statement of fact and a statement of opinion.

Directions Read the following passage. Then complete the diagram and answer the questions below.

When I grow up, I want to hunt for fossils like Mary Leakey. We seem to be a lot alike. She wanted to find fossils. So do I. She wanted to learn about early humans. So do I. I read all about her discoveries in Africa. I think her most exciting discovery was the skull from the Stone Age, which was almost two million years old. Her work in Africa gave us new information about stone tools and Stone Age cultures. In 1962, she and her husband, Louis Leakey, won the National Geographic Society's highest honor.

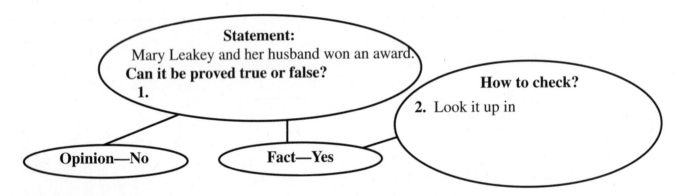

Statement:
Mary Leakey and her husband won an award.
Can it be proved true or false?
1.

How to check?
2. Look it up in

Opinion—No

Fact—Yes

3. How do you know "We seem to be a lot alike" is a statement of opinion?

Because there is no way to _____

4. Which sentence contains both a fact and an opinion?

_____

_____

5. In the eighth sentence, the author expresses an opinion that the discovery of the Stone Age skull was the most exciting. What kind of details would support this opinion?

Details about how other people _____

 Home Activity Your child read a short passage and identified facts and opinions. Read a news article and have your child make a list of facts and opinions in the passage.

R2.5 Distinguish facts, supported inferences, and opinions in text.

Schedule

A **schedule** is a kind of table with **rows** and **columns**. The rows and columns meet at boxes that are called **cells**. Schedules show times, dates, and locations for airplanes, trains, buses, activities, and sporting events.

Directions Use this train schedule to answer the questions.

Departure Schedule for Trains to Chicago

		A.M.	A.M.	A.M.	P.M.	P.M.	P.M.
Waukekee		5:01	7:30	11:30	1:00	3:30	5:00
Hampton		5:45	8:15	12:15	1:45	4:15	5:45
Rainville	*	6:15	8:45	12:45	2:15	4:45	6:15
Harbor Park	*	7:00	9:30	1:30	3:00	5:00	7:00
Arrive in Chicago		**8:00**	**10:30**	**2:30**	**4:00**	**6:00**	**8:00**

* Indicates food service.

1. How many trains go to Chicago every day? Which train leaves Waukekee in the morning and arrives in Chicago in the afternoon?

_____

2. Counting Waukekee, how many stops does the train make? What is the fourth stop?

_____

3. You live in Rainville. You want to meet your friends in Chicago at 10:30 A.M. What time do you have to catch the train in Rainville to be on time? How much extra time will you have when you arrive in Chicago?

_____

4. You live in Harbor Park and have to take the train that leaves at 7:00 A.M. for Chicago. You don't have time to fix yourself breakfast. Will you be able to get something to eat on the train? How do you know?

_____

5. You live in Hampton. Every Monday at 5:00 P.M., you have violin lessons in Rainville. To be on time, which train do you have to catch? Will you have time to spare?

_____

R2.1 Understand how text features (e.g., format, graphics, sequence, diagrams, illustrations, charts, maps) make information accessible and usable.

Directions Use this camp schedule to answer the questions.

Camp Want-To-Get-Away Schedule

	Monday	**Tuesday**	**Wednesday**	**Thursday**	**Friday**	**Saturday**	**Sunday**
8 A.M.	Breakfast in Olson Hall	Breakfast in Olson Hall	Breakfast in Olson Hall	Breakfast in Olson Hall	Breakfast in Olson Hall	Breakfast in Olson Hall	Breakfast in Olson Hall
10 A.M.	Swimming at Lake Beluga	Play Rehearsal	Archery	Swimming at Lake Beluga	Band Practice	You Choose	Play Rehearsal
1 P.M.	Crafts	Crafts	Horseback Riding	Letters Home	Horseback Riding	You Choose	Parents Visit
4 P.M.	Group Games	Archery	Water Sports	Group Games	Hiking	Group Games	Swimming at Lake Beluga
8 P.M.	Lights Out	Lights Out	Lights Out	Lights Out	MOVIE	Campfire Stories	Lights Out

6. How many time slots for each day are listed on this schedule? How many days are listed?

_____

7. You want to sharpen your swimming skills. What days and times can you go swimming?

_____

_____

8. You want your parents to come for a visit. What day and time is best?

_____

9. What time can you eat breakfast every day? Where is breakfast held?

_____

10. You love to act. What is a good activity to take part in? When is this activity available?

_____

Home Activity Your child learned about reading schedules. Look at the schedule of a sports team your child likes. Find out when the next game is and whether or not it takes place during school hours.

R2.1 Understand how text features (e.g., format, graphics, sequence, diagrams, illustrations, charts, maps) make information accessible and usable.

Card Catalog/Library Database

- You can use a **card catalog** or **library database** to find books, magazines, audiotapes, videotapes, CD-ROMS, and other materials in the library. You can search for materials by author, title, or subject. A card catalog is a box of drawers filled with cards containing detailed information about books and other library materials. A library database is an electronic version of a card catalog.

- If you don't know exactly what you are searching for in the library database, you can use "keywords." Be sure to type and spell words carefully. If you use more than one keyword in your search, put the word "AND" between the keywords.

- Both card catalog and library databases contain certain types of basic information. For instance, call numbers are used by libraries to identify and organize the items in their collections. Nonfiction books, videos, and recordings are arranged on library shelves by call number. Fiction books are arranged in alphabetical order by the author's last name.

Directions Look at the starting search screen for a library database below. For each of the numbered items, tell which of the six categories you would choose for each search. Then write the information you would enter into the library database.

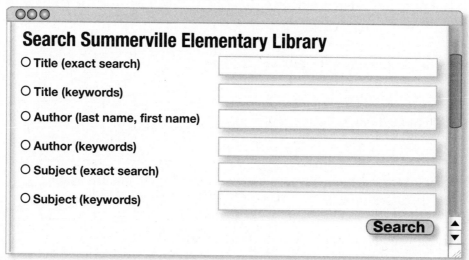

1. Ray Charles's autobiography

_____

2. a Louis Armstrong recording on CD, audiotape, or vinyl LP

_____

3. a biography of Louis Armstrong

_____

4. *Mahalia: A Life in Gospel Music*

_____

5. a critical history of Motown Records

_____

G4W1.6 Locate information in reference texts by using organizational features (e.g., prefaces, appendixes).

Research and Study Skills   175

Directions Use the following sample card from a library card catalog to answer the questions below.

> L424.7 RE
>
> **Roots of Blues Music**
>
> Parker, Mark, 1959-
>
> Blues has influenced many different types of music today. It changed the way many people felt about music, as well. Blues emerged after slavery was abolished and changed the way singers approached music. Blues is still a popular form of music played today.
>
>   Publisher: Wilson Musical Reference
>
>   Pub date: c2001.
>
>   Pages: 313 p.
>
> ISBN: 0534212311

6. Who is the author of this reference book?

_____

7. What is the book's call number?

_____

8. What is the title of the book?

_____

9. How many pages does this book have? When was it published, and by whom?

_____

10. What do you learn about the book from the card's summary?

_____

_____

_____

© Pearson Education, Inc., 5

Home Activity Your child learned about using a library database and a card catalog. Visit the library with your child. Take turns searching for subjects that interest one or both of you.

G4W1.6 Locate information in reference texts by using organizational features (e.g., prefaces, appendixes).

Family Times

Summary

Special Effects in Film and Television

Have you ever wondered how movie monsters and dinosaurs can seem so real? In this article, we follow the process of a group of special effects artists as they create a miniature model of a prehistoric landscape, complete with dinosaurs that move!

Activity

Your Own Miniature Model Using materials you find around the house and outside, such as scrap wood, cardboard, construction paper, rocks, and sand, create a miniature model of a scene from a favorite story that you would like to see made into a movie.

Comprehension Skill

Graphic Sources

Graphic sources are visual materials such as pictures, time lines, maps, charts, and diagrams that make information easy to understand. Previewing graphic sources before reading a story or article can help you predict what it will be about.

Activity

Get the Picture? Take turns describing stories or articles that this picture might accompany. Create as many captions as you can for the picture.

Lesson Vocabulary

Words to Know

Knowing the meanings of these words is important to reading *Special Effects in Film and Television*. Practice using these words.

Vocabulary Words

background the part of a picture or scene toward the back

landscape a view of scenery on land

miniature smaller in size or scale than others of its type

prehistoric of or belonging to periods before recorded history

reassembled came or brought together again

Grammar

Prepositions and Prepositional Phrases

A **preposition** is a word that shows a relationship between a noun and another noun. *For example: Maria stood between her parents.* The *preposition* "between" shows where Maria (a noun) stood in relation to her parents (also a noun).

A **prepositional phrase** begins with a preposition and ends with a noun called the **object of the preposition**. *For example: Samuel crawled under the porch.* "Under" is the *preposition*, "porch" is the *object of the preposition*, and "under the porch" is the *prepositional phrase*.

Activity

Where Are You Going? Many prepositions describe location. Write five prepositional phrases that answer the question, "Where are you going?" Have a family member write the object of the preposition for each of your phrases, and then check their work. When you are done, switch roles.

Practice Tested Spelling Words

_____ _____ _____ _____

_____ _____ _____ _____

_____ _____ _____ _____

_____ _____ _____ _____

_____ _____ _____ _____

Graphic Sources

- Some graphic sources are maps, time lines, charts, diagrams, and pictures with captions.
- A graphic source makes information easy to see and understand.

Directions Study the circle graph below. Then answer the following questions.

Small Films Company Annual Budget for Special Effects

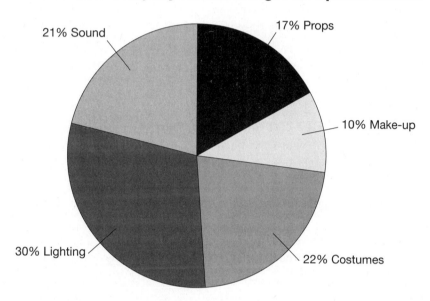

1. What do the percentages show?

_____

2. On what special effect did the company spend the most money?

_____

3. How much more of the budget went toward costumes than make-up?

_____

4. In what kind of article might you see a circle graph?

_____

_____

5. What prior knowledge did you use to help you understand the graphic source?

_____

_____

Home Activity Your child learned how to interpret a graphic source. Together, imagine you are both writing an article about a favorite subject. Draw a graphic source that could be included in the article.

R2.1 Understand how text features (e.g., format, graphics, sequence, diagrams, illustrations, charts, maps) make information accessible and usable.

Name_____

Vocabulary

Directions Choose the word from the box that best matches each definition. Write the word on the line.

_____ 1. of or belonging to periods before recorded history

_____ 2. put back together again

_____ 3. view of scenery on land

_____ 4. done or made on an extremely small scale

_____ 5. the part of a picture or scene toward the back

Directions Choose the word from the box that best completes the sentence. Write the word on the line shown to the left.

_____ 6. Three hours after the storm, the set for the movie had already been _____.

_____ 7. In preparing for the movie, the crew created a _____ village.

_____ 8. The film crew built a ruined temple to appear in the _____ of the scene.

_____ 9. The dinosaur film used models of huge, _____ creatures.

_____ 10. The park provided a perfect _____ for the film.

Write a Movie Review

On a separate sheet of paper write a review of a movie that had lots of special effects. Describe the special effects and how they worked. Use as many vocabulary words as you can.

Home Activity Your child identified and used vocabulary words from *Special Effects in Film and Television*. Read the review of a movie with your child. Have him or her point out unfamiliar words. Work together to try to figure out the meaning of each word.

G3R1.8 Use knowledge of prefixes (e.g., *un-, re-, pre-, bi-, mis-, dis-*) and suffixes (e.g., *-er, -est, -ful*) to determine the meaning of words.

© Pearson Education, Inc., 5

Vocabulary • Prefixes

- A **prefix** is added at the beginning of a base word to change its meaning.
- Prefixes do not stand alone in sentences. They usually have their own definitions listed in dictionaries, as well as their origins, such as the Greek or Latin languages.
- The prefixes *re-,* meaning "to do over," and *pre-,* meaning "before," come from Latin.

Directions Read the following passage. Then answer the questions below.

On our first trip to Los Angeles, we toured a special-effects studio. In one room the workers had just reassembled a landscape scene with prehistoric animals. Huge reptile-like birds with feathers flew in the background. In another room we saw a miniature village. Tiny houses were placed among even tinier bushes and trees.

Next, we visited the basement. We heard explosions going off. We were told that technicians were testing small explosive devices and that we should be careful. Down the hall we saw a room full of what looked like snow and ice. It was going to be used as an Arctic landscape with below-zero temperatures.

By the end of the afternoon, we were weary but eager to redo the tour soon. We felt like we had been treated to our own sneak preview of several of the coolest movies coming out in the future.

1. What does *reassembled* mean? What prefix helped you to determine the meaning?

_____

2. What does *prehistoric* mean? What does its prefix mean?

_____

3. If you replaced the prefix in *preview* with the prefix *re–,* how would the meaning change?

_____

_____

4. Can you use a prefix to determine the meaning of *real*? Why or why not?

_____

5. Write at least three examples of words that either begin with the prefix *re–* or *pre–.*

_____

Home Activity Your child identified the meanings of words with prefixes. Make a list of all the words you can think of that begin with the prefixes *re–* or *pre–*. Then, have a silly conversation in which you try to use as many words on the list as possible.

G3R1.8 Use knowledge of prefixes (e.g., *un-, re-, pre-, bi-, mis-, dis-*) and suffixes (e.g., *-er, -est, -ful*) to determine the meaning of words.

Author's Purpose

Directions Read the passage. Then answer the questions below.

Jack had studied dinosaurs for twenty years, and he'd lived in Dinosaur Park for all twenty of them. Nothing about dinosaurs could surprise him. This thought calmed his nerves as he walked toward the lodge at the other end of the park.

After an hour, he pulled out his GPS-DL (dinosaur locator) to check the position of the dinosaurs. The path was still clear for miles. So why did he feel so uneasy? Sweat was running down his cheeks. He felt dizzy.

Then a thundering blast filled the air. The earth shook. A foul smell hit him like a punch. A roar split the sky. It was like nothing he'd heard before. And it was coming straight toward him.

1. What is the author's purpose?

_____

2. How do you know?

_____

3. Do you think the author met his or her purpose for writing? Why or why not?

_____

_____

4. Notice the sentences get shorter in the second half of the passage. Why do you think the author did this?

_____

_____

5. How did the author's purpose affect your reading pace?

_____

_____

Home Activity Your child has read a fictional passage and identified the author's purpose for writing it. Choose a story to read. Have your child preview the story first, looking at the cover, title, and pictures, to predict the author's purpose. Read the story to find out if the prediction was correct.

 R3.7 Evaluate the author's use of various techniques (e.g., appeal of characters in a picture book, logic and credibility of plots and settings, use of figurative language) to influence readers' perspectives.

Name_____

Graphic Sources

- Some graphic sources are maps, time lines, charts, diagrams, and pictures with captions.
- A graphic source makes information easy to see and understand.

Directions Study the diagram for a miniature neighborhood below. Then answer the questions that follow.

Miniature Neighborhood Layout Diagram

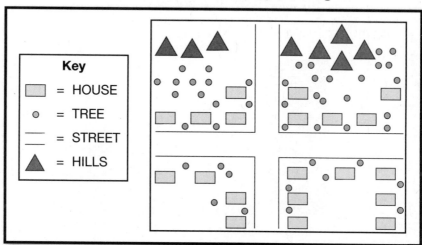

1. What does this diagram show?

_____

_____

2. What shape represents a tree?

_____

3. How many more houses than hills are there?

_____

4. Why would this diagram be helpful to special-effects artists?

_____

_____

5. What prior knowledge did you have about this topic that helped you understand it?

_____

_____

© Pearson Education, Inc., 5

Home Activity Your child used a graphic source to answer questions. Together, make a diagram of your home. Create a title and a key for your diagram. Challenge your child to use prior knowledge of diagrams to construct it.

R2.1 Understand how text features (e.g., format, graphics, sequence, diagrams, illustrations, charts, maps) make information accessible and usable.

Graphic Sources

- Some graphic sources are maps, time lines, charts, diagrams, and pictures with captions.
- A graphic source makes information easy to see and understand.

Directions Study the bar graph. Then answer the questions.

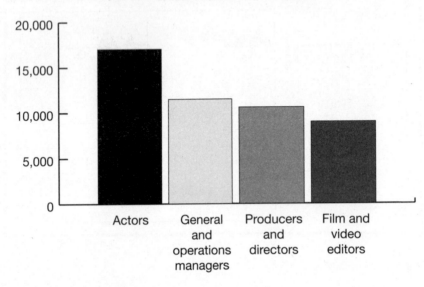

**Employment in the Motion Picture Industry for 2002
(numbers have been rounded)**

1. What does this bar graph show?

_____

2. What kind of article might include this graphic source?

_____

_____

3. How many editor jobs were there in 2002?

_____

4. Which group had the most jobs?

_____

5. What prior knowledge helped you understand this subject and graph?

_____

_____

Home Activity Your child used a graphic source to answer questions. Look at the graphic sources in a newspaper. Challenge your child to study them on his or her own and then explain them to you.

R2.1 Understand how text features (e.g., format, graphics, sequence, diagrams, illustrations, charts, maps) make information accessible and usable.

Graphics/Symbols

- **Graphics** aid in the use of instructions and communication. They identify and summarize information.
- **Graphics** have an effect on the user's understanding of material and provide additional meaning to the text that they accompany.
- **Symbols** and icons can be used to represent ideas, concepts, and information.

Directions Study the Web page below.

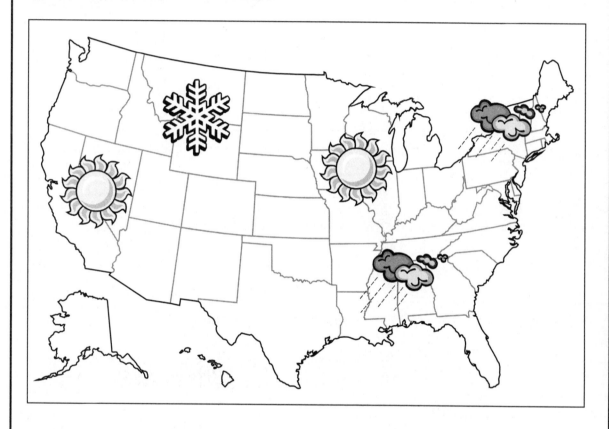

Weather World

Search

Ask an Expert

Weather around the World

**Questions about this site?
E-mail the webmaster.**

Copyright © 2004 Weather World, Inc.

R2.1 Understand how text features (e.g., format, graphics, sequence, diagrams, illustrations, charts, maps) make information accessible and usable.

1. What is the name of this Internet site? How do you know?

_____

_____

2. What do the graphics on the weather map tell you?

_____

3. What does the rain cloud symbol mean?

_____

4. What type of weather will the Midwest have?

_____

5. Why do you think this Web designer placed graphics in the tool bar?

_____

_____

6. If one of the links in the tool bar was to the archives of historical weather, what graphic could be used?

_____

7. What does the © symbol stand for? Where have you seen it before?

_____

_____

8. What would probably happen if you clicked "E-mail the webmaster."?

_____

_____

9. Why do people use symbols?

_____

_____

10. How do the graphics on the weather map limit the amount of information you know?

_____

_____

Home Activity Your child learned about the use of graphics and symbols as visual representations of information. Look at a Web page or book that uses graphics and symbols. Challenge your child to explain what the graphics and symbols mean.

G4W1.6 Locate information in reference texts by using organizational features (e.g., prefaces, appendixes).

Family Times

Selection Summaries

Week 1 The Fabulous Perpetual Motion Machine

The science fair will never be the same, thanks to the Pérez twins' amazing project.

Week 2 Leonardo's Horse

What is it about this horse statue that makes it impossible for the great Leonardo da Vinci to complete it?

Week 3 The Dinosaurs of Waterhouse Hawkins

Finding dinosaurs took the skill of scientists, but bringing them to life took the unique vision of a remarkable artist.

Week 4 Mahalia Jackson

In this story, a grandfather tells his granddaughter about the music he loves, and about one of the greatest blues singers of them all.

Week 5 Special Effects in Film and Television

Movies and TV have created a whole new kind of artist—one who can make us think we see things that don't exist.

Activity

Tell a member of your family more about each of the five stories. Tell which one is your favorite, and why you liked it best.

Comprehension Skills Review

In Unit 3, you learned and used many skills while reading the stories and selections.

- Every piece of writing contains the **author's viewpoint,** or how the author feels about the topic. Some authors show a strong **bias** for or against their topic.

- The **main idea** of a piece of writing is what the text is mostly about.

- A **fact** can be proved true. An **opinion** is what someone thinks or believes and cannot be proved true.

- A **graphic source** shows or explains information in the text. Pictures, tables, charts, diagrams, time lines, and maps are all graphic sources.

Activity

What do you imagine? Do you dream of castles and knights, or of fantastic flying machines? Imagination is essential for artists, singers, writers, scientists, and inventors. Talk with a trusted family member about imagination and what you would like to do with your life.

Unit Vocabulary Skills

Multiple-Meaning Words

Multiple-meaning words are words that have more than one meaning.

Activity Read a newspaper and look for words with multiple meanings. List the words and their different meanings.

Greek and Latin Roots

Many English words have **Greek and Latin roots.** You can use a dictionary to find out a word's roots.

Activity As you read, check word roots in a dictionary; make a list of words that come from Latin or Greek.

Multiple-Meaning Words

Multiple-meaning words are words that have more than one meaning.

Activity Choose one multiple-meaning word. Use a dictionary to understand the many meanings, and try writing sentences that use each meaning.

Antonyms

Antonyms are words that mean the opposite of other words.

Activity Use a thesaurus to find the antonyms of words you have learned recently.

Prefixes

A **prefix** is a word part added to the beginning of a word to change its meaning.

Activity Make a list of words in your reading that have the prefix *pre-*, and add their meanings from the dictionary.

Unit Spelling Rules

Schwa

In many words, the schwa in an unaccented syllable gives no clue to its spelling. Any vowel can stand for the schwa sound.

Compound Words

A compound word is smaller words joined together. To decode a compound word, divide it and sound out each smaller word.

Consonant Sounds /j/, /ks/, /sk/, /s/

These consonant sounds can be spelled in different ways:

- /j/ can be spelled *g*, *j*, and *dge*, as in *ginger*, *journal*, and *dodge*.
- /ks/ can be spelled *x*, as in *excuse*.
- /sk/ can be spelled *sch*, as in *schedule*.
- /s/ can be spelled *sc*, as in *scene*.

One Consonant or Two

When the same consonant appears twice in a row in a word, it stands for a single sound.

Prefixes *un-*, *de-*, *dis-*

When the prefixes *un-*, *de-*, and *dis-* are added to a base word, the base word does not change. These three prefixes all mean "not" or "the opposite of."

⊙ Multiple-Meaning Words

Running six miles can *tire* you out.

He fixed the flat *tire* on his bicycle

Words To Know

applauds
browsing
fabulous
inspecting
project

A **multiple-meaning word** is a word that has more than one meaning. In the pictures above identify the multiple-meaning word and its two different meanings.

Practice

Read the following sentences. Fill in the blanks using the Words to Know. Then choose the definition that best matches the underlined word.

1. Kyle's <u>homework</u> for his science fair _____ includes observing magnets.

   a. an assignment   b. stick out from   c. forecast

2. Even the <u>judge</u> who is _____ it can't quite understand the machine.

   a. one at a trial   b. one at a contest   c. one with an opinion

3. Kyle explains his _____ machine prevents deer from
   _____ in people's <u>gardens</u>.

   a. land for plants   b. public place   c. raises vegetables

4. "When the deer <u>approach</u>, the machine _____," Kyle says, "scaring the deer away without hurting them."

   a. to deal with something   b. to land   c. draw near to

On Your Own

As you read "The Baseball Mitt," look for multiple-meaning words.

School + Home

Home Activity Your child used context clues to determine the correct meanings of multiple-meaning words. With your child, make a list of as many multiple-meaning words as you can.

⊙ Author's Viewpoint/Bias

The **author's viewpoint** is the attitude the author expresses in the writing. **Bias** is a strong attitude in favor of (positive bias) or against (negative bias) a certain topic or thing. You can identify bias in writing by looking for words that make judgments, such as *most beautiful, amazing, ridiculous,* and so on.

Viewpoint

Bree is the tallest girl in the class.

Practice

In the boxes below, write the words that identify the bias in each sentence. Tell whether the bias is positive or negative.

1. Bree is unbelievably lucky to be so tall.   **2.** Bree's height is very peculiar.

Bias Words	Positive or Negative?

Bias Words	Positive or Negative?

On Your Own

Use what you know about author's viewpoint and bias as you read "The Baseball Mitt." Make a list of words in the reading selection that identify bias and viewpoint.

School + Home **Home Activity** Your child reviewed using the skill identifying author's viewpoint and bias. Share a newspaper editorial discuss the author's viewpoint and any bias you discover.

R3.7 Evaluate the author's use of various techniques (e.g., appeal of characters in a picture book, logic and credibility of plots and settings, use of figurative language) to influence readers' perspectives.

⊙ Greek and Latin Roots

Many English words come from ancient Greek and Latin words. Sometimes you can use **Greek and Latin roots** to figure out the meaning of an unfamiliar word.

The Greek root *sophia* means "knowledge." The Latin root *spect* means "look at." The Greek root *bio* means "life."

Practice

Read the following sentences. Fill in the blanks using the Words to Know. Then choose the definition that best matches the underlined word.

> ### Words To Know
>
> achieved
> architect
> bronze
> cannon
> depressed
> fashioned
> midst
> philosopher
> rival

1. The _____ designed the skyscraper, and she _____ such fame that the building is mentioned in her <u>biography</u>.

   a. a book about someone's life   b. a book about building

2. The building <u>inspector</u> came to see the finished structure, which was a statue of the famous _____ Plato, _____ totally of _____.

   a. one who creates   b. one who examines

3. A _____ from another firm was _____ to see his <u>philosophy</u> of design being used by a competitor.

   a. knowledge about a topic   b. desire to study a new topic

4. On the day of the grand opening, <u>spectators</u> stood in the _____ of a large crowd, while a memorial _____ gave a grand salute.

   a. people who watch an event   b. people who compete in an event

On Your Own

As you read "The Wizard of Menlo Park," look for words with Greek or Latin roots.

Home Activity With your child, list as many words as you can with the same root words as *philosopher* and *architect*.

R1.4 Know abstract, derived roots and affixes from Greek and Latin and use this knowledge to analyze the meaning of complex words (e.g., *controversial*).

Vocabulary 191

⊙ Main Idea

The **main idea** of a piece of writing is what the piece of writing is mostly about. Details help support and expand on the main idea.

Bree is a tall girl.	Her parents, brother, and sister are all tall too.	Bree does not feel self-conscious about her height.	She says being tall can come in handy.

Practice

Fill in the graphic organizer below with the main idea and details.

Main Idea	**Detail**	**Detail**	**Detail**

On Your Own

Use what you know about main idea as you read "The Wizard of Menlo Park." List the details that support the main idea.

School + Home **Home Activity** Your child reviewed main idea. Work with your child to make a graphic organizer that shows the main idea and supporting details of an article about an artist.

R2.3 Discern main ideas and concepts presented in texts, identifying and assessing evidence that supports those ideas.

⊙ Multiple-Meaning Words

A **multiple-meaning word** is a word that has more than one meaning. A dictionary can help you determine what meaning of a multiple-meaning word an author is using.

Practice

Read the following sentences. Fill in the blanks using the Words to Know. Then choose the definition that best matches the underlined multiple-meaning word. Use a dictionary to help you.

Words To Know

erected
foundations
mold
occasion
proportion
tidied
workshop

1. The <u>opening</u> of the new play was a(n) _____ of immense _____ for the talented young playwright.

   a. a hole or gap   b. a clearing   c. a first performance

2. She had started the <u>script</u> during a(n) _____ in college, setting down the _____ of the story during a single week.

   a. a written text   b. cursive handwriting   c. a list of instructions

3. After a storm flooded her house, she had thought her work lost, but found a <u>copy</u> in one of the only boxes not covered with _____.

   a. a duplicate   b. material to print   c. do the same as

4. Not only is her play on <u>stage</u>, but her home is now being _____ again, soon after the storm debris has been _____ away.

   a. a part of a rocket   b. a raised platform   c. a step in a process

On Your Own

As you read "The Wizard of Menlo Park," make a list of the multiple-meaning words you find. Then look up the multiple-meaning words in a dictionary.

Home Activity Your child reviewed multiple-meaning words. Invite your child to show you how to find multiple-meaning words in the dictionary and how to determine the correct meaning based on context.

G6R1.2 Identify and interpret figurative language and words with multiple meanings.

Vocabulary 193

⊙ Fact and Opinion

Fact and Opinion A **fact** is something that can be proved true or false. An **opinion** is a belief or judgment that cannot be proved true or false.

Read each statement. If it is a fact, write F on the line. If it is an opinion, write O.

_____ The playwright's name is Starr Smith.

_____ Her house was flooded by a storm.

_____ The play is really great.

_____ The actor playing the lead could have been better.

_____ I would like to see the play again.

Practice

Read the following passage. Underline the statements of fact.

> Starr Smith's new play, *Chasing Roger*, opened last night before a full house at the Hippodrome Theater. The playwright is only 25 years old, but I was pleasantly surprised by the play's quality. The play is a comedy about a man trying to track down an ex-roommate who took some of his property. Lead actor William Dunst took several scenes to become comfortable in the role, which was unfortunate. With a better actor in the lead role, *Chasing Roger* may have been the best play of the year. The play ran for two hours, with a fifteen-minute intermission. I think we can expect great things from Ms. Smith in the future.

On Your Own

Use what you know about fact and opinion as you read "The Wizard of Menlo Park." Decide which are facts and which are opinions in the selection.

Home Activity Your child reviewed fact and opinion. Discuss the ways in which you can tell facts from opinions and how they differ.

R2.5 Distinguish facts, supported inferences, and opinions in text.

Name_____

⊙ Antonyms

An **antonym** is a word that means the opposite of another word. A thesaurus is a useful tool for finding antonyms.

Practice

Answer each question with one of the Words to Know. Use a thesaurus to look up any words you do not know.

Words To Know

- appreciate
- barber
- choir
- released
- religious
- slavery
- teenager

1. Which word means the opposite of *soloist?*

_____

2. Which word means the opposite of *freedom?*

_____

3. Which word means the opposite of *captured?*

_____

4. Which word means the opposite of *disparage?*

_____

5. Which word means the opposite of *secular?*

_____

6. Which word means the opposite of *adult?*

_____

On Your Own

As you read "The Wizard of Menlo Park," notice how the author uses antonyms. Make a list of the antonyms you find.

© Pearson Education, Inc., 5

Home Activity Your child reviewed antonyms. Play a game with one of you saying a word and the other answering with the word's antonym. Use a thesaurus for help if you get stumped.

G4R1.2 Apply knowledge of word origins, derivations, synonyms, antonyms, and idioms to determine the meaning of words and phrases.

⊙ Main Idea

The **main idea** of a piece of writing is what the piece of writing is mostly about. Details help support and expand on the main idea.

| Louis was born in 1900. | He liked to play with other kids. | Then he discovered the trumpet. | Louis Armstrong grew up to be a famous musician. |

Practice

Fill in the graphic organizer below with the main idea and details.

Main Idea	Detail	Detail	Detail

On Your Own

Use what you know about main idea as you read "The Wizard of Menlo Park." Decide what the main idea is and what details support the main idea in the selection.

© Pearson Education, Inc., 5

Home Activity Your child reviewed main idea. Together, read a magazine article and determine the main idea of the article.

R2.3 Discern main ideas and concepts presented in texts, identifying and assessing evidence that supports those ideas.

Prefixes

Prefixes A **prefix** is a word part added to the beginning of a word to change its meaning. The prefix *pre-* means "before" or "the opposite of." The prefix *re-* means "again" or "back."

Add the prefix *pre-* or *re-* to the words below and write the new words formed.
Then write a definition for each new word.

re + cycle   =   _____

pre + record =   _____

pre + teen   =   _____

re + new   =   _____

> **Words To Know**
>
> **background**
> **landscape**
> **miniature**
> **prehistoric**
> **reassembled**

Practice

Read the following sentences. Fill in the blanks with one of the Words to Know. Then answer the question about the underlined word in each sentence.

1. For their science diorama of a _____ era, Lashawn and Queen went online to <u>review</u> depictions of early mammals.

   Review probably means: a. look at again   b. repeat

2. They were fascinated by a Web site that <u>re-created</u> a _____ where _____ horses lived.

   Re-created probably means: a. made previously   b. made again

3. Because the clay trees they made drooped, they _____ the background, using <u>precut</u> broccoli crowns from the grocery store.

   Precut probably means: a. cut again   b. cut before

On Your Own

As you read "The Wizard of Menlo Park," look for antonyms and how they are used in the story. Make a list of the antonyms you find.

Home Activity Your child reviewed prefixes. Choose a common prefix and see who can list the most words with the prefix in a minute.

G3R1.8 Use knowledge of prefixes (e.g., *un-, re-, pre-, bi-, mis-, dis-*) and suffixes (e.g., *-er, -est, -ful*) to determine the meaning of words.

Vocabulary   197

© Pearson Education, Inc., 5

◉ Graphic Sources

Graphic sources, such as maps, charts, tables, illustrations, and diagrams, make information easy to understand and use. Graphic sources depict information that would take a great deal to describe in words visually in a small amount of space.

Practice

Science Project Timetable: Ms. Carter's Class

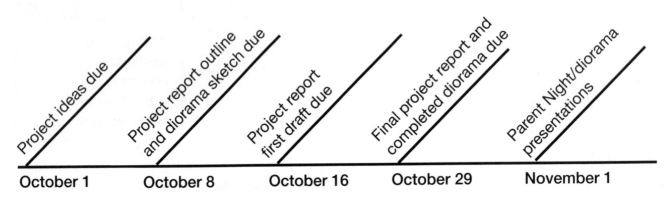

Project ideas due	Project report outline and diorama sketch due	Project report first draft due	Final project report and completed diorama due	Parent Night/diorama presentations
October 1	October 8	October 16	October 29	November 1

1. On what date do Ms. Carter's students have to give her their project ideas?

_____

2. What is due to Ms. Carter on October 8?

_____

_____

3. By what date must the students hand in their completed dioramas?

_____

_____

4. At what event will the class present their projects?

_____

On Your Own

Use what you know about graphic sources as you read "The Wizard of Menlo Park."

Home Activity Your child reviewed graphic sources. Flip through a magazine or newspaper and count how many different graphic sources you can find.

R2.1 Understand how text features (e.g., format, graphics, sequence, diagrams, illustrations, charts, maps) make information accessible and usable.

The Wizard of Menlo Park

Every time we turn on a light, we should feel grateful to Thomas Alva Edison. Edison officially created and patented more inventions than anyone in history. Some of these inventions, such as the phonograph, the motion picture camera, and the incandescent light bulb, had a huge impact on American society.

Early Years

Edison was born in 1847 and spent his childhood in Port Huron, Michigan. His mother, a teacher, educated her son at home and exposed him to many different subjects. Edison quickly became a book-lover with a passion for chemistry, machinery, and electricity.

Driven by his interest in locomotives, the young Edison took a job selling newspapers and candy on the train. When he eventually had enough money saved, the ambitious boy bought printing equipment. He then published and sold his own newspapers to the train passengers. In addition to this business, Edison was given permission to set up a small laboratory in the train's baggage car. The eager boy-scientist conducted experiments there, until an accidental fire brought the locomotive lab to an abrupt end.

Telegraphy and Edison's First Invention

In 1862, when Edison was still a teenager, he risked his life to save a three-year-old boy from an oncoming train. The boy's father thanked Edison by teaching him about the telegraph, a way of sending messages over wires using electricity. At the time, the telegraph was the chief method for communicating across long distances. Edison soon became a skilled telegraph operator, working around the country.

In 1869, Edison patented his very first invention: the electric vote-recording machine. Patents are handed out by the United States government. When someone gets a patent for a new invention, it means that he or she will get money if people use their idea. But Edison's vote machine didn't sell. No politicians were interested in using it! Despite this failure, Edison's first official invention taught him a valuable lesson. From that moment on, he would be sure to invent devices that people would use.

⊙ **DAY 2** Main Idea
What is the topic of this passage?

_____

⊙ **DAY 3** Fact and Opinion Is the first sentence of the passage a fact or an opinion? Explain your answer.

_____

_____

_____

_____

_____

_____

⊙ **DAY 3** Multiple-Meaning Words
What is the meaning of *train* as it is used in the passage?

_____

_____

What is another meaning for *train* not used in the passage?

_____

_____

R2.0 Students read and understand grade-level appropriate material.

"The Wizard of Menlo Park" **199**

Edison's Career Takes Flight

Edison eventually landed a well-paying job and achieved several successful patents and good business deals. After he had enough money saved, he built what he called "an invention factory" in Newark, New Jersey. He hired dozens of engineers and produced numerous products. His work was so successful that he eventually moved his creative workshop to a larger facility in Menlo Park, New Jersey, and later again to West Orange, New Jersey. As his fame grew, he became known as the "Wizard of Menlo Park."

His Most Famous Inventions

Of the more than 1,000 patents that Edison received during his lifetime, a few of his inventions stand out above the rest. First, he decided to rework Alexander Graham Bell's telephone, improving its sound quality and clarity. Then in 1877, Edison invented the phonograph, or record player, a device that would play back sound.

Edison, though, was most famous for his work on the incandescent light bulb. Other inventors had already discovered that when an electric current was sent through a wire, the wire became hot and glowed. This glowing was known as incandescence—the giving off of light. The wire that people used, however, only lasted for a short time before burning out. It was Edison who discovered that a thin piece of scorched cotton thread would provide light for many hours without burning out too quickly.

After the invention of the incandescent light bulb, Edison also collaborated with his assistant, William Dickson, to create a motion picture camera and viewer, known respectively as the Kinetograph and the Kinetoscope. These early devices helped to lay the groundwork for modern movies.

Over his lifetime, Edison was granted more than 1,000 patents, at times receiving an average of one patent for an invention every five days. He achieved great success and his hard-working philosophy made him famous throughout the world. Today, our cultural landscape would not be the same if weren't for the Wizard of Menlo Park.

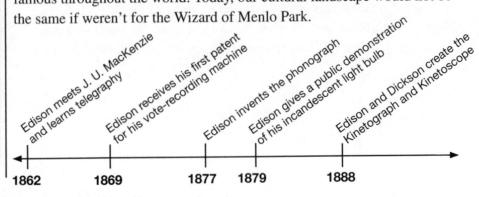

- ⊙ **DAY 4** Antonyms What is an antonym for *numerous?*

  _____

  _____

- ⊙ **DAY 4** Main Idea What is the main idea of the first paragraph?

  _____

  _____

  _____

  _____

  _____

- ⊙ **DAY 5** Prefixes What is the prefix in *rework?*

  _____

- ⊙ **DAY 2** Greek and Latin Roots What word on this page contains the Greek root *philo-?*

  _____

- ⊙ **DAY 5** Graphic Sources Circle the date on the time line that tells you when Edison presented his light bulb to the public.

Time line:
- 1862 Edison meets J. U. MacKenzie and learns telegraphy
- 1869 Edison receives his first patent for his vote-recording machine
- 1877 Edison invents the phonograph
- 1879 Edison gives a public demonstration of his incandescent light bulb
- 1888 Edison and Dickson create the Kinetograph and Kinetoscope

Home Activity Your child read a selection and used comprehension and vocabulary skills from Unit 3. Have your child summarize the main ideas of the selection, using the time line to help with the summary.

R2.0 Students read and understand grade-level appropriate material.

The Baseball Mitt

Rico woke up on Monday morning when his bed tossed him onto the floor. *I guess I'll need to do some work on my mattress alarm,* he thought while rubbing his head. Then he looked at his watch and yelped. He was running fifteen minutes behind schedule! Quickly, he activated his A.M. Machine and watched his room slip into action. His bedroom light flipped on, his bureau drawer flew open, and his bedspread rolled neatly into place. Within minutes, Rico was dressed, his room was tidy, and he was ready to head down for breakfast.

"Morning, Rico," his mother said, handing him a piece of toast. Rico ate it hungrily and gathered his things for school. In the corner of the kitchen, his little brother sat in a high chair busily coating himself in oatmeal. Rico made a mental note to invent some stain-resistant fabric for later.

Right before Rico left for school, his father called him over. "Don't forget, kiddo," his dad said. "Baseball practice starts today. I'll see you on the field."

Rico gave a weak smile and stared uncomfortably at his feet. Rico's father was the baseball coach, and this year, he'd signed up his son for the team. Rico hadn't had the heart to tell his father he would rather be home working on whatever new project he'd invented. That was more fun for him than running bases or fielding balls.

At least Rico had one new invention that might help him out on the baseball field. He ducked into the garage and carefully slipped his secret baseball glove into his backpack. Already he was dreading the afternoon practice, but there was nothing he could do to stop it.

At lunch, Rico sat with his friend, Jamil, discussing his practice game plan. "All I need to do is flip the glove's switch," Rico said, "and the vacuum will suck up the ball. I'll never have to worry about catching a thing. The glove will do it all for me."

"Let's hope it works," Jamil said. "If it does, I'm hiring you to make me some special baseball running shoes."

The rest of the day passed by in a blur. When the school bell rang, Rico dragged himself down to the boys' locker room and slowly got dressed for practice. Everyone around him, including Jamil, was excited for the start of the baseball season. It seemed like Rico was the only one wishing he were somewhere else. Carefully, he pulled his secret glove out of his backpack and headed for the baseball diamond.

⊙ **DAY 1** Author's Viewpoint/Bias Do you think the author likes the character Rico? Why or why not?

_____

_____

_____

_____

_____

© Pearson Education, Inc., 5

R2.0 Students read and understand grade-level appropriate material.

⊙ **DAY 1** Multiple-Meaning Words
What is the meaning of *sentence* as it is used in the passage?

_____

_____

What is another meaning for *sentence* not used in the passage?

_____

_____

_____

⊙ **DAY 1** Author's Viewpoint/Bias Do you think the author believes Rico's inventions are a waste of time? Explain your answer.

_____

_____

_____

_____

_____

_____

_____

_____

When the team had assembled on the field, Rico's dad began to speak. "Okay, guys. Let's try some fielding. Everyone get out there and show your stuff!" Rico swallowed hard. He felt like a prisoner awaiting his sentence.

When no one was looking, he flipped the switch on his glove. It made a noise like a small vacuum cleaner, but none of his teammates seemed to notice. For several minutes, Rico waited for a ball. He was just beginning to wonder if one would come his way when suddenly a pop fly began plummeting in his direction. *Please work*, he thought to himself as he squeezed his eyes shut and held up his glove.

A moment later, Rico felt a hard and solid thud in his hand. He opened his eyes to see the ball resting firmly in his glove. "Nice job, Rico," his father called from home plate. Rico stared in astonishment. His invention had worked!

"Here comes one more," his father yelled. In a flash, Rico's glove grabbed the second ball, too. Now Rico began to panic. He hadn't expected so many baseballs to fly at him all at once. In desperation, he held out his mitt, accidentally sucking up two more pop flies meant for other teammates.

By now, a curious crowd had gathered in a circle. "What's going on, Rico?" his father shouted over the noise of the vacuum.

Finally, Rico flipped the glove's switch and four baseballs promptly fell to the ground. "I invented this glove," Rico said. "It makes the catch for you."

His father's eyes were thoughtful as he started inspecting the mitt. "Rico, this is a fabulous invention—I'm proud that you made it! But it wouldn't be fair to use it when we're playing. We all need to use our own skills—not a glove that does the work for us."

"I know," Rico admitted. "But maybe I can use the mitt to collect the baseballs after fielding practice is over."

Rico's father laughed. "Sounds like a deal," he said. "Now everyone," he continued, turning to his team, "let's play ball!"

© Pearson Education, Inc., 5

Home Activity Your child read a selection and used comprehension and vocabulary skills from Unit 3. Have your child retell the selection, focusing on the author's viewpoint and bias regarding the characters.

R2.0 Students read and understand grade-level appropriate material.

Connect Text to Text

Reading Across Texts

Think about the selections "The Wizard of Menlo Park" and "The Baseball Mitt." Complete the Venn diagram below with details that show similarities and differences between the two texts.

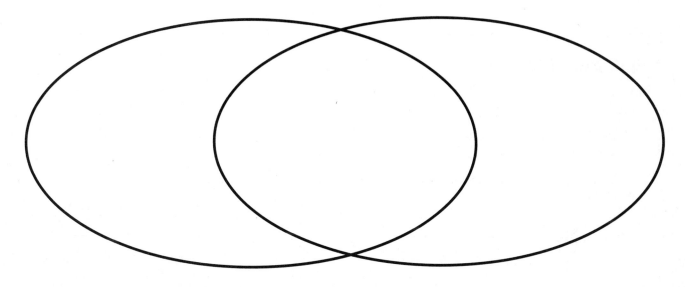

Writing Across Texts

Imagine you have the chance to invent something important. What would you invent and why?

_____

_____

_____

_____

_____

_____

_____

_____

© Pearson Education, Inc., 5

School + Home **Home Activity** Your child read two selections this week. Have your child explain to you how they were alike and how they were different.

Summarize Your Learning

What do people gain from the work of inventors and artists?

- *The Fabulous Perpetual Motion Machine*   • *Leonardo's Horse*
- *The Dinosaurs of Waterhouse Hawkins*   • *Mahalia Jackson*
- *Special Effects in Film and Television*

Think About It!

Think about the selections you read in this unit.

- How were they alike? How were they different?
- Were the selections you read this week similar to others you have read?
- What did you learn?

Write three big ideas about how artists and inventors can inspire others around them.

- _____
- _____
- _____

Question It!

What if you had a chance to meet a famous artist or inventor? Write three questions that you would ask him or her.

- _____
- _____
- _____

Talk About It!

Discuss your questions with a partner.

- What questions did your partner have? Were they similar to yours?
  Were they different from yours?
- What things did you and your partner want to know?
- What feelings and ideas did you and your partner have about artists and inventors?

© Pearson Education, Inc., 5

Home Activity Your child reviewed and discussed the selections from Unit 3. Have your child describe to you the big ideas about the work of artists and inventors from this unit.

Family Times

Summary

American Slave, American Hero

In 1804, the Corps of Discovery, headed by Meriwether Lewis and William Clark, set out by boat on the Missouri River to explore the western portion of the North American continent. York, a slave of Clark, became a hero of the journey.

Activity

One for the Books There are many times when everyone in the family must adapt to a difficult situation. With your family, talk about some time when you all went on a trip or had to work together to get a job done. Write a journal entry about the event as if it were an important historical occasion. Include details about how each of you had to make an extra effort to get through the event.

Comprehension Skill

Author's Viewpoint/Bias

• A **viewpoint** is how an author looks at a subject from past experience or knowledge.

• A **bias** is an author's feelings or preferences for or against something.

• Examining the author's beliefs may help you understand the author's viewpoint.

• A bias in an author's writing may be revealed by the types of evidence the author uses to support his or her viewpoint.

Activity

One side of the story Even when family members experience the same event, memories of the details are often different. One reason for this is that every person sees things through his or her own viewpoint. With your family, think of an occasion where you were all present. Then, separately, write down a list of details about this event. Get together when you are finished to compare differences in what you wrote. Talk about what might cause your memories to be unique.

Lesson Vocabulary

Words to Know

Knowing the meaning of these words is important to reading *American Slave, American Hero*. Practice using these words.

Vocabulary Words

accurate without errors or mistakes

advanced move forward

dwindled became smaller and smaller

edible fit to eat

extraordinary very unusual

unexplainable unable to be given reasons for

uprooted torn away, removed, or displaced completely

Conventions

Pronouns and Antecedents

A **pronoun** is a word that replaces a noun or noun phrase. *For example: I, you, he, she, it, me, him, her, we, you, they, us.* The word or words that a pronoun stands for—such as *Julie, my father,* or *our cat Mouffette*—is called the pronoun's **antecedent.** *For example: Laurene saw George, so she waved to him.* In the example, the nouns "Laurene" and "George" are the *antecedents* of the *pronouns* "she" and "him."

Activity

Creative Captions With a family member, look through a picture book with which you both are familiar. Write captions on a separate piece of paper for the pictures that you see. Circle each pronoun that appears in your captions.

Practice Tested Spelling Words

_____   _____   _____   _____

_____   _____   _____   _____

_____   _____   _____   _____

_____   _____   _____   _____

_____   _____   _____   _____

Author's Viewpoint/Bias

- A **viewpoint** is how an author looks at a subject from past experience or knowledge. Examining the author's beliefs may help you understand the author's viewpoint.
- A **bias** is an author's feelings or preferences for or against something. A bias in an author's writing may be revealed by the types of evidence the author uses to support his or her viewpoint.

Directions Read the following passage. Then answer the questions below.

April 3rd
Dear Diary—
I let Gina talk me into going with her to a Parkour "jam." Parkour is a combination of sport, dancing, and martial arts. Gina says it's the art of moving from one place to another with speed and precision. She says the athletes treat anything that gets in their way like a jungle gym. They jump over walls and climb over just about anything. I told her that sounds silly. I've been doing gymnastics for three years. You have to train hard to do those things. You can't just pretend you're some kind of super-hero.

April 5th
Dear Diary—
Wow! Was I wrong about Parkour! It's fun, but it's hard. Gina's instructor taught us to make accurate jumps and land safely. He placed an extraordinary value on preventing injuries. I thought just because I'm a gymnast, I'd be better than everyone. My overconfidence dwindled quickly. I learned that Gina's Parkour team develops physical fitness and strong friendships because the sport is non-competitive. I'm going to add Parkour to my exercise program and adapt my gymnastic skills to help me train.

1. Does the author have a bias for or against Parkour in her first diary entry?

_____

2. From what viewpoint does the author form an opinion about Parkour?

_____

_____

3. Is the author's bias understandable? Why or why not?

_____

_____

4. How does the author's bias change in the second diary entry?

_____

Home Activity Your child identified an author's viewpoint and bias in a short passage. With your child, think of a place that one person in the family likes to go for recreation but another does not. Discuss what differences in viewpoint cause each person's biases.

R3.7 Evaluate the author's use of various techniques (e.g., appeal of characters in a picture book, logic and credibility of plots and settings, use of figurative language) to influence readers' perspectives.

Comprehension 217

Vocabulary

Directions Choose the word from the box that best matches each definition. Write the word on the line.

_____ 1. became smaller and smaller

_____ 2. fit to eat

_____ 3. without errors or mistakes

_____ 4. move forward

_____ 5. torn away, removed, or displaced completely

> **Check the Words You Know**
>
> ___ accurate
> ___ advanced
> ___ dwindled
> ___ edible
> ___ extraordinary
> ___ unexplained
> ___ uprooted

Directions Choose the word from the box that best completes each sentence. Write the word on the line to the left.

_____ 6. Swimming the English Channel was one of Larry's most _____ athletic accomplishments.

_____ 7. Her _____ poor grades began to worry Jessie's parents because she was normally a good student.

_____ 8. My interest in computer games _____ after my interest in rock climbing increased.

_____ 9. When you pick berries, always go with someone who knows the difference between _____ and poisonous berries.

_____ 10. I can't make an _____ guess about the value of this antique coin until I learn more about where it came from.

Write a Newspaper Article

On a separate piece of paper, write a newspaper article about an imaginary group of explorers who travel to another planet and encounter serious challenges. Use as many of the vocabulary words as you can.

Home Activity Your child identified and used vocabulary words from *American Slave, American Hero*. Together, look through newspapers or magazines for stories about people who adapt to face physical, emotional, or mental challenges. Discuss what gives people the determination to persevere.

R1.0 Word Analysis, Fluency, and Systematic Vocabulary Development

Vocabulary • Unfamiliar Words

- When you find a word you do not know in a text, look for clues to its meaning.
- You can find **context clues** among the words around the unfamiliar word.

Directions Read the following passage about facing a different kind of challenge. Then answer the questions below.

> Anita's friend Jessica asked her a hard question. "Anita, what is it like to live with your disability? Is it hard for you to be in a wheelchair?"
>
> Anita thought carefully about how she would answer. "I don't mind using a wheelchair. I get around in it very well. But because I have cerebral palsy, it's difficult for people to understand what I'm saying. Sometimes my words can sound very confusing. Sometimes my speech sounds muddled, like I have something in my mouth."
>
> Jessica said, "But I can understand you just fine."
>
> "You are used to me," said Anita. "I go to a speech therapist every week to help me learn how to speak more clearly. I want people to better understand what I'm saying."

1. What does *wheelchair* mean? What context clues helped you to determine the meaning?

_____

_____

2. What does *disability* mean? What context clues helped you to determine the meaning?

_____

3. What does *muddled* mean? What context clues help you to determine the meaning?

_____

4. How would using context clues help you determine the meaning of *speech therapist*?

_____

_____

5. What context clues helped you understand what *cerebral palsy* means?

_____

_____

_____

Home Activity Your child identified and used context clues to understand new words of a passage. Have a discussion with your child in which you use context clues to give clues to the meanings of new words.

G3R1.6 Use sentence and word context to find the meaning of unknown words.

Graphic Sources

Directions Look at the circle graph and read the caption below it. Then answer the questions below.

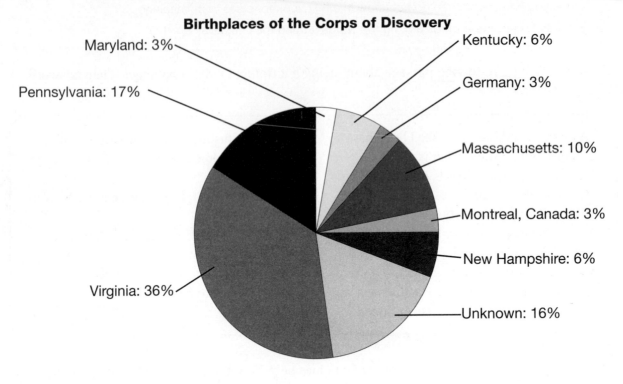

Birthplaces of the Corps of Discovery

Maryland: 3%

Kentucky: 6%

Germany: 3%

Pennsylvania: 17%

Massachusetts: 10%

Montreal, Canada: 3%

New Hampshire: 6%

Virginia: 36%

Unknown: 16%

This graph shows the percentage of members of the Corps of Discovery who came from the countries and states listed.

1. Where did the largest percentage of corps members come from? What was the percentage?

_____

_____

2. Where did the smallest percentage come from?

_____

3. Where did 16% come from?

_____

4. After Virginia, where did the greatest percentage come from?

_____

5. Kentucky and what other state had 6%?

_____

School + Home

© Pearson Education, Inc., 5

R2.1 Understand how text features (e.g., format, graphics, sequence, diagrams, illustrations, charts, maps) make information accessible and usable.

Author's Viewpoint/Bias

- A **viewpoint** is how an author looks at a subject from past experience or knowledge. Examining the author's beliefs may help you understand the author's viewpoint.

- A **bias** is an author's feelings or preferences for or against something. A bias in an author's writing may be revealed by the types of evidence the author uses to support his or her viewpoint.

Directions Read the following passage. Then answer the questions below.

Review of *The Legacy of Luna: The Story of a Tree, a Woman and the Struggle to Save the Redwoods*

The biggest challenge I had writing a review of this book was trying not to laugh. "Luna," a redwood tree in a California forest, became home to Julia "Butterfly" Hill, a young woman who seems to think that saving the environment is more important than making honest money.

Ms. Hill's book tells the story of the 738 days she lived in the tree, trying to "save" it from loggers. It seems strange that, after building her "nest" in the 180-foot tree, sleeping through raging storms, and keeping warm in the dead of winter, she wrote a book printed on paper. I wonder if the paper was recycled. Let's help Ms. Hill recycle—throw a copy of her new book into the nearest recycling bin, immediately! Sure, she saved the tree from being cut down. I wonder who will save her readers from the book she wrote?

1. Does the author have a bias for or against Julia Hill's effort to save the tree?

_____

2. What clue reveals what the author's bias is?

_____

3. What would you guess might be the author's viewpoint?

_____

_____

4. Does knowing the author's bias and viewpoint make you want to read the book? Why or why not?

_____

_____

Home Activity Your child identified an author's viewpoint and bias in a short passage. With your child, think of a book or movie that one person in the family really likes but another does not. Discuss what differences in viewpoint cause each person's biases.

R3.7 Evaluate the author's use of various techniques (e.g., appeal of characters in a picture book, logic and credibility of plots and settings, use of figurative language) to influence readers' perspectives.

Author's Viewpoint/Bias

- A **viewpoint** is how an author looks at a subject from past experience or knowledge. Examining the author's beliefs may help you understand the author's viewpoint.
- A **bias** is an author's feelings or preferences for or against something. A bias in an author's writing may be revealed by the types of evidence the author uses to support his or her viewpoint.

Directions Read the following passage. Then answer the questions below.

Dear Editors,

Your readers have probably never heard of my country, Tuvalu. I own one of the only hotels in my country, which has the smallest population of any country in the United Nations. We are very worried about the predicted rise of sea levels, since the highest point in Tuvalu is only 16 feet above sea level. If global warming continues and Earth's polar ice melts, our country might disappear!

My people migrated from the Polynesian islands three thousand years ago. Since then we have struggled. First, we farmed and fished to survive. When we could not farm enough to feed ourselves, we printed beautiful postage stamps for collectors. When the Internet grew, our country was given the Internet suffix ".*tv*" instead of ".*com*". Our country now earns money by charging companies to use Internet addresses ending in .tv. Clearly, Tuvaluans can adapt to almost anything. But we cannot learn to breathe underwater! We ask your readers to do all they can to stop global warming.

1. From what viewpoint does the author write this letter to the editor?

_____

_____

2. How might the author's ownership of a hotel affect his bias about global warming?

_____

3. What type of evidence does the author use to share his viewpoint with readers?

_____

4. What is the one thing the author says Tuvaluans cannot adapt to?

_____

R3.7 Evaluate the author's use of various techniques (e.g., appeal of characters in a picture book, logic and credibility of plots and settings, use of figurative language) to influence readers' perspectives.

Telephone Directory

A **telephone directory** is an alphabetical index of names and telephone numbers for a selected geographical area. The **white pages** list entries for individual people and businesses. The **yellow pages** list entries and ads for businesses. Entries are grouped by category or type of business, such as *restaurants.* This information is available in reference books or on the Internet. You can search online to find phone numbers for people and businesses in other cities, states, and even countries.

Directions The computer screen shows you how to search a directory of online white pages. Use the computer screen to answer the questions that follow.

Enter the first and last name of the person and click *Find!*

For better results, enter the city and state also.

Last Name (required)	
First Name	
City	**State**
Country	

Find!   If you need help, click here.

1. What entries will you get if you type "Reyes" in the field for Last Name, "Philadelphia" in the City field, and "PA" (for Pennsylvania) in the State field?

_____

_____

2. You know Sue Costello lives in Florida. Tell how to find her phone number and address.

_____

_____

3. Would typing "Julia" in the First Name field and "Texas" in the State field give you good search results? Explain.

_____

_____

4. How does using an online telephone directory rather than a telephone book increase the information you can get?

_____

R2.1 Understand how text features (e.g., format, graphics, sequence, diagrams, illustrations, charts, maps) make information accessible and usable.

Research and Study Skills 223

Directions The computer screen shows you how to search a directory of online yellow pages. Use the computer screen to answer the questions that follow.

Enter a business category or name. Then click *Find!*

City [_____] State [_____]

Find! If you need help, click here.

---

5. What will you get if you enter the category "state park" and "FL" for State?

_____

_____

6. If you want information on Nancy & Beth's Catering Services in St. Louis, Missouri, what should you enter?

_____

_____

7. If you want to find a bike rental in Phoenix, Arizona, what should you enter?

_____

_____

8. If you enter "toy store" in the category field, will this produce good search results? Explain.

_____

_____

9. Which of the three fields could you leave blank? Explain how filling in this field would narrow your search.

_____

_____

10. Can you use an online telephone directory if you don't know how to spell the name of a business? Explain.

_____

_____

Home Activity Your child learned about using telephone directories. Look at an online telephone directory together. Ask your child to locate emergency phone numbers, maps, and phone numbers of local businesses and residences.

W1.4 Create simple documents by using electronic media and employing organizational features (e.g., passwords, entry and pull-down menus, word searches, a thesaurus, spell checks).

Family Times

Summary

The Gymnast

What is it like to try gymnastics? As a young boy, Gary envies his cousin who takes gymnastics. Gary tries to learn too. He vividly describes his feelings as he rolls, flips, and cartwheels for the first time.

Activity

Sports Center With your family, recall outstanding sports moments you each have seen or experienced. Then talk with family members about what sport they would like to succeed at.

Comprehension Skill

Draw Conclusions

A **conclusion** is a decision you reach when you think about facts and details. Draw conclusions as you read. Your conclusions should be logical and well supported.

Activity

How Was Your Day? Ask a family member to tell you about the things that happened during his or her day. When you have heard your family member's story, decide whether he or she probably felt it was a good day or a bad day. Explain the thinking you used as you drew your conclusion.

Lesson Vocabulary

Words to Know

Knowing the meanings of these words is important to reading *The Gymnast*. Practice using these words.

Vocabulary Words

bluish somewhat blue; somewhat like the color of the clear sky in daylight

cartwheels sideways handsprings with the legs and arms kept straight

gymnastics a sport in which very difficult exercises are performed

hesitation act of failing to act promptly; doubt; indecision

limelight center of public attention and interest

skidded slipped or slid sideways while moving

somersault to run or jump, turning the heels over the head

throbbing beating rapidly or strongly

wincing drawing back suddenly; flinching slightly

Grammar

Who and Whom

Use **who** as the subject of a sentence. *For example: Who is calling?* Use **whom** as the object of a preposition such as *to, for,* or *from,* or as a direct object. *For example: Whom is that from? Whom are you calling?* To check whether you should write *who* or *whom* in a question, think of a sentence with *he* or *him* in place of *who* or *whom.* If *he* is correct, then write *who.* If it is not correct, write *whom.*

Activity

Boo-Who Play this game with your family. In teams, make up questions that use *who/whom,* such as *Who/Whom does the quarterback pass to?* The other team's job is to decide whether *who* or *whom* is correct in that sentence. Call out "boo-who" if the team answers incorrectly.

Practice Tested Spelling Words

_____ _____ _____ _____

_____ _____ _____ _____

_____ _____ _____ _____

_____ _____ _____ _____

Draw Conclusions

- A **conclusion** is a sensible decision you make after you think about facts or details that you read.
- Drawing conclusions may also be called making inferences.
- Use your prior knowledge to help you draw conclusions.

Directions Read the following passage. Then complete the diagram below.

Enrique is a young gymnast who is training for the Olympics. He goes to live at the Olympic Training Center in Colorado Springs. There he trains twelve hours a day with other athletes. In addition, he regularly takes part in competitions to test his skills. Enrique sets goals for himself. He wants to improve in gymnastics skills and to learn routines that are more difficult. His training schedule is so demanding, he does not have time to go to a regular school. He studies all of his school subjects with a tutor. After more years of training, Enrique hopes to make the Olympic team.

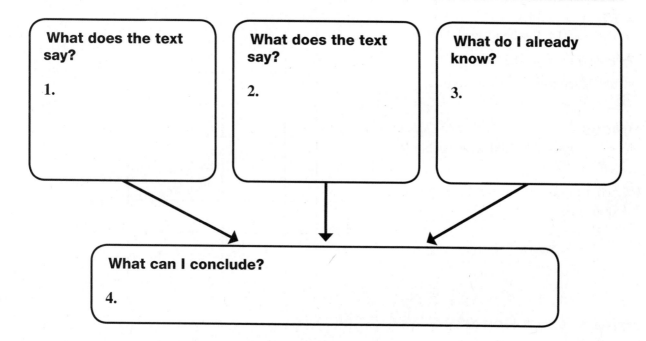

What does the text say?

1.

What does the text say?

2.

What do I already know?

3.

What can I conclude?

4.

5. Visualize Enrique studying with his tutor. What conclusion can you draw about the advantages or disadvantages of studying with a tutor rather than studying at a regular school?

_____

Home Activity Your child read a short passage and drew a conclusion based on the details in it. Tell your child a story about an athlete you know about. Ask your child to visualize the details as you describe them. Ask your child to draw a conclusion based on the details you provide.

R2.4 Draw inferences, conclusions, or generalizations about text and support them with textual evidence and prior knowledge.

Name_____

Vocabulary

Directions Choose the word from the box that best matches each definition below. Write the word on the line.

_____ 1. to run or jump, turning the heels over the head

_____ 2. a sport in which very difficult exercises are performed

_____ 3. act of failing to act promptly

_____ 4. somewhat blue

_____ 5. sideways handsprings with the legs and arms kept straight

Directions Choose the word from the box that matches the clues and complete the crossword puzzle.

DOWN
6. the pain I felt when I broke my toe
7. the color of a pale sky
8. the place the star wants to be

ACROSS
9. what my bicycle did when I slammed on the brakes
10. what I am doing when I eat food I don't like

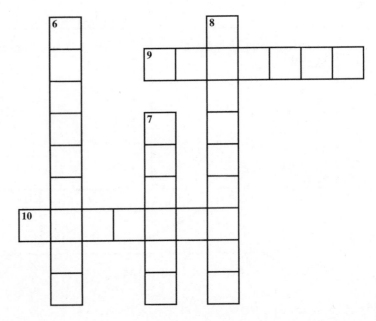

Write a News Report

Imagine you're a sports reporter covering a gymnastics meet. On a separate sheet of paper write a news report. Use as many vocabulary words as you can.

Home Activity Your child identified and used vocabulary words from *The Gymnast*. Skim the articles about a single sport in the sports section of a newspaper. Point out and define the vocabulary word that is used to describe each type of sport.

R1.0 Word Analysis, Fluency, and Systematic Vocabulary Development

© Pearson Education, Inc., 5

Name_____

Vocabulary • Suffixes

- A **suffix** is a syllable added to the end of a base word to change its meaning or the way it is used in a sentence. For example, the suffix *-ish* means "somewhat," as in *childish*. The suffix *-ion* means "the act or state of being _____," as in *determination*. The suffix *-ics* means "study or system," as in *athletics*. You can use suffixes to help you figure out the meanings of words.
- In dictionaries, the definition of a base word with the suffix added is usually found near that of the base word. The base word's definition is helpful in understanding a word's meaning.

Directions Read the following passage. Notice the words with suffixes as you read. Then answer the questions below.

The gymnastics meet started with a spectacular balance beam routine by Amy's main competitor. Then Amy hopped onto the beam and started her routine with no hesitation. She did fine on her somersaults and cartwheels, but on one backflip she had a bad landing. Her ankle felt like a knife had ripped through it, and she saw bluish stars in front of her eyes. Still, she finished her routine, wincing with the pain. When the numbers came up, she scored the highest! Although her ankle was throbbing, she stepped to the judges' table and accepted her medal.

1. What is the suffix in *gymnastics*? How does the suffix change the meaning of the base word?

_____

_____

2. What is the suffix in *hesitation*? How does the suffix change the meaning of the base word?

_____

_____

3. What is the suffix in *bluish*? How does the suffix change the meaning of the base word?

_____

4. Change the suffix of *competitor* from *-or* to *-ion*. What is the meaning of the new word?

_____

5. Write two other words that use suffixes. Write a definition for each word.

_____

_____

Home Activity Your child read a short passage and identified and used suffixes to understand new words. Work with your child to identify unfamiliar words with suffixes. Then ask your child how the suffixes help him or her to understand the meanings of the new words. Confirm the meanings by looking them up in a dictionary.

G3R1.8 Use knowledge of prefixes (e.g., *un-, re-, pre-, bi-, mis-, dis-*) and suffixes (e.g., *-er, -est, -ful*) to determine the meaning of words.

Generalize

Directions Read the passage. Then answer the questions below.

> Many schools require every student to play at least one sport. By playing sports, many young people say that they meet new friends. By being on a team, a young person can learn cooperation and fair play. Playing a sport can build strength, flexibility, and endurance, and improve fitness. Many experts say young people get a boost in self-confidence as they succeed with new skills they learn through playing sports. Finally, for most young athletes, playing sports is simply a lot of fun.

1. Based on the passage, what is a generalization you can make about playing sports?

_____

_____

2. Which detail from the passage supports this generalization?

_____

_____

3. What other detail supports this generalization?

_____

_____

4. What is a generalization that is stated in the passage?

_____

_____

5. Write a generalization of your own about sports. Write at least one detail to back it up.

_____

_____

_____

_____

_____

Home Activity Your child read a short passage and made a generalization based on the passage. Tell your child some specific details about a subject you think is important. Ask him or her to make a generalization about the subject.

R2.4 Draw inferences, conclusions, or generalizations about text and support them with textual evidence and prior knowledge.

Draw Conclusions

- A **conclusion** is a sensible decision you make after you think about facts or details that you read.
- Drawing conclusions may also be called making inferences.
- Use your prior knowledge to help you draw conclusions.

Directions Read the following passage. Then answer the questions below.

When Lance Armstrong was 20, he made the U.S. Olympic cycling team. Three years later, he won an important cycling race, the Tour Du Pont, a premier U.S. cycling event. In 1996, he made the U.S. Olympic team again. That same year, he was diagnosed with cancer. He suffered terrible pain during his treatments and fought hard to get back to cycling. Five months after his diagnosis, he was training again determined to return to the sport he loved. Even though he was weakened from the disease, he wouldn't give up. In 1998, he finally returned to professional cycling. In 1999 he won the Tour de France. In 2005, he became the first seven-time winner of the Tour de France. Lance Armstrong inspires many people with his courage and abilities.

1. What conclusion can you draw about Lance Armstrong's character?

_____

_____

2. What is one detail from the passage that supports your conclusion?

_____

3. What is another detail from the passage to support your conclusion?

_____

4. What conclusion can you draw about how Lance Armstrong inspired other people?

_____

_____

5. How does visualizing help you understand what you read about Lance Armstrong?

_____

_____

© Pearson Education, Inc., 5

Home Activity Your child read a short passage and drew conclusions based on details in the passage. Read a newspaper or magazine article about a famous athlete with your child. Ask your child to visualize the details. Afterward, ask your child to draw a conclusion about this sports star.

R2.4 Draw inferences, conclusions, or generalizations about text and support them with textual evidence and prior knowledge.

Draw Conclusions

- A **conclusion** is a sensible decision you make after you think about facts or details that you read.
- Drawing conclusions may also be called making inferences.
- Use your prior knowledge to help you draw conclusions.

Directions Read the following passage. Then complete the diagram below.

Gymnastics has existed for more than five thousand years. It dates back to ancient Egyptian times. In modern times, gymnastics developed first in Germany and then came to the United States in the 1800s. For many years it was based in local clubs and organizations. U.S. schools then began teaching gymnastics at the end of the nineteenth century. Still, gymnastics was not popular in schools and grew mainly through clubs outside of school. The first world competitions for gymnastics began about a hundred years ago, in 1903. Women did not compete in Olympics gymnastics until 1928. Finally, in 1970 the U.S. Gymnastics Federation was formed to oversee the sport in this country. By then gymnastics had earned its place as a competitive sport in the United States.

What does the text say?	What does the text say?	What does the text say?	What do I already know?
1. Gymnastics began _____ _____	2. In the 19th century, _____ _____	3. _____ _____ _____	4. _____ _____ _____

What can I conclude?

5. It took many years for _____

_____

Home Activity Your child read a short passage and drew a conclusion based on the facts in the passage. Together with your child, read an article about an unfamiliar sport. Have your child draw a conclusion about why people participate in that sport.

R2.4 Draw inferences, conclusions, or generalizations about text and support them with textual evidence and prior knowledge.

Graphs

Graphs show information visually. You can use graphs to compare different pieces of information. Look at the title of a graph to see what is being compared. There are many types of graphs, but two types of graphs are bar graphs and circle graphs. A **bar graph** uses horizontal and vertical lines. Words or numbers along each line explain what is being compared. A **circle graph**, which is also called a pie chart, compares the parts of a whole.

Directions Use this graph to answer the questions below.

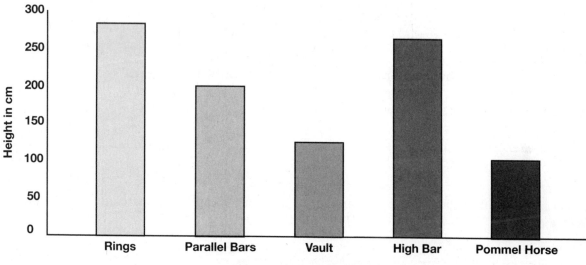

1. Explain what kind of graph this is and how you know.

_____

_____

2. What is the tallest piece of equipment? What is the shortest piece of equipment?

_____

_____

3. How many pieces of equipment are being compared?

_____

4. Approximately how tall are the parallel bars? The high bar?

_____

5. Would this graph be a good source for finding out information about equipment used by female gymnasts? Explain.

_____

R2.1 Understand how text features (e.g., format, graphics, sequence, diagrams, illustrations, charts, maps) make information accessible and usable.

Name_____

Directions Use this graph to answer the questions below.

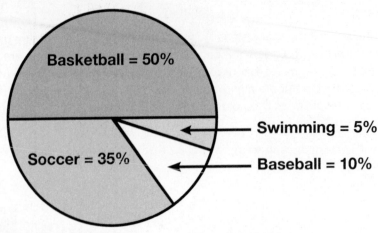

Favorite Sports of Sawyer School Fifth Graders

6. What kind of graph is this? How do you know?

_____

_____

7. What is the favorite sport of the fifth graders at Sawyer School? What percent of students prefer that sport?

_____

_____

8. What sport is second-most popular? What percent of students prefer that sport?

_____

_____

9. What sport is the least popular? What percent of students prefer that sport?

_____

_____

10. What is being compared in this graph? Explain why you think this type of graph displays this information effectively.

_____

_____

Home Activity Your child learned about using graphs as resources. With your child, look at a graph that appears in the newspaper or in a brochure. Ask your child what information is being compared. Ask your child specific questions about information the graph shows.

254 Research and Study Skills

R2.1 Understand how text features (e.g., format, graphics, sequence, diagrams, illustrations, charts, maps) make information accessible and usable.

Family Times

Selection Summaries

Week 1 *Weslandia*

Wesley uses his imagination and some of the things he learned at school to start a very special garden.

Week 2 *American Hero*

Without the help of York, a slave, the Lewis and Clark expedition might never have succeeded.

Week 3 *Exploding Ants*

From soldier ants that self-destruct to save their colony to owls that literally gulp down their dinner, animals have developed amazing adaptations.

Week 4 *The Stormi Giovanni Club*

Stormi decides making friends isn't worth the pain of saying goodbye to them. But on the second day of school, she changes her mind.

Week 5 *The Gymnast*

Gary tells his experiences as he learns to roll, flip, and cartwheel in gymnastics.

Activity

Retell in your own words one of the selections from the unit to a family member. Explain why you chose that selection.

Comprehension Skills Review

In Unit 4, you learned and used many skills while reading the stories and selections.

- When you **draw a conclusion**, you form an opinion based on what you know or on the facts and details in a text.

- An **author's viewpoint** is how the author feels about the topic. Some authors show a strong **bias** for or against their topic.

- A **graphic source** shows or explains information in the text. Pictures, tables, charts, and maps are all graphic sources.

- An author may write similar details about different things or people, and these details can be used to **generalize** about the things or the people.

Activity

Sometimes we have to learn to do things differently, such as when we start a new grade with a different teacher or move to a new home. Write about a time when you've had to adapt to something new. Tell what was good about it, and what was not so good.

Suffixes

A **suffix** is attached to the end of a word to change its meaning. You can check the meanings of suffixes in the dictionary.

Activity Look for words that contain suffixes as you read the selections, and make a list of what you find.

Unfamiliar Words

When you come across an **unfamiliar word,** use context clues—the words and sentences near the word—to help you figure out the word's meaning.

Activity As you read, look for words you are not familiar with and make a list of them. Use context clues to figure out their meanings, and check the dictionary.

Synonyms

A **synonym** is a word that has a similar meaning to another word. You can find synonyms in a thesaurus.

Activity As you read, keep a list of any adjectives you find. Use a thesaurus to find synonyms for those words.

Unfamiliar Words

When you come across an **unfamiliar word,** use context clues—the words and sentences near the word—to help you figure out the word's meaning.

Activity As you read, look for words you are not familiar with and make a list of them. Use context clues to figure out their meanings, and check the dictionary.

Words from Many Cultures

Many words in English come from other languages. These may have unexpected spellings that do not follow the usual English spelling rules.

Prefixes *over-, under-, sub-, super-, out-*

When these prefixes are added to words, the base word stays the same. The base word is also pronounced the same way as it was before the prefix was added.

Homophones

A homophone is a word that sounds exactly like another word but has a different spelling and meaning (for example, *sent*, *cent*, and *scent*).

Suffixes *-ible, -able*

When adding these suffixes, there are no sound clues to help you decide which form to use. The vowel sound spelled by the letters *ib* and *ab* in these suffixes is the schwa sound and can be spelled many different ways.

Negative Prefixes

The prefixes *il-*, *in-*, *im-*, and *ir-* all mean "not." When adding these prefixes, make no change in the base word. Remember that vowels before double consonants usually have a short sound. These prefixes have a short vowel sound in words like *impossible* and *illegal*.

⊙ Suffixes

A **suffix** is attached to the end of a word to change its meaning. Remember that the suffix *-ation* can mean "the act or state of." What Word to Know contains this suffix?

Practice

Read the following sentences. Fill in the blanks using the Words to Know. Then circle the letter of the definition that best matches the underlined word.

Words To Know

blunders
civilization
complex
envy
fleeing
inspired
rustling
strategy

1. The _____ she felt at the older students'
   <u>graduation</u> _____ Lucy to become a better student.
   a. the act of graduating   b. a person who is graduating

2. Her _____ was to become an expert on everything
   taught in her classes, from the history of European <u>immigration</u> to
   the ancient _____ of Rome.
   a. the act of immigrating   b. spectators

3. Lucy decided to increase her <u>exploration</u> of science, and wrote a paper about why the mice were
   always _____ and running around in the classroom cage.
   a. the act of exploring something   b. an expert who explores something

4. But no one can master so many _____ subjects without making some
   _____, and Lucy's teachers asked her to give the other students a chance for
   <u>participation</u> in class.
   a. a person who participates   b. the act of participating

5. Lucy's <u>hesitation</u> about what to do next gave her time to think before she decided that
   _____ the classroom in embarrassment wasn't needed.
   a. failing to act promptly   b. deciding very quickly

On Your Own

As you read "City Blues," keep a list of words with suffixes that you recognize. Tell how these suffixes give you clues about the words' meanings.

Home Activity Your child studied suffixes and how they change a word's meaning. With your child, look for additional words with suffixes. Make a list of suffixes you recognize and discuss how they change words' meanings.

G4R1.4 Know common roots and affixes derived from Greek and Latin and use this knowledge to analyze the meaning of complex words (e.g., *international*).

Vocabulary 257

⊙ Draw Conclusions

When you **draw a conclusion**, you use what you already know and the facts you get from the text to form an opinion.

When you read something, check your conclusion by asking: Does it make sense? Are the facts correct?

Fact: Jack's plan for becoming famous involved building a toothpick tower.
Fact: He wanted to break the world's record.
Conclusion: Jack would become famous if he broke the world's record.

Fact: The team made mistakes while building the tower.
Fact: The tower collapsed.
Conclusion: Jack did not succeed in breaking the world's record.

Practice

Read the facts. Draw a conclusion and write it in the box.

1. Fact: Jack designed the toothpick tower. Fact: The tower fell over.

2. Fact: Jack really wants to become famous. Fact: His first plan to become famous failed.

On Your Own

Use what you know about drawing conclusions while you read "City Blues." Make a conclusion about life in the city.

Home Activity Your child reviewed drawing conclusions. Together, read a newspaper article and see what conclusions you can draw.

258 Comprehension

G6R2.7 Make reasonable assertions about a text through accurate, supporting citations.

◎ Unfamiliar Words

When you come across an **unfamiliar word**, look at the words and sentences around it. These context clues can help you figure out its meaning.

Practice

Fill the blanks with the Words to Know. Then use context clues to choose the definition that best matches the underlined word.

Words To Know
accurate
dwindled
edible
extraordinary
unexplainable
uprooted

1. When I looked out the window one morning, I saw the branches of
   a most _____ and unusual <u>conifer</u> towering over
   the house.

   a. bush   b. shrub   c. tree

2. Its <u>instantaneous</u> growth and _____ cones were simply
   _____.

   a. absurd   b. quick   c. tall

3. Even though the <u>cynical</u> newspaper reporter, at first, refused to believe that the tree had
   grown overnight, a professor from the local college confirmed that our assertions were

   _____.

   a. someone who   b. someone who   c. someone who
      doubts what other   studies hard to   tries to show
      people tell her   understand things   kindness to all

4. Our cranky neighbor wanted to have the tree _____, but her hopes
   _____ as the crowds <u>swelled</u>, from a few people to many hundreds,
   to see our marvelous tree!

   a. divided   b. grew   c. visited

On Your Own

As you read "Urban Wildlife," use context clues to determine the meanings of unfamiliar words.

Home Activity Your child has reviewed using context clues to determine the meanings of unfamiliar words. Together, read a story and look for unfamiliar words. Use context clues to determine their meanings, and check your ideas with a dictionary.

G3R1.6 Use sentence and word context to find the meaning of unknown words.

Name_____

⊙ Author's Viewpoint / Bias

Every piece of writing contains the **author's viewpoint**, or how the author feels about the topic. Some authors show a strong **bias** for or against their topic.

Dear Editor:
I saw the front-page article about that strange tree. I live next door to it. For the life of me, I don't know why that monstrosity is allowed to remain! It is too tall and too green. Pine trees don't belong in the city. I don't know where it came from, but it should be cut down.
Sincerely,
Frances Brown

Dear Editor,
Thank you for the article about that amazing tree! No other tree I know of has ever grown 75 feet overnight! Unlike other conifers, its edible cones taste like popcorn. I believe this astonishing tree needs to be protected and preserved.
Sincerely,
Holt Harrison

Practice

Read the two letters. Then answer the questions.

1. Which letter writer is biased in favor of the tree?

_____

2. Which letter writer is biased against the tree?

_____

3. What words in the second letter indicate the writer's bias?

_____

4. Describe the feelings of the first letter writer about the tree.

_____

_____

On Your Own

Use what you know about author's viewpoint and bias as you read "Urban Wildlife." Write what the author's viewpoint and bias are in the passage.

School + Home **Home Activity** Your child reviewed author's viewpoint and bias. Read several letters to the editor and discuss the different viewpoints of the writers.

R3.7 Evaluate the author's use of various techniques (e.g., appeal of characters in a picture book, logic and credibility of plots and settings, use of figurative language) to influence readers' perspectives.

© Pearson Education, Inc., 5

⊙ Synonyms

A **synonym** is a word that means the same or almost the same as another word. A thesaurus lists the synonyms of words.

Practice

Fill in the blanks with Words to Know. Then use a thesaurus to help you find the answers to the questions that follow.

Words To Know
critical
enables
mucus
scarce
specialize
sterile

Dr. Muldoon is an epidemiologist. Epidemiologists _____ in studying disease. For her work, it is _____ that she obtains samples, such as _____. She examines the samples under _____ conditions, which _____ her to determine what bacteria and viruses are present. People who do her job are pretty _____.

1. Which Word to Know means the same or almost the same as *rare?*

   _____

2. Which Word to Know means the same or almost the same as *vital?*

   _____

3. Which Word to Know means the same or almost the same as *helps?*

   _____

4. Which Word to Know means the same or almost the same as *clean?*

   _____

5. Which Word to Know means the same or almost the same as *concentrate?*

   _____

6. Which Word to Know means the same or almost the same as *slime?*

   _____

On Your Own

As you read "Urban Wildlife," look for synonyms of words that you already know. Write them in a list in alphabetical order. Then look up the words in a thesaurus.

Home Activity Your child reviewed synonyms. Read a magazine together and make a list of words you want to find synonyms for.

© Pearson Education, Inc., 5

R1.3 Understand and explain frequently used synonyms, antonyms, and homographs.

Vocabulary 261

⊙ Graphic Sources

A **graphic source** shows or explains information in the text. Pictures, tables, charts, diagrams, time lines, and maps are all graphic sources.

Illnesses Studied by Dr. Muldoon		
Name	Caused by	Studied since
Chicken Pox	Virus	1984
Flu	Virus	1996
Lyme Disease	Bacteria	2005
Mumps	Virus	1977
Salmonella	Bacteria	2001
Strep	Bacteria	1989

Practice

Use the table above to answer the following questions. Circle the letter in front of your answer.

1. In what year did Dr. Muldoon start studying strep?

   a. 1977　　　　　　　b. 1989　　　　　　　c. 1996

2. Dr. Muldoon has been studying salmonella about _____ years longer than she has been studying Lyme Disease.

   a. 2　　　　　　　　b. 4　　　　　　　　c. 6

3. Which three illnesses shown on the chart are caused by a virus?

   a. chicken pox, flu, and mumps

   b. chicken pox, mumps, and salmonella

   c. flu, Lyme Disease, and strep

4. According to the table, which illness has Dr. Muldoon been studying for the longest time?

   a. flu　　　　　　　b. Lyme Disease　　　　　　　c. mumps

On Your Own

Use what you know about graphic sources as you read "Urban Wildlife." Make a chart that shows the reasons for the changes in urban wildlife population.

© Pearson Education, Inc., 5

School + Home　**Home Activity** Your child reviewed using graphic sources to obtain information. Together, look through a how-to book and talk about how the graphic sources make the information easier to understand.

🐻 **R2.1** Understand how text features (e.g., format, graphics, sequence, diagrams, illustrations, charts, maps) make information accessible and usable.

Name_____

Name_____

Name _____

Name _____

⊙ Unfamiliar Words

When you come across an **unfamiliar word**, look at the words and sentences around it. These context clues can help you figure out its meaning.

Practice

Read the following sentences. Fill in the blanks using the Words to Know. Then use context clues to figure out the meaning of the underlined word.

Words To Know

- cavities
- combination
- demonstrates
- episode
- profile
- strict

1. Kelsey once again forgot her locker _____,

   and to Mr. Hall that _____ that she is in <u>dire</u> need of

   getting organized.

   a. bland   b. professional   c. serious

2. After that <u>mortifying</u> _____, Kelsey tried to keep a low

   _____ in school.

   a. attractive   b. embarrassing   c. rowdy

3. However, Mr. Hall is _____ when he wants a student to do something. He followed up with Kelsey by providing her with a school <u>agenda</u>, to help her organize her time and activities each day.

   a. list of topics   b. motive   c. planner

4. "This will help fill any _____ in your memory," Mr. Hall <u>asserted</u>.

   a. laughed   b. said slowly   c. said with certainty

On Your Own

As you read "City Blues," look for words unfamiliar to you and use context clues to figure out their meanings. Check your ideas in the dictionary.

Home Activity Your child reviewed unfamiliar words. With your child, read a magazine article and use context clues to figure out their meanings.

G3R1.6 Use sentence and word context to find the meaning of unknown words.

⊙ Generalize

To **generalize** is to use a broad statement or rule that applies to many examples. Clue words such as *all, most, every, always, usually,* and *generally* signal generalizations.

| Ted usually has a hard time with the livestock. | Roslyn has always had a way with animals. | Their cousin Lyra is afraid of all animals. |

Practice

Look at the pictures above. Based on the generalizations you have read, choose the letter in front of the person's name that the statement is most likely about.

1. handles the animals well

   a. Lyra   b. Roslyn   c. Ted

2. is uncomfortable on a farm

   a. Lyra   b. Roslyn   c. Ted

3. might decide to become a veterinarian

   a. Lyra   b. Roslyn   c. Ted

4. should ask for help handling the animals

   a. Lyra   b. Roslyn   c. Ted

5. has probably not spent lots of time with animals

   a. Lyra   b. Roslyn   c. Ted

On Your Own

Use what you know about generalization as you read "City Blues." Make a list of generalizations as you read the passage.

School + Home   **Home Activity** Your child reviewed making generalizations. Talk about how generalizations can be useful, but how they have their limits too.

R2.4 Draw inferences, conclusions, or generalizations about text and support them with textual evidence and prior knowledge.

⊙ Suffixes

A **suffix** is attached to the end of a word to change its meaning. The suffix *-ish* means "similar to something, or like something." The suffix *-ion* means "the act or state of being."

Practice

Read the following sentences. Fill in the blanks with one of the Words to Know. Then choose the meaning of each underlined word. You can use a dictionary to help you.

Words To Know

- bluish
- cartwheels
- gymnastics
- hesitation
- limelight
- skidded
- somersault
- throbbing
- wincing

1. Chris asked Sara to teach her _____, and Sara found herself _____ at the request because Chris lacks <u>coordination</u>.

   a. a person who is coordinated
   b. the state of being coordinated

2. Yet Sara agreed without _____ because Chris is her dearest friend, even though Sara knew the gymnastics lesson might be <u>nightmarish</u>.

   a. the opposite of a nightmare
   b. similar to a nightmare

3. After tumbles and _____, Chris tried a disastrous _____ and stood up holding her arm. Her <u>fascination</u> with gymnastics had turned a bit painful!

   a. the state of being fascinated by something
   b. a good reason to be fascinated by something

4. Chris admitted that her arm was _____, but she didn't want to be <u>childish</u>, so she didn't cry.

   a. similar to or like a child
   b. much older than a child

5. A few weeks later, to show her <u>appreciation</u> for the gymnastics lesson, Chris taught Sara to skate. Now Chris was in the _____, while Sara was clumsy as she _____ across the _____ ice and fell.

   a. the act of appreciating something
   b. not ever appreciating anything

On Your Own

As you read "City Blues," look for words that have suffixes. List them and remove the suffix, then look up the base word in the dictionary.

Home Activity Your child reviewed suffixes. Work together to list as many words as you can that end with suffixes you know. Discuss the suffixes' meanings.

🐻 **G3R1.8** Use knowledge of prefixes (e.g., *un-, re-, pre-, bi-, mis-, dis-*) and suffixes (e.g., *-er, -est, -ful*) to determine the meaning of words.

Vocabulary 265

⊙ Draw Conclusions

Drawing conclusions is forming an opinion based on what you know or on the facts and details in a text.

| Chris is showing Sara how to skate. | At first, Sara feels wobbly on the ice. | But after a while, Sara can skate by herself. |

Practice

Look at the pictures and read the captions above. Then answer these questions.

1. Which girl is a better skater? Tell how you know.

_____

2. List the details in the pictures and the captions that help you know that Sara is just learning to skate.

_____

_____

3. Do you think Sara is learning to be a better skater? Why or why not?

_____

_____

4. Based on the pictures and captions, what kind of a friend is Chris?

_____

_____

On Your Own

Use what you know about drawing conclusions as you read "City Blues." Make a conclusion about the main character's feelings about living in the city.

School + Home **Home Activity** Your child reviewed drawing conclusions. With your child, talk about any conclusions you can reach after reading a newspaper article together.

🐻 **R2.4** Draw inferences, conclusions, or generalizations about text and support them with textual evidence and prior knowledge.

© Pearson Education, Inc., 5

Urban Wildlife

If you've ever noticed a pigeon flying past city buildings or a cockroach scuttling along the kitchen floor, then you've witnessed urban wildlife. Sure, pigeons and cockroaches aren't the most glamorous of animals, but when you think about how these creatures have made their homes in our cities, it's easy to see how remarkably talented they are.

Plenty of species are visible right outside our doors. Birds, squirrels, deer, raccoons, bats, insects, and mice are just a few of the animals that suburban- and urban-dwellers are likely to see on any given day. But there are countless other species too. Some are living in, under, or on top of our homes! Scientists believe, in fact, that the number of urban species is increasing due to cities' expansion and improved urban environmental actions.

Where exactly do these wild animals make their homes? Our streets, buildings, gardens, streams, and railroads are just some of the places they choose to live. What's more, plentiful food supplies—including our steady stream of garbage—provide creatures with a choice of tasty snacks and meals.

Amazingly, some animals whose numbers have dwindled in their natural habitats have made a comeback in urban areas. One such animal is the redstart bird, which has recently been found throughout abandoned factories and city rooftops in London. Peregrine falcons have also made a comeback, particularly in New York City. These swift birds can hurtle down toward their prey, traveling at over one hundred fifty miles per hour! Many people have helped these extraordinary creatures by placing special peregrine nesting boxes on ledges high off the ground.

Birds will find places to roost in just about every urban nook and cranny. Look at highway overpasses, train tunnels, hidden corners in churches and skyscrapers—even streetlights and stoplights—for signs of these animals. Beneath the skies and in the waters, the number of fish and waterfowl has also increased thanks to cleaner rivers and other waterways.

But the news isn't always good. One of the reasons that animals have moved into our neighborhoods is because we have encroached on their territory. As our cities grow past their limits, natural habitats can become scarce.

⊙ **DAY 2** Author's Viewpoint/Bias Think about the words *remarkably talented.* How do they reveal the author's viewpoint about pigeons and cockroaches?

_____

_____

_____

_____

_____

⊙ **DAY 5** Draw Conclusions Why does garbage attract animals?

_____

_____

⊙ **DAY 3** Synonyms What is a synonym for *swift?*

_____

_____

⊙ **DAY 5** Suffixes What is the suffix in *expansion?*

_____

⊙ **DAY 2** Unfamiliar Words Underline the words in the passage that help you understand the meaning of *encroached.*

R2.0 Students read and understand grade-level appropriate material.

"Urban Wildlife" 267

⊙ **DAY 2** Author's Viewpoint/Bias How do you think the author feels about animals? Explain your answer.

_____

_____

_____

_____

_____

⊙ **DAY 5** Draw Conclusions How might foreign species affect native species?

_____

_____

_____

_____

⊙ **DAY 3** Graphic Sources According to the chart, what types of animals might you see in the air?

_____

_____

Another reason that animals have moved away from their natural habitats is because of the chemicals and pesticides being used on farmland. Due to these poisons, open meadows and forests are no longer as friendly to living creatures as they once were. Plants are disappearing, along with the species that relied on them. Fortunately for us, some types of animals, such as butterflies and beetles, are finding their needed food sources in the woodsy parts of suburbs, where pesticides and other chemicals are not widely used.

Some urban wildlife may also be affected by non-native species that have shifted to the area. For example, two birds—the house sparrow and the starling—were originally brought to the United States in the 1800s and have since multiplied in cities and suburbs across North America. Some people believe they have brought down the numbers of other native birds, such as bluebirds and woodpeckers.

Yet regardless of whether species are native or foreign, nature conservationists agree that it is important to care for all wildlife. Several organizations throughout the United States provide resources and information for people interested in getting to know their wild neighbors. Are you curious about what lives in your region? Then hit the streets and see what urban animals you can find.

City Slickers in the Limelight Wild animals live among us in our cities and towns. Which animals can you find near you?

On Land	In the Sky	In the Ocean
Skunks	Bats	Fish
Mice	Birds	Frogs
Lizards	Butterflies	Turtles

© Pearson Education, Inc., 5

School + Home Home Activity Your child read a selection and used comprehension and vocabulary skills from Unit 4. Have your child summarize the selection, drawing conclusions about the author's viewpoint and bias.

268 "Urban Wildlife"

R2.0 Students read and understand grade-level appropriate material.

City Blues

At five in the morning, Jada woke up to the sound of a motorcycle revving its loud engine down her busy street. She moaned and pulled the pillows over her head. Sleeping would be so much easier if she could simply turn off the noises of the city.

Moments later, when the deafening sound of a garbage truck rumbled beneath her window, Jada threw her pillows onto her bed and decided it was time to get up. She grabbed her journal and got herself some cereal. Then she sat on her parents' new couch that still smelled like the furniture store.

Day 5, Jada wrote in her journal. *Note to self: buy earplugs. Still miss Gran and her garden. Living here is the pits.*

Jada stared out of her tenth-story apartment window at the highway just a few blocks away. Leaving Gran behind had been the worst part of Jada's move. Back at home, it was Gran who had taken Jada for fish tacos and root beer at the Cactus Café. It was Gran who had explained the ins and outs of every soap opera episode and the strategies behind game shows. And it was Gran who had taught Jada about the desert plants that grew across her dusty backyard.

Now Jada was living three hours away in a new civilization, one that was full of concrete and cars. There wasn't so much as a single cactus in sight. The only thing cities were good for were sirens and office buildings.

Just as Jada was finishing her last bite of breakfast cereal, her mother padded into the living room. "Morning, honey," she yawned. "You're up early, again."

"Couldn't sleep," Jada said. She turned on her dad's computer and began checking her e-mail, where she found a new message from Gran. *Dear Jays,* she read. *My cactus, George, is missing you. It's hotter than blue blazes here. Hope you're keeping cool. Love, G.*

Jada sighed. A twinge of envy rippled through her body. How she wished she were with Gran on her back porch, staring at the brown and jagged mountain skyline.

A few hours later, when the sun had risen high overhead, Jada's father asked her if she wanted to go for a swim. "There's a new pool at the recreation center down the street," he explained. "Might as well take advantage of it, now that we're here!"

© Pearson Education, Inc., 5

⊙ DAY 1 Suffixes
What is the suffix in *moaned*?

_____

⊙ DAY 1 Draw Conclusions Why does Jada want to buy earplugs?

_____

_____

_____

⊙ DAY 4
Generalize Look at the fifth paragraph. Underline the generalization that Jada makes about the city.

⊙ DAY 4 Unfamiliar Words What do you think *jagged* means?

_____

_____

What nearby words help you to determine the meaning of *jagged*?

_____

R2.0 Students read and understand grade-level appropriate material.

"City Blues" 269

⊙ **DAY 1** Draw
Conclusions Why do
you think Jada is so
upset when her book
gets wet?

_____

_____

_____

_____

⊙ **DAY 4**
Generalize Before
Jada meets George,
how do you think
she feels? Make a
generalization about
her attitude.

_____

_____

_____

_____

"I guess so," Jada said, though she wasn't too convinced.

A combination of adults and kids were swimming in the pool by the time Jada and her parents got there. Jada had to admit that the cool water looked inviting, but she knew she had better things to do with her time. Finding a chair in a shady spot, she sat down to browse through her new book on desert plants. The book had been a good-bye present from Gran. *By the time you come back to visit me,* she'd said, *you'll be telling me what to do with my garden.*

Jada was in the midst of admiring the pictures when a piercing voice rang through the air. "Cannonball!" the voice cried. Instantly, Jada was splashed from head to toe by a boy who had jumped into the pool. She looked down at her new book to find it sopping wet.

"Sorry about that!" she heard someone say. Jada looked up to see the boy standing in front of her with water dripping down his hair and nose. She felt like fleeing back to her apartment and bit her lip to hold back the tears.

"You ruined my book," she said quietly.

The boy's face fell. "Hey, I'm sorry. I didn't mean to." He stared at the wet pages apologetically, then noticed the book's photographs and took a closer look. "Actually," he said in surprise, "my dad has lots of books like this one. He gets them from working at the botanical gardens. He'd let you borrow one if you want."

"There are botanical gardens here?" Jada asked in astonishment. "I thought nothing grew in the city."

"Of course things grow," the boy said. "This isn't the planet Mars, you know. Are you new here or something?"

Jada flushed. "Kind of," she said.

"Well, come over any time," the boy told her, "and I'll show you some of my dad's books. My name's George, by the way."

Just like Gran's cactus, Jada thought to herself, with a small smile. Then she introduced herself and looked toward the pool. "Maybe I'll go in," she said. "I've already gotten wet anyway."

"How about a water race?" George asked with a gleam in his eye.

"You're on," Jada said, leaping into the pool.

© Pearson Education, Inc., 5

Home Activity Your child read a selection and used comprehension and vocabulary skills from Unit 4. Have your child retell the selection, making generalizations and drawing conclusions about the characters.

270 "City Blues"

R2.0 Students read and understand grade-level appropriate material.

Connect Text to Text

Reading Across Texts

Think about the selections "Urban Wildlife" and "City Blues." Complete the Venn diagram below with details that show similarities and differences between the two texts.

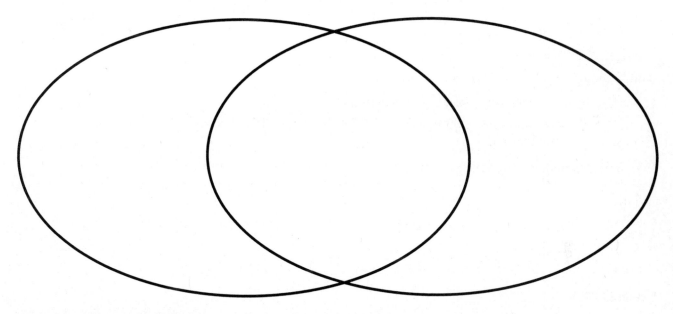

Writing Across Texts

Imagine you are living somewhere new. Where would you be and how would you adjust to the situation?

_____

_____

_____

_____

_____

_____

_____

_____

_____

Home Activity Your child read two selections this week. Have your child explain to you how they were alike and how they were different.

Summarize Your Learning

How do people and animals adapt to different situations?

- *Weslandia*   - *American Slave, American Hero*   - *Exploding Ants*
- *The Stormi Giovanni Club*   - *The Gymnast*

Think About It!

Think about the selections you read in this unit.

- How were they alike? How were they different?
- Were the selections you read this week similar to others you have read?
- What did you learn?

Why might people or animals need to adapt to new situations? Write three reasons.

- _____

- _____

- _____

Question It!

Write three questions that you might ask someone who is adjusting to a new situation.

- _____

- _____

- _____

Talk About It!

Discuss your questions with a partner.

- What questions did your partner have? Were they similar to yours?
  Were they different from yours?
- What things did you and your partner want to know?
- What feelings and ideas did you and your partner have about adjusting to
  new situations?

© Pearson Education, Inc., 5

 School + Home   **Home Activity** Your child reviewed and discussed the selections from Unit 4. Have your child describe to you the big ideas about adaptation from this unit.

Family Times

Summary

The Skunk Ladder

Creativity turns to chaos when two friends decide to dig a hole as a way to pass the time. Unfortunately, some ideas are destined to cause trouble no matter what. All it takes is a curious skunk and a suspicious father to fall into the trap of youthful imagination.

Activity

I Remember When... Children are often forbidden to do some things because their families know from experience that the results will be disastrous. With your family, discuss some of the brilliant yet misfired ideas they had when they were young. Discuss how those experiences compare with some of your "brilliant" ideas.

Comprehension Skill

Character and Plot

Traits are the qualities shown by a story's **characters,** such as bravery or shyness. We see their traits in their words, actions, and how other characters treat them. The **plot** is the pattern of events in a story.

Activity

What's She Like? Think about a character you know from a book, movie, or television show. How would you describe him or her to someone? Sit down with a family member and describe him or her. Think about the character's personality traits as well as how he or she looks.

Lesson Vocabulary

Words to Know

Knowing the meanings of these words is important to reading *The Skunk Ladder*. Practice using these words.

Vocabulary Words

abandoned gave up on, dismissed

attempt try or make an effort

bellow shout or roar like a bull

cavern a large cave

feat a difficult or skillful act

immensely very greatly

savage wild, ferocious, angry

Conventions

Contractions and Negative Contractions

A **contraction** is a shortened form of two words. An apostrophe takes the place of one or more letters. Contractions can be formed from a pronoun and a verb. *For example: I + am = I'm; she + will = she'll; you + are = you're.*

A **negative contraction** is when you combine a verb with *not*. An apostrophe takes the place of the letter *o* in *not*. *For example: do + not = don't; are + not = aren't; will + not = won't.*

Activity

Cut It Down Newspapers usually avoid using contactons in their articles. Choose a newspaper article and read a few sentences to a family member. Then read the sentences again, this time using contractions wherever you can. Discuss with your family member how this changes the way the article sounds.

Practice Tested Spelling Words

_____ _____ _____ _____

_____ _____ _____ _____

_____ _____ _____ _____

_____ _____ _____ _____

_____ _____ _____ _____

Character and Plot

- **Traits** are the qualities, such as bravery or shyness, of **characters,** or the people and animals in a story. We see characters' traits in their words and how other characters treat them.
- The **plot** is the pattern of events in a story. Usually, the events are told in sequence, from start to finish.

Directions Read the following passage. Then fill in the diagram.

Darcy Evans had been a rebel all her life. As a young woman, she marched for civil rights. She protested a plan to build the first mall in her small hometown. She was at the first Earth Day celebration in the 1970s, supporting efforts to protect the environment. Save the dolphins, save the whales, save the trees: Darcy could always find a good cause to support, no matter how old she was. So nobody was surprised when 83-year-old Darcy Evans was leading the fight to save the 200-year-old City Hall building in her hometown. "I'm nearly as old as City Hall," she joked. But everyone knew that if Darcy was fighting for it, the building must be worth saving.

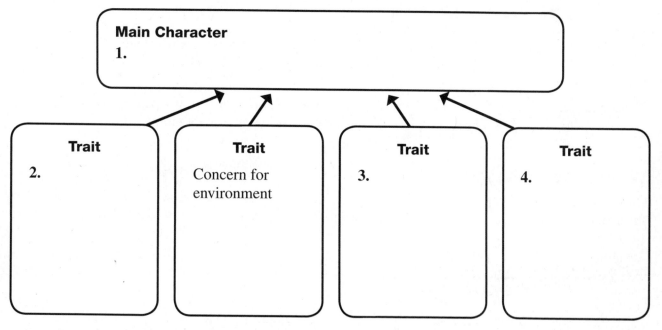

Main Character
1.

| Trait | Trait | Trait | Trait |
| 2. | Concern for environment | 3. | 4. |

5. Why does Darcy fight on behalf of various causes?

_____

© Pearson Education, Inc., 5

School + Home **Home Activity** Your child answered questions about characters and plot in a fictional passage. Have him or her describe to you a favorite character from a book.

R3.3 Contrast the actions, motives (e.g., loyalty, selfishness, conscientiousness), and appearances of characters in a work of fiction and discuss the importance of the contrasts to the plot or theme.

Comprehension 275

Vocabulary

Directions Draw a line to connect each word on the left with its definition on the right.

1. bellow   gave up on, dismissed

2. savage   try or make an effort

3. attempt   shout or roar like a bull

4. feat   wild, ferocious, angry

5. abandoned   a difficult or skillful act

**Check the Words
You Know**

___abandoned
___attempt
___bellow
___cavern
___feat
___immensely
___savage

Directions Choose a word from the box that best matches each sentence. Write the word on the line.

_____ **6.** The outlaw buried the gold in the _____ just before his arrest.

_____ **7.** For her latest brave _____ , the escape artist freed herself from chains just in time to pull the cord on the parachute.

_____ **8.** Their _____ to hike the entire Appalachian Trail in two months had little chance of success.

_____ **9.** The _____ popular rock music star was greeted at the coliseum by thousands of his adoring fans.

_____ **10.** The _____ expression on her face would not have been out of place on a panther or some other wild animal.

Write a News Report

On a separate sheet of paper, write an imaginary news report that describes two local youth who surprise everyone by succeeding at a difficult task. Use as many vocabulary words as you can.

Home Activity Your child identified and used vocabulary words from the story *The Skunk Ladder*. Together, come up with a list of accomplishments that you or your child performs regularly, but that might seem amazing to other people.

R1.0 Systematic Vocabulary Development

Vocabulary · Greek and Latin Roots

- Many English words are based on **Greek** and **Latin** root words. Sometimes you can use Greek and Latin roots to figure out the meaning of an unfamiliar word.
- The Latin root *spec* means "look" or "see," as in the word *inspect.* The Latin root *sect* means "to cut," as in the word *dissect.* The Latin root *pond* means "to weigh," as in the word *ponderous.*

Directions Read the following passage. Then answer the questions below. Look for Greek and Latin roots to help you determine the meaning of the words in italics.

> The toughest section of Thursday was the morning, when I drove into town with my great-uncle Al. He couldn't see his hand in front of his face without his *spectacles.* So as we approached the stoplight with Uncle Al at the wheel, you can imagine my fright when I noticed he didn't have his glasses on. I *pondered* my options: Do I yell something? Do I scream and point? But then I saw his glasses sitting on top of his head. Not wanting to *distract* Uncle Al with any unnecessary *interaction,* I reached over and gently tapped his glasses. They slid right onto his nose, perfectly in place. We came to an easy stop at the red light.

1. What is the root of the word *section*? What does the word mean?

_____

_____

2. How does the Latin root of the word *spectacles* help you understand the meaning of the word?

_____

3. How does the Latin roots in the word *interaction* help you understand the meaning of the word?

_____

_____

4. The Latin root word *distrahere* means "to pull away." Which word above comes from that root?

_____

5. How does the Latin root of the word *pondered* help you understand the meaning of the word?

_____

_____

 Home Activity Your child identified and answered questions about Latin and Greek roots in words. Have your child look in the dictionary and find other words with Latin or Greek roots. Have him or her tell you the meanings of the roots he or she found. Together think of other words with the same roots.

G4R1.4 Know common roots and affixes derived from Greek and Latin and use this knowledge to analyze the meaning of complex words (e.g., *international*).

Literary Elements · Author's Purpose

Directions Read the article. Then answer the questions below.

The restless look on Winnie's face made me nervous. "There's nothing to do around here," she complained. She was right. Our town was boring. "We should protest something," Winnie declared. Winnie loved to protest. She became energized when she made signs and handed out flyers.

Suddenly, Winnie's face brightened. "What about the senior center?" she asked.

"Winnie, our town doesn't have a senior center," I said.

"Exactly!" she exclaimed. "We'll demand that the town turn the abandoned factory downtown into a senior center. It'll be our best protest ever!" she said. "After we succeed, the senior citizens will be so grateful that they will give us a hand in our next protest!"

1. What is the author's purpose in the passage above?

_____

_____

2. Does the narrator or Winnie make the big decision in the story?

_____

_____

3. What do the narrator and Winnie plan to do?

_____

_____

4. What is the motivation, or purpose, behind Winnie's plans?

_____

_____

5. Does the author succeed at his or her purpose? Why or why not?

_____

_____

_____

Home Activity Your child has answered questions about an author's purpose in a fictional passage. Read a short story with your child and identify how the author succeeds or fails to write a humorous or dramatic tale.

R3.7 Evaluate the author's use of various techniques (e.g., appeal of characters in a picture book, logic and credibility of plots and settings, use of figurative language) to influence readers' perspectives.

Character/Plot

- **Traits** are the qualities, such as bravery or shyness, of **characters,** or the people and animals in a story. We see characters' traits in their words and how other characters treat them.
- The **plot** is the pattern of events in a story. Usually, the events are told in sequence, from start to finish.

Directions Read the following passage. Then answer the questions below.

Every day, Nipper, Jack's favorite sheepdog, and Bowser, the German Shepherd, ran through the pastures on Jack's farm, protecting and corralling Jack's large sheep herd. The main job for the dogs was to keep the sheep from wandering too close to the woods, where a pack of wolves was known to live. A wolf could be very dangerous to a sheep.

One day a large grey wolf wandered onto the farm. It snuck around the farmhouse, crept slowly up behind the herd, and was getting ready to pounce on one of the sheep. From across the field, Nipper and Bowser sprang into action. They raced like rockets across the field, barking like crazy. They ran straight toward the wolf. The wolf ran as fast as it could back into the woods. Jack drove up in his pickup truck shortly after the wolf ran away. He walked over, petted the dogs and asked, "Why do you guys seem so excited?"

1. Who are Nipper and Bowser?

_____

2. What traits might describe the dogs?

_____

3. What do Nipper and Bowser do when they see the wolf get ready to pounce on the sheep?

_____

4. Are they successful? How do you know?

_____

5. If Nipper and Bowser could have answered Jack's question, what might they have said?

_____

School + Home **Home Activity** Your child answered questions about plot and character based on a short passage. With your child, describe a character from a favorite book or movie.

R3.3 Contrast the actions, motives (e.g., loyalty, selfishness, conscientiousness), and appearances of characters in a work of fiction and discuss the importance of the contrasts to the plot or theme.

Comprehension 279

Name_____

Character/Plot

- **Traits** are the qualities, such as bravery or shyness, of **characters,** or the people and animals in a story. We see characters' traits in their words and how other characters treat them.
- The **plot** is the pattern of events in a story. Usually, the events are told in sequence, from start to finish.

Directions Read the following passage. Fill in the diagram below.

Finding that old bottle did something to Maribel. As it turned out, the bottle was just her first discovery of many from a two-hundred-year-old dump. After finding the bottle, Maribel became immensely interested in history. She wanted to know everything about the lives of the people who had lived on her street in the 1800s.

Maribel cautiously dug up more bottles, pottery, and other artifacts from the past.

She delicately cleaned them and took them to the local historical museum, where a museum employee helped her identify what the bottles were used for. Soon Maribel's history grades improved. She also started to enjoy writing and faithfully kept a journal of all her historical finds. When her teacher asked where Maribel's new enthusiasm for learning came from, her father answered, "She found it in a junk pile."

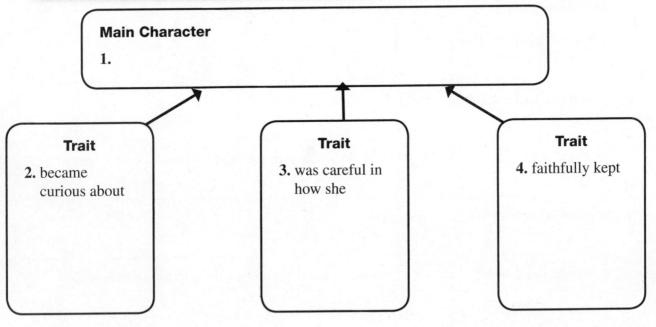

Main Character

1.

Trait

2. became curious about

Trait

3. was careful in how she

Trait

4. faithfully kept

© Pearson Education, Inc., 5

Home Activity Your child answered questions about character and plot in a fictional passage. Have your child come up with words that describe some of the traits he or she admires in a best friend or relative.

R3.3 Contrast the actions, motives (e.g., loyalty, selfishness, conscientiousness), and appearances of characters in a work of fiction and discuss the importance of the contrasts to the plot or theme.

Print Sources

- Libraries contain many sources of information for students to use. You can use a library database or a card catalog to identify and locate these materials. In both cases, you can search for materials by author, title, or subject.
- **Print sources** include encyclopedias, newspapers, magazines, dictionaries, and other reference books.

Directions Read the following list of school library print sources for a report on U.S. Presidents.

Encyclopedias

Encyclopedia of U.S. Presidents, Vols. I & II

World History Encyclopedia, Vols. I–XX

Encyclopedia of American History, Vols. I–XII

Encyclopedia of Modern Science, Vols. I–VI

Encyclopedia of Entertainment, Vols. I–III

Newspapers

World News Daily (metropolitan paper)

Weekly Wrap-Up (community paper)

Kingsley Chronicle (school paper)

Magazines

News Weekly

The Historical Reader

History for Children

Skateboard Life

U.S. and the World

Dictionaries

Student Dictionary of American History

Cultural Dictionary of the United States

Anders' Dictionary of Places & Events

Dictionary of Who's Who & What's What

G4W1.8 Understand the organization of almanacs, newspapers, and periodicals and how to use those print materials.

Research and Study Skills 281

Directions Pretend you are writing a report on U.S. Presidents in the twentieth century. Use the list of print sources to answer the questions below.

1. Which type of print sources might be valuable to use for this report?

2. Which would be the best source with which to start your report?

3. Would all the magazines be valuable to your report? Why or why not?

4. Suggest a topic you might research in a library's card catalog for your report.

5. If you knew an author had written a good book about U.S. Presidents, how could you use this knowledge to get information for your report?

6. Explain how a newspaper would be helpful if you extended your report to include U.S. Presidents in the twenty-first century.

7. How helpful would any of the newspapers be in gathering information for your report? Why?

8. If you didn't understand something that was referred to in the magazine *History for Children*, where would be a good place to find out what the reference meant?

9. If you wanted to find out how many Presidents were from a certain state, where would you look?

10. Would encyclopedias be more useful if you were writing a report on U.S. Presidents in the twentieth century or a report on children's movies currently showing in your neighborhood? Why?

© Pearson Education, Inc., 5

Home Activity Your child answered questions about print and media sources. Discuss where media sources are located at your local library or bookstore. How are they organized? How are they organized similarly or differently from the print sources?

G4W1.6 Locate information in reference texts by using organizational features (e.g., prefaces, appendixes).

Draw Conclusions

- **Drawing conclusions** is forming an opinion based on what you already know or on the facts and details in a text. Facts and details are the small pieces of information in an article or story.
- Facts and details "add up" to a conclusion. Conclusions formed by the author or the reader must make sense.

Directions Read the following passage. Then answer the questions below.

Jenna looked at the blank screen of the device in her hand and cursed her luck. The Global Positioning Satellite (GPS) receiver, a computer a little larger than a cell phone, could pinpoint her exact location anywhere in the world. The only problem was that the batteries were dead.

Jenna was part of a team of archaeologists, people who study ancient cultures. The team was in a remote part of Alaska, looking for an ancient Inuit settlement. It was Jenna's job to scout out a path to a valley the team saw from their airplane. Thankfully, Jenna was an expert at finding directions with a compass. She dug through her backpack and found the traditional navigation tool that didn't need batteries.

1. Why was Jenna's team in the Alaskan wilderness?

_____

2. What technology did Jenna usually use to help her find directions?

_____

3. How did this technology fail to help her?

_____

4. What traditional navigation tool did she end up using to help find her way back to camp?

_____

5. What conclusion or conclusions can be drawn from Jenna's experience?

_____

_____

 Home Activity Your child drew conclusions about technology based on information in a short passage. Discuss with your child some of the kinds of technology used by your family each day. Talk about what alternatives you could use if these devices broke down.

R2.4 Draw inferences, conclusions, or generalizations about text and support them with textual evidence and prior knowledge.

Vocabulary

Directions Draw a line to connect each word on the left with its definition on the right.

1. cramped

2. sonar

3. interior

4. ooze

5. debris

soft mud or slime

scattered fragments, ruins

device for finding water depth or underwater objects

shut into a small space

inner surface or part

Check the Words You Know

____cramped
____debris
____interior
____ooze
____robotic
____sediment
____sonar

Directions Choose words from the box to complete the crossword puzzle.

DOWN

6. litterbugs leave this behind

7. moving but not living

ACROSS

8. opposite of *exterior*

9. collected at the bottom of the ocean

10. locates objects underwater

Write a Journal Entry

Pretend you are a passenger on a huge cruise ship crossing the ocean. On a separate sheet of paper, write your first journal entry as the ship sets sail. Use as many vocabulary words as you can.

Home Activity Your child identified and used vocabulary words from the story *The Unsinkable Wreck of the R.M.S. Titanic.* Have your child narrate a recent adventure he or she has experienced.

R1.0 Word Analysis, Fluency, and Systematic Vocabulary Development

© Pearson Education, Inc., 5

Name_____

Vocabulary • Unfamiliar Words

- A dictionary lists words in alphabetical order and gives their meanings, part of speech, and pronunciations. A glossary is an alphabetical list of important words and their meanings that are used in a book. Glossaries are located at the back of a book.
- Sometimes an **unfamiliar word** doesn't have context clues to help you find its meaning. Then you should look up the word in a dictionary or glossary.

Directions Read the following passage. Then use the glossary in the back of your book or a dictionary to answer the questions below.

One of the pioneers of underwater research was Jacques Cousteau. He invented the "Aqua-Lung" in 1943. The Aqua-Lung was the first compressed air diving tank that allowed divers to stay underwater for long periods of time. This tank allowed Cousteau to move freely among the fish he studied. Cousteau also helped invent a camera for filming underwater. His television series, *The Undersea World of Jacques Cousteau*, was extremely popular. People were compelled by images of the deep sea that they were able to view without leaving their homes.

1. What is the meaning of *compressed*?

_____

2. What is the meaning of *pioneer*? Is *pioneer* used as a verb or a noun in this passage?

_____

_____

3. What is the meaning of *invent*?

_____

4. Look up *Jacques Cousteau* in your dictionary. Did you find him listed under *C* or *J*? When was he born?

_____

5. Find an unfamiliar word in the passage. Write a sentence using this word.

_____

_____

© Pearson Education, Inc., 5

Home Activity Your child read a short passage and used a dictionary and glossary to find the meanings of unfamiliar words. Read an article together and pick a few unfamiliar words. If your child cannot find context clues to help with the meanings, ask him or her to find the meanings in a dictionary.

R1.2 Use word origins to determine the meaning of unknown words.

Main Idea and Details

Directions Read the passage. Then answer the questions below.

NASA has developed many materials for astronauts that are later used in everyday products. A recent invention, thermoplastic polymers, are materials that become hard when cooled and soft when heated. Scientists at NASA use them as a protective covering on space vehicles, but they can also be used for purposes more common than space flight. Thermoplastics are designed to protect against the sun's ultraviolet rays, so they could have many uses. They could be used as a coating for outdoor statues, other art pieces, and house paint. They could also be used to protect the delicate parts of radios and CD players from the sun's heat.

1. What is the topic of the passage?

_____

2. What is the main idea of the above passage?

_____

_____

3. What is one detail that supports the main idea?

_____

_____

4. What is another detail that supports the main idea?

_____

_____

5. Write a summary of the passage in one or two sentences.

_____

_____

_____

Home Activity Your child read a short passage and identified its main idea and supporting details. Read a newspaper or magazine article with your child and have him or her identify the main idea and supporting details in the article.

R2.3 Discern main ideas and concepts presented in texts, identifying and assessing evidence that supports those ideas.

Draw Conclusions

- **Drawing conclusions** is forming an opinion based on what you already know, or based on the facts and details in a text. Facts and details are the small pieces of information in an article or story.

- Facts and details "add up" to a conclusion. Conclusions formed by the author or the reader must make sense. This means you should be able to support your conclusions with evidence from the selection or from real life.

Directions Read the following passage. Then answer the questions below.

> The image on the video monitor shows what looks like an alien landscape. The men and women watching are tense as the images show the inside of what appears to be an underwater cave. The leader of the team, Dr. Black, speaks quietly into a microphone. "Keep going," she says. The image, transmitted from a remote camera, tilts and shows a break in the walls of the "cave." "Stop," says Dr. Black. The camera, attached to a tiny robot known as Zeus, stops moving. Now the doctors can get to work. They are looking, not at an underwater cave, but at the inside of a blood vessel leading to a patient's heart.
>
> Microscopic tools controlled by computer now can do surgery. Because of this, doctors can now achieve precision never before possible. Not long ago, doctors had to saw a patient's rib cage in half to gain access to the heart. Healing took a long time. Now the Zeus robot lets doctors perform heart operations through a two-inch hole in the patient's chest. The patient recovers in one day and goes home with an almost unnoticeable scar.

1. What does the surgical robot "Zeus" allow doctors to see?

_____

2. How is Zeus controlled?

_____

3. How does the surgeon see what is going on during the surgery?

_____

4. Based on the information in the passage, do you think surgery done by robots is as safe as older, more traditional ways of performing surgery?

_____

_____

Home Activity Your child drew conclusions about robotic heart surgery based on the information in a short paragraph. Looking around at the different technologies in your home, work with your child to draw conclusions about the future of these devices based on the changes you have witnessed in the past few years.

R2.4 Draw inferences, conclusions, or generalizations about text and support them with textual evidence and prior knowledge.

Draw Conclusions

- **Drawing conclusions** is forming an opinion based on what you already know or based on the facts and details in a text. Facts and details are the small pieces of information in an article or story.
- Facts and details "add up" to a conclusion. Conclusions formed by the author or the reader must make sense.

Directions Read the following passage. Then answer the questions below.

A pioneer in science fiction, Jules Verne used his imagination to explore the future of technology many years before science made it possible. In *From the Earth to the Moon*, which Verne wrote in 1865, three astronauts liftoff from a launch pad in Florida and then make exciting discoveries about the Earth's atmosphere, the moon, and asteroids. They learn about weightlessness, or what happens when a person is free of Earth's gravity.

Somehow, Verne predicted the science and technology of space flight a century ahead of time. In his 1869 story *Twenty Thousand Leagues Under the Sea*, he described the science that would go into the first practical submarine. His last published story was *Paris in the 20th Century*, written in 1863 but not made public until 1994. In this story Verne imagined air conditioning, gasoline-powered automobiles, the Internet, and television.

1. What Jules Verne story predicted the technology of space flight?

_____

2. Why are Verne's predictions about space interesting?

_____

3. How might ideas about technology in science fiction stories turn into science realities?

_____

_____

4. When were Verne's predictions about the future in *Paris in the 20th Century* made public?

_____

5. What can you conclude about the role of imagination in science and science fiction?

_____

Home Activity Your child drew conclusions about the connection between science and science fiction described in a short passage. With your child, discuss a movie or story that makes predictions about the future. Talk about evidence you can see today that suggests the predictions will or will not come true.

R2.4 Draw inferences, conclusions, or generalizations about text and support them with textual evidence and prior knowledge.

Note Taking

Taking notes about what you read can help you understand and remember the text better. It can also help you organize information to study for a test or to include in a research report. There is no one right way to take notes. You might make a list, an outline, or a story map or paraphrase what you've read. When you **paraphrase**, you rewrite what you've read using your own words. When you record findings, you synthesize, or combine information. Use key words, phrases, or short sentences when taking notes.

Directions Read the following article. On a separate sheet of paper, take notes as you read.

Remotely-operated vehicles, or ROVs, are the primary means for underwater exploration to take place in deep waters. The first ROV was created by a Russian photographer, Demitri Rebikoff, in 1953. Since the first ROV, which was connected by rope or cable above water, many improvements have been made to the technology. The earliest innovations in ROV technology were made by the U.S. Navy in the 1960s. The Navy used CURV, Cable-Controlled Underwater Recovery Vehicle, to recover a hydrogen bomb lost off the coast of Spain. CURV was also used to save the lives of the pilots of a submersible that sunk off the coast of Cork, Ireland, in 1973. In the past two decades, private oil companies have searched ever deeper for new oil resources. As a result, they are responsible for the greatest developments in ROV technology.

The most famous development in ROV technology, however, came in 1986 when *Alvin* was "flown" down to the wreck of the *Titanic* in the Atlantic Ocean. Created by the scientists at Woods Hole Oceanographic Institution, *Alvin* was a human-driven submersible tethered by a line that reached the water's surface. A person was able to steer it and operate the camera equipment attached to the exterior. Scientist Martin Bowen was the first person to take *Alvin*, to the wreck of the *Titanic*, some 13,000 feet below sea level. Because the pressure at such a depth is far too great for the human body to withstand, only a protective submersible like *Alvin* could provide the necessary protection for such a journey.

Currently, more advanced ROVs, like Triton XL (which is about the size of a small car), can perform a variety of tasks deep underwater. Construction, underwater surveying, and pipeline maintenance are a few of the things these advanced ROVs can accomplish.

G4W1.5 Quote or paraphrase information sources, citing them appropriately.

Research and Study Skills 291

Name_____

Directions Answer the questions below based on the article you read and the notes you took.

1. When was the first ROV developed?

_____

2. Why did the U.S. Navy develop ROV technology?

_____

3. Why was *Alvin* developed?

_____

4. How far below sea level is the wreck of the *Titanic* located?

_____

5. Paraphrase the last two sentences of the first paragraph.

_____

_____

6. Synthesize the information in the second paragraph.

_____

_____

_____

7. How would you organize your notes about this article? Why?

_____

_____

8. Why is it important for you to take notes about what you read?

_____

_____

9. How does paraphrasing help you to understand and recall material that you read?

_____

_____

10. On a separate piece of paper, make a simple time line of the major developments in ROV technology.

Home Activity Your child read a short article, took notes, and recorded findings from it. With your child, read an article from a newspaper or magazine and practice taking notes and recording findings from the article.

G4W1.5 Quote or paraphrase information sources, citing them appropriately.

Author's Purpose

- The **author's purpose** is the main reason an author writes a selection. An author may write to persuade, to inform, to entertain, or to express ideas or feelings.
- Sometimes an author may write with more than one purpose in mind.
- What the author says and the details given help you figure out the author's purpose.

Directions Read the following passage and fill in the diagram below.

Jenna dreamed of being an astronaut. She read books about astronauts, she watched documentaries on TV about space exploration, and she even insisted her parents take her on vacation to the NASA launch site in Florida. At school, Jenna's science projects always had something to do with the planets or space or famous astronauts. It seemed she knew more about the space shuttle than some of her teachers did. Although she had only been in an airplane once, she spent the whole three-hour flight staring out the window at the clouds and the vast sky. Jenna wasn't sure how long it would take, but she knew one day she would see the Earth from as far away as the moon.

AUTHOR'S PURPOSE	1.
DETAIL What is one example of Jenna's interest in astronauts?	2.
DETAIL What is another example of Jenna's interest in astronauts?	3.

4. Does the author meet his or her purpose successfully? Why do you feel this way?

_____

_____

5. If you did not understand the passage, what could you do to help yourself understand?

_____

School + Home **Home Activity** Your child answered questions about an author's purpose in a fictional passage. Read a favorite book and have your child describe the author's purpose for writing.

R3.7 Evaluate the author's use of various techniques (e.g., appeal of characters in a picture book, logic and credibility of plots and settings, use of figurative language) to influence readers' perspectives.

Vocabulary

Directions Draw a line to connect each word on the left with its definition on the right.

1. monitors

part played in real life

2. role

the force that causes objects to move or tend to move toward the center of the Earth

3. gravity

computer screens

4. accomplishments

definite

5. specific

achievements

Directions Choose a word from the box that best matches each clue. Write the word on the line.

_____ 6. what gets the most attention

_____ 7. this keeps our feet on the ground

_____ 8. they show information

_____ 9. things you can successfully complete

_____ 10. not just anything

Write a Scene from a Play

On a separate sheet of paper, write a short scene from a play about an astronaut telling his granddaughter what it was like to fly to the moon. Use as many vocabulary words as you can.

Home Activity Your child identified and used vocabulary words from the interview *Talk with an Astronaut*. Have your child interview you about the work you do.

R1.0 Word Analysis, Fluency, and Systematic Vocabulary Development

Vocabulary • Multiple-Meaning Words

- Some words have more than one meaning. They are called **multiple-meaning words.**
- If you read a word that you recognize, but it is used in an unfamiliar way, look for clues about its meaning in the words nearby. Then use a dictionary to help you understand its meaning.

Directions Read the following passage. Then answer the questions below. Look for context clues to help you understand words with multiple meanings.

> You could say astronomers are monitors of the skies. They focus in on the details of our vast universe so we can understand the bigger picture. Even though the serious work astronomers do has a lot of gravity, most of them will admit they feel as excited as kids when a major discovery is made.
>
> To become an astronomer, you have to study many elements of science, such as gravity, with a dedication and focus most people find hard to have. But once you complete your education and are a working astronomer studying space, the sky truly is the limit.

1. How would you define the word *monitors* as it is used in the passage?

_____

_____

2. What is another definition for the word *monitors*?

_____

_____

3. What context clues helped you understand the way the word *gravity* was used in the passage the first time?

_____

4. What does *focus* mean the first time it is used in the passage?

_____

_____

5. What does *focus* mean the second time it is used in the passage?

_____

_____

Home Activity Your child used context clues to help define words with multiple meanings. Work together to try to use other words with multiple meanings to make up a silly poem.

Name_____

Graphic Sources

Directions Study the diagram of the Space Shuttle and answer the questions below.

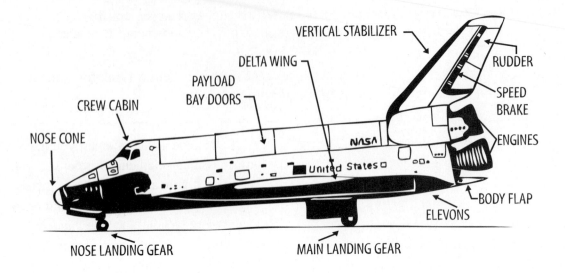

1. What does the Space Shuttle use to land when returning to Earth?

_____

2. According to this diagram, what part of the Shuttle do you think is the *most* different from a non-military airplane?

_____

_____

3. Where is the large equipment stored for each mission?

_____

4. How do you think the Shuttle is designed like an airplane?

_____

_____

5. Pretend you are an airplane pilot flying the Space Shuttle for the first time. On a separate sheet of paper, describe what you think would be different when landing the Shuttle compared to an airplane.

© Pearson Education, Inc., 5

Home Activity Your child has answered questions about a graphic source. Find an owner's guide to a piece of equipment in the house (oven, microwave, car, radio) and look at the detailed diagram with your child.

298 Comprehension

R2.1 Understand how text features (e.g., format, graphics, sequence, diagrams, illustrations, charts, maps) make information accessible and usable.

Author's Purpose

- An **author's purpose** is the reason or reasons an author has for writing.
- An author may write to persuade, to inform, to entertain, or to express ideas or feelings.
- Authors often have more than one reason for writing.

Directions Read the following passage. Then answer the questions below.

Sally Ride was the first American woman in space. But as a teenager, Ride was more interested in sports than space. She trained to be a tennis player from a very early age. She even dropped out of college to pursue a pro tennis career, but she soon left the pros and decided to return to college. She was studying astrophysics when she read that NASA was looking for new astronauts.

Ride was one of 8,000 people who applied. She began the training program in 1977. In 1983, she was aboard the space shuttle *Challenger,* becoming the first American woman in space. Over the next four years, she would log 343 hours of space travel. As a child Sally Ride might have had her eye on the ball, but as an adult, her head was in the clouds.

1. What is the author's main purpose for writing the above passage?

_____

2. When she was a little girl, what did Sally Ride want to be when she grew up?

_____

3. Based on the number of years it took for Ride to reach outer space from the time she began her astronaut training, do you think it is easy to become an astronaut? Why or why not?

_____

_____

4. Based on her hours of space flight, approximately how many days was Sally Ride in space?

_____

5. If you needed to answer questions about Sally Ride, what fix-up strategies could you use to do so?

_____

_____

Home Activity Your child answered questions about an author's purpose and fix-up strategies. Have your child practice taking notes while reading an article about space.

R3.7 Evaluate the author's use of various techniques (e.g., appeal of characters in a picture book, logic and credibility of plots and settings, use of figurative language) to influence readers' perspectives.

Comprehension 299

Name_____

Author's Purpose

- An **author's purpose** is the reason or reasons an author has for writing.
- An author may write to persuade, to inform, to entertain, or to express ideas or feelings.
- Authors often have more than one reason for writing.

Directions Read the following passage and fill in the diagram below.

Carl Allen was sure of one thing: if he was too young to fly to the Moon with the real astronauts, he would start training for it on his own. Carl set out a training schedule for himself. He ran around his yard a lot, he monitored the temperature everywhere in his house, and he practiced floating in the bathtub on his back, pretending to be weightless. Then

Carl discovered a refrigerator box by a neighbor's trash. He started making it into his own space capsule. He had his mom help cut out a window and a small door, and he spent weeks drawing and pasting a control board inside the capsule. Even though he was still in his house, when Carl sat in his box with his football helmet on, it was like he was on the Moon!

AUTHOR'S PURPOSE	1. The author is writing to
DETAIL What did Carl make his space capsule from?	2.
DETAIL Name two things Carl did as part of his astronaut training.	3. Carl ran 4. Carl monitored

5. Did the author meet his or her purpose successfully? Why do you feel this way?

_____

_____

© Pearson Education, Inc., 5

School + Home **Home Activity** Your child answered questions about author's purpose in a fictional passage. Discuss the author's purpose in one of your child's favorite stories.

R3.7 Evaluate the author's use of various techniques (e.g., appeal of characters in a picture book, logic and credibility of plots and settings, use of figurative language) to influence readers' perspectives.

Readers' Guide to Periodical Literature

- The **Readers' Guide to Periodical Literature** is a set of books that lists, alphabetically by author and subject, the articles that are published in more than 200 periodicals. Each entry provides an article's title, author, volume, pages, and date.
- You can find a *Readers' Guide* in most libraries.

Directions Read the following page, which is similar to one you would find in the *Readers' Guide to Periodical Literature*. Then answer the questions below.

ASTRONAUTS—
   See also
   Moonwalk
   NASA
   Shuttle
Astronaut interviews. *School Zone* v496 p18 Ja '02
Astrophysics. L. Jones. *Science Explorers* v117 p87 My '02
Calling Earth [astronaut talks about mission] G. Calwell. *The Northwest Herald* Sec D p1
   Au 17 '02
Miraculous Adventure [astronaut orbits Earth] R. Gold. *Discover the World* v198 p29 Jy '03
Where is NASA's Latest Mission? S. Bobrick. *Mysteries of Space* v48 p31 Mr '03
The Years Before Space Exploration [training astronauts in 1950s] A. Hether. *Our Times* p44
   F '03

1. Which article would probably be the best to read if you were writing a research paper on the training of the first astronauts?

_____

2. In each listing, where does the title of the article appear?

_____

3. What do the words in brackets tell you?

_____

4. Are there any books listed in this section? How do you know?

_____

5. Why is the *Readers' Guide to Periodical Literature* a valuable tool?

_____

_____

W1.3 Use organizational features of printed text (e.g., citations, end notes, bibliographic references) to locate relevant information.

Research and Study Skills 301

© Pearson Education, Inc., 5

Directions Read the following page. Then answer the questions below.

MARS

     See also
     Martians
     Red Planet
     Solar System–Planets
     Space Exploration
Are the Martians Coming? A. Wilson. *Mysteries of Space* v22 p24 D '03
Astral Recordings. *Science Sounds* v6 p33 F '04
Earth's Neighbors [Venus and Mars] T. Charleston. *The Jersey Times* Sec 1 p3 O 7 '03
Ice on Mars [NASA's report on ice deposits] W. M. Walters. *This Great Planet* v8 p29 Ja '04
Life on Mars? [research by University of Minnesota] L. Fulkner. *Science Research Weekly* p8
   S 18 '03
The Trouble with Hubble [information on Hubble] J. Randolph. *Astrophysical Magazine* v68
   p356 Mr '04

---

6. Why do you think the *"See also"* references are placed at the top of the listing?

_____

7. According to the listing above, what is the focus of the article in *The Jersey Times?*

_____

_____

8. If you were writing a report on the possibility of water existing on Mars, which article or articles would be most helpful?

_____

_____

9. How would you describe one of the major differences between a library card catalog and the *Readers' Guide*?

_____

_____

10. If you were writing a research paper, why might you use the *Readers' Guide?*

_____

_____

Home Activity Your child answered questions about the *Readers' Guide to Periodical Literature*. Together, gather several magazines and create your own *Readers' Guide* listings for them. Encourage your child to catalog as many articles from the magazines as possible.

Family Times

Selection Summaries

Week 1 *The Skunk Ladder*

Two friends dig a marvelous hole, and then discover they have an unwelcome visitor.

Week 2 *The Unsinkable Wreck of the R.M.S. Titanic*

Seventy-four years after the *Titanic*'s tragic collision with an iceberg, two explorers viewed the wreck from a mini-submarine.

Week 3 *Talk with an Astronaut*

NASA astronaut Ellen Ochoa answers questions from students around the country.

Week 4 *Journey to the Center of the Earth*

In an excerpt from a classic novel, Harry and his uncle witness a titanic battle underground between two fearsome creatures.

Week 5 *Ghost Towns of the American West*

Searching for land and riches, people headed west and built towns. When the expected windfall didn't come, they abandoned the towns, which became ghost towns.

Activity

Think about the different ways the selections told their stories. Share your thoughts with a family member. Tell which selection was your favorite, and why.

Comprehension Skills Review

In Unit 5, you learned and used many skills while reading the stories and selections.

- **Plot** is what happens in a story. **Characters** are the people who experience the events.
- When you **draw a conclusion**, you form an opinion based on what you know or on the facts and details in a text.
- The **author's purpose** is the reason the author writes a story.

- **Sequence** is the order in which events happen.
- To **generalize** is to make a broad statement that applies to several examples.

Activity

Adventures can be found in faraway places or right down the street. Write about a time when you had an adventure.

Unit Vocabulary Skills

Greek and Latin Roots

Many English words come from Latin and Greek. Use a dictionary to find out more about **Greek and Latin roots.**

Activity As you read, make a list of Greek and Latin roots you find.

Unfamiliar Words

With an **unfamiliar word**, use context clues and then use the dictionary.

Activity Look for unfamiliar words. Check their meanings in the dictionary. Then create a list of new words and write several sentences using them.

Multiple-Meaning Words

When you come across a **multiple-meaning word**, look the word up in the dictionary or a glossary.

Activity Write two sentences using a multiple-meaning word. The word should have a different meaning in each sentence.

Synonyms

Synonyms have similar meanings to other words. You can find synonyms in a thesaurus.

Activity How many synonyms does a thesaurus list for the word *school?*

Prefixes

A **prefix** is attached to the beginning of a word to create a new word. Check the meanings of prefixes in the dictionary.

Activity Look up the prefix *over-*. List ten words that begin with it.

Unit Spelling Rules

Multisyllabic Words

When spelling words with many syllables, look carefully at each word part. Often, whether a syllable is stressed or not determines how it is spelled.

Unusual Spellings

Some words have letters you don't hear. For example, the *b* in *dou̲bt* is silent. In other words, the sound you hear gives no clue as to the word's spelling. For example, the *x* in *an̲x̲ious* sounds like the combination of letters *ksh*.

Greek Word Parts

Many English words are formed from Greek word parts. Sometimes the Greek word parts are spelled differently when forming an English word.

Latin Roots

Latin roots show up in many English words—for example, *ject*, meaning "throw," and *aud*, meaning "hear." Not all words that have these letters in them, however, are using the Latin roots. For example, you can see the root *aud* in words like *inaudible*, *audience*, and *auditorium*. However, *gaudy*, meaning "bright or showy," contains *aud* but has nothing to do with hearing.

Related Words

Related words often have parts that are spelled the same but are pronounced differently: *major, majority*. When you say these words, pay close attention to where the stress is placed.

⊙ Greek and Latin Roots

Many words in English have their roots in the older languages Greek and Latin.
Look at the roots below to review their meanings.

Practice

ex ("out of")	+	cave ("hollow")	+	ation ("act or process of")	=	excavation ("the act of digging up something")

Read the following sentences. Fill in the blanks using the Words to
Know. Then circle the letter of the correct definition for each underlined
word. Use what you know about word roots to help you. A dictionary
can also help if you get stuck.

Words To Know

- abandoned
- attempt
- bellow
- cavern
- feat
- immensely
- savage

1. The crowd pounded their feet with <u>anticipation</u> as the proud

   explorer, Carl Weisner, began his _____ to reach

   the depths of the _____.

   a. to stop anticipating
      or looking forward to

   b. the act or process of
      anticipating

2. Weisner felt _____ confident about heading down into the <u>cavernous</u> space,

   although the _____ was not easy and other experts had failed.

   a. small and full

   b. large and hollow

3. Just as the explorer found his first foothold, a _____ yell erupted from deep

   within the fissure. It was a terrifying _____, like the painful roar of someone
   getting a <u>cavity</u> painfully filled at the dentist!

   a. the hard outside part of a tooth

   b. a hole or hollow space in a tooth

4. Automatically, everyone thought the attempt would be _____, but Weisner
   insisted on continuing down—so the <u>exploration</u> went on.

   a. the act or process of exploring

   b. being in danger while exploring

On Your Own

As you read "On the Hunt," watch out for words that have Greek or Latin roots. Check your ideas
against the dictionary.

Home Activity Your child studied Greek and Latin roots. Ask your child to show you how to look for clues
to roots in the words.

G4R1.4 Know common roots and affixes derived from Greek
and Latin and use this knowledge to analyze the meaning of complex
words (e.g., *international*).

⊙ Character and Plot

A **character** is a person or an animal that takes part in the events of a story. The **plot** is what happens in a story.

The **plot** is the sequence of events in a selection. The plot starts with a *problem* or *conflict*, continues with *rising action* as the conflict builds, and reaches a *climax* when the problem or conflict is faced. The plot ends with a *resolution* or *outcome*.

Practice

Read the story. Answer the questions below.

Problem	Rising action	Climax	Resolution
Carl Weisner was beginning to explore a cave live on TV when a huge roar came out of the cavern.	The terrible roar frightened everyone except the explorer. They begged him not to go down into the dark cave.	He continued his descent into the cavern.	The explorer discovered a rival explorer in the cave who pretended to be a monster.

1. Who is Carl Weisner?

_____

2. What is Weisner's problem?

_____

3. What is the climax of the story?

_____

_____

4. What is the resolution?

_____

_____

On Your Own

Use what you know about character and plot as you read "On the Hunt."

Home Activity Your child reviewed character and plot. Retell one of your favorite books or movies. Discuss who the characters are. Have your child explain the problem, rising action, climax, and resolution of the book or movie.

R3.3 Contrast the actions, motives (e.g., loyalty, selfishness, conscientiousness), and appearances of characters in a work of fiction and discuss the importance of the contrasts to the plot or theme.

© Pearson Education, Inc., 5

⊙ Unfamiliar Words

When you come across an **unfamiliar word**, use a dictionary or glossary to find out its meaning. Dictionaries and glossaries list words in alphabetical order.

Practice

Fill the blanks with the Words to Know. Then use context clues to choose the definition that best matches the underlined word. Use a dictionary to check your work.

Words To Know
cramped
debris
interior
ooze
robotic
sediment
sonar

1. Dr. Taylor decided to get a <u>specimen</u> of ocean-floor

_____ to complete her research.

  a. example   b. mark

2. Yet she found the _____ of the submarine

_____ and began to feel <u>claustrophobic</u>.

  a. comfortable to be in a small space   b. confined or trapped in a small space

3. The situation <u>necessitated</u> the use of the _____ sub to gather the

_____ that was required.

  a. required   b. tried

4. Although <u>gratified</u> by the success, she was saddened by the large amount of

_____ indicated by the ship's _____.

  a. surprised   b. pleased

On Your Own

As you read "Diamond Discoveries," look up the meanings of unfamiliar words in the dictionary. Make a list of new words as you learn them.

© Pearson Education, Inc., 5

Home Activity Your child has reviewed using the dictionary to determine the meanings of unfamiliar words. Together, practice using a print or online dictionary to find new and unusual words.

R1.2 Use word origins to determine the meaning of unknown words.

Vocabulary 327

⊙ Draw Conclusions

When you **draw a conclusion**, you form an opinion based on what you know or on the facts and details in a text.

Dr. Taylor piloted the robot sub.

The sub reached the ocean floor after several hours of descent.

The sub collected ooze where it was too dark and cold for human divers.

Dr. Taylor got her sample.

Practice

Read the story above. Then answer the questions.

1. What was the robot sub able to do?

_____

_____

2. What detail tells you it was necessary to use a robot?

_____

_____

3. What clues tell you that the ocean floor is very far below the surface?

_____

_____

4. Without the robot sub, what would have happened?

_____

_____

_____

On Your Own

Use what you know about drawing conclusions as you read "Diamond Discoveries." Make a list of details in the passage that help you draw a conclusion.

School + Home **Home Activity** Your child reviewed drawing conclusions. As you watch a television program together, practice drawing conclusions based on the actions.

R2.4 Draw inferences, conclusions, or generalizations about text and support them with textual evidence and prior knowledge.

© Pearson Education, Inc., 5

⊙ Multiple-Meaning Words

A **multiple-meaning word** is a word that has several different meanings. To determine which meaning an author is using in a text use **context clues**. You can also check the word in the dictionary.

Practice

Fill in the blanks with Words to Know. Then choose the correct meaning of the underlined multiple-meaning word. Use a dictionary to help you.

> ### Words To Know
> **accomplishments**
> **focus**
> **gravity**
> **monitors**
> **role**
> **specific**

1. Jamal <u>managed</u> some real _____ this year.
   a. controlled the use of   b. succeeded in reaching

2. His _____ _____ was to improve his <u>scores</u> in math and science.
   a. grades in school   b. musical compositions

3. Even the television _____ at home and in the community center did not distract him from his <u>goal</u>.
   a. the finish line in a race   b. something that is desired

4. Now a _____ model for younger students, Jamal said that he is working toward

   his dream of experiencing zero _____ as an astronaut in <u>space</u>.
   a. an area of ground of   b. the area beyond
      a certain size   Earth's atmosphere

On Your Own

As you read "Diamond Discoveries," look for multiple-meaning words and use the dictionary to find their meanings. Use the new words in sentences.

Home Activity Your child reviewed multiple-meaning words. Together, read a newspaper article and look up any multiple-meaning words in a print or online dictionary.

G6R1.2 Identify and interpret figurative language and words with multiple meanings.

⊙ Author's Purpose

Review

The **author's purpose** is the reason the author writes a story. Authors can write to inform, persuade, entertain, and express themselves.

Local student is a fine example to others

Jamal Williams, a student at Centerville Middle School, is an outstanding example of how hard work leads to success. Once a D student, Jamal recently earned all As in his classes. Was this remarkable accomplishment due to some educational video? No, says the young man, it was just deciding he wanted to do better and figuring out how to reach that goal....

Practice

Read the article and answer the questions.

1. Why was the article about Jamal written?

_____

_____

2. What does the article's author think of Jamal?

_____

_____

3. Which words helped you identify how the author felt?

_____

4. What was Jamal's 'remarkable accomplishment'?

_____

On Your Own

Use what you know about author's purpose as you read "Diamond Discoveries." Write about the author's purpose in this passage. Did the author succeed?

Home Activity Your child reviewed author's purpose. Read several articles in a magazine and discuss the different purposes of the writers.

R3.7 Evaluate the author's use of various techniques (e.g., appeal of characters in a picture book, logic and credibility of plots and settings, use of figurative language) to influence readers' perspectives.

Name _____

⊙ Synonyms

A **synonym** is a word that means the same or almost the same as another word. The thesaurus lists a word's synonyms.

Practice

Fill in the blanks with Words to Know. Then use a thesaurus to help you find the answers to the questions that follow.

Words To Know

armor
encases
extinct
hideous
plunged
serpent

1. "What a _____ creature!" exclaimed Jade as she peered into the case.

2. "Oh, it's not so bad," said Efraim. "It's just a _____."

3. "I don't care," said Jade with a shudder. "I don't like them. I wish they were all _____."

4. "Jade, that's a terrible thing to say!" Efraim said "Without them, we'd be _____ into a world filled with vermin!"

5. Jade grimaced and said, "All right, they can stay. But I'm going to make sure a suit of

   _____ _____ me before I touch one!"

6. Which Word to Know means the same or almost the same as *nonexistent?* _____

7. Which Word to Know means the same or almost the same as *ugly?* _____

8. Which Word to Know means the same or almost the same as *snake?* _____

9. Which Word to Know means the same or almost the same as *wraps?* _____

10. Which Word to Know means the same or almost the same as *dunked?* _____

On Your Own

As you read "On the Hunt," list the adjectives you find and look up a synonym for each in a thesaurus. Make a list of the synonyms you find.

© Pearson Education, Inc., 5

Home Activity Your child reviewed synonyms. With your child, read a magazine article and use a thesaurus to find synonyms of words.

R1.3 Understand and explain frequently used synonyms, antonyms, and homographs.

Name _____

⊙ Sequence

Sequence refers to the order of events in nonfiction, or the steps in a process. Clue words, such as *first*, *next*, and *then* can help you follow the sequence of events. Phrases such as "three weeks later" are also clues as to when events happened.

Practice

Read the story about the life cycle of the timber rattlesnake. Then answer the questions below.

First, the female snake gives birth to six to ten baby snakes.	The snakes are 10 to 13 inches long at birth.	The snake gets a new button on its rattle every year when it sheds its skin.	After seven years, the snakes are full grown. They are three to five feet long.

1. What was the first step in the sequence?

   _____

2. How many babies are born at a time?

   _____

3. List the sequence clue words in each of the captions.

   _____

4. How long does it take for the snake to reach its full growth?

   _____

On Your Own

Use what you know about sequence as you read "On the Hunt." Make a list of the sequence of events in the story.

Home Activity Your child reviewed sequence. With your child, list the sequence of events for doing a chore, such as the dishes or the laundry.

R2.2 Analyze text that is organized in sequential or chronological order.

⊙ Prefixes

- A **prefix** is attached to the beginning of a word to make a new word. You can check the meanings of prefixes in the dictionary. The dictionary will list the prefix by itself and also as part of many words.
- Remember that *in-* can mean "not," and that *over-* means "too much."

Practice

Read the following sentences. Fill in the blanks with one of the Words to Know. Then circle the letter of the correct meaning of each underlined word.

> **Words To Know**
>
> **economic**
> **independence**
> **overrun**
> **scrawled**
> **vacant**

1. My friend Amanda started her own business selling her old puzzles and <u>inactive</u> board games. She hoped that the extra money would give her more _____.

   a. being used very often
   b. not being used right now

2. Though the idea sounded like a huge project to her <u>overcautious</u> brother Joe, she _____ a few signs and hung them around the neighborhood.

   a. being too careful
   b. not being careful

3. To Joe's surprise, Amanda was _____ by eager customers, all of whom were <u>incomprehensibly</u> excited to purchase her puzzles!

   a. not easy to understand
   b. very easy to understand

4. Now her old puzzle closet is _____, and she is no longer working <u>overtime</u> to get _____ freedom. Soon, though, she will need to find another creative way to earn some money.

   a. less time than usual
   b. more time than usual

On Your Own

As you read "Diamond Discoveries," look for words that have prefixes. List them and look up the meanings of the prefixes in the dictionary.

Home Activity Your child reviewed prefixes. Work together to list as many words as you can that begin with prefixes.

G3R1.8 Use knowledge of prefixes (e.g., *un-, re-, pre-, bi-, mis-, dis-*) and suffixes (e.g., *-er, -est, -ful*) to determine the meaning of words.

Name _____

⊙ Generalize

A **generalization** is a broad statement or rule that applies to many examples. Clue words such as *all*, *most*, *always*, *usually*, and *often* can signal generalizations.

Generalizations that are supported by text evidence and by logic are called *valid generalizations*. Generalizations that are not well supported are called *faulty generalizations*.

Amanda is in fifth grade. She often paints after school.

Joe is also in fifth grade. He often plays guitar after school.

Practice

Look at the pictures, and read each generalization below. Circle the correct answer to show if you think it is a valid generalization or a faulty generalization. Then explain your answer.

1. Amanda usually enjoys painting.

   a. valid generalization   b. faulty generalization

   _____

   _____

2. Joe always has his guitar with him.

   a. valid generalization   b. faulty generalization

   _____

   _____

3. Amanda and Joe never play sports.

   a. valid generalization   b. faulty generalization

   _____

   _____

On Your Own

Use what you know about making generalizations as you read "Diamond Discoveries." List several generalizations you find in the passage.

School + Home **Home Activity** Your child reviewed making generalizations. Together, read a magazine article. Identify any generalizations the writer has made.

R2.4 Draw inferences, conclusions, or generalizations about text and support them with textual evidence and prior knowledge.

Diamond Discoveries

If you look at a map of Canada, you will spot the chilly area of the Northwest Territories. These territories cover over 500,000 square miles and consist mainly of forests and frozen lands. During the winters, temperatures can plummet down to –25 degrees Fahrenheit. Only lichen and moss will grow there. The human population is so sparse that, on average, one person lives every twelve and a half miles.

Although this area may seem very remote, one geologist named Charles Fipke braved the cold, harsh climate for a hoard of treasure. His journey first began in 1978 when he was hired by a company to complete a specific task: to locate priceless diamonds in the Canadian wilderness.

Diamonds were expensive, and there was just no telling how much profit could be made. Billions of dollars might be up for grabs. Because the stakes were so high, Fipke wasn't even allowed to tell his team of explorers why they were exploring!

Fipke first set out to search the Colorado Rockies, making his way up past the Canadian border. He knew that finding diamonds would take both talent and a whole lot of luck. Diamonds are located in kimberlite pipes—long channels in the ground created ages ago during volcanic eruptions. Since these pipes are very difficult to find, diamond-hunters may also look for "indicator minerals." These special minerals, such as garnets and chromites, are often found near the kimberlite pipes. Not all pipes, however, have diamonds in them. Many pipes are empty, while others are just too small to mine.

By 1981, Fipke and his team had moved farther east, into the Northwest Territories. When Fipke heard that competitors were looking for diamonds just a hundred miles away, he decided to spy on their operation. The information that he gathered from the soil and sediment samples there helped to further his own mission.

Soon after the espionage incident, Fipke's employer abruptly ended the diamond search. But that wasn't about to stop Fipke from looking on his own! Without any help from an outside company, Fipke and a fellow geologist, Stewart Blusson, pooled their economic resources together and started on their own diamond quest.

⊙ **DAY 2**
Unfamiliar Words Circle the nearby word that helps you to understand *plummet*.

⊙ **DAY 2** **Draw Conclusions** Give one reason why the population might be so sparse in the Northwest Territories.

_____

_____

_____

⊙ **DAY 3** **Author's Purpose** After reading the first two paragraphs, what do you think is the author's purpose?

_____

_____

_____

_____

_____

⊙ **DAY 3** **Multiple-Meaning Words** What is the meaning of *company* as it is used in the passage?

_____

_____

R2.0 Students read and understand grade-level appropriate material.

"Diamond Discoveries" 335

⊙ **DAY 2** Draw
Conclusions What
might have happened
if others found out
about the expeditions?

_____

_____

_____

_____

⊙ **DAY 5** Prefixes
What is the prefix in
insanely?

_____

⊙ **DAY 5**
Generalize Underline
a generalization in the
fourth paragraph.

⊙ **DAY 3** Author's
Purpose Do you think
the author achieved
her purpose? Why or
why not?

_____

_____

_____

_____

_____

⊙ **DAY 5**
Generalize What
generalization could
you make about
Fipke?

_____

_____

The pair made their way farther east to an area now known as the Barren Lands. Concerned that rivals would hear about their explorations, they kept extra quiet and took many precautions. They hiked through areas they knew didn't have diamonds, just to throw competitors off the scent. Blusson would also fly a helicopter without telling anyone where he was going. He was afraid that others would track his flight patterns and then head in the same direction in search of diamonds. Once when Blusson was alone in the icy wasteland, his freezing helicopter would not restart. Since no one knew of his location, he had to save himself. Blusson eventually built a fire, heating the plane's engine until it was warm enough to turn on again.

For years, the men searched for diamond traces while suffering through insanely cold winter temperatures and vicious summer mosquitoes. Their expeditions were enormously expensive, and still no kimberlite pipes were in sight.

Work continued at a constant pace with the help of other funds. Then in the late 1980s, newly published geological research helped Fipke to pinpoint a potential diamond source located in an area among thousands of tiny lakes.

While Blusson was on other expeditions, Fipke and a new team set up a camp near this new lake area. Fipke was feverish with anticipation, and his team began racing against the clock. Everyone was afraid that rivals would hear about their location and soon swoop down to look for diamonds themselves.

Tensions mounted. Where was the kimberlite? It had to be around there somewhere.

Finally, Fipke found a kimberlite pipe beneath one of the many lakes—and yes, there were diamonds inside! With the help of a large company, he quickly staked his claim of land. After years and years of searching, Fipke's fortune was finally made, and his accomplishments were announced to the world!

© Pearson Education, Inc., 5

Home Activity Your child read a selection and used comprehension and vocabulary skills from Unit 5. Have your child summarize the selection, drawing conclusions about the facts and making generalizations about the text.

R2.0 Students read and understand grade-level appropriate material.

On the Hunt

The gym was full of excitement as the fifth-grade school scavenger hunt was about to start. Deval, Sofia, and Evan chattered together eagerly as the sky grew dark outside. They were determined to win the scavenger hunt and the prize of the free movie passes.

When all of the kids had settled down, Principal Taylor began to speak. "Good evening, everyone," she said. "I know you're all eager to begin, so I'll make this introduction quick. Your teachers and I will soon be passing out the list of scavenger hunt questions. First team to answer all of the questions correctly wins the prize! When the game is over, we'll finish the evening with a pizza party here in the gym." At the end of this announcement, the entire fifth grade erupted in shouts and cheering.

Papers were quickly handed out, and the teams plunged into action. Deval, Sofia, and Evan high-fived and ran to their starting location: Ms. Kyle's first-grade classroom. Evan looked at the paper and read clue number one aloud. "My name is Ted. I like to rhyme. I wrote *Green Eggs* in little time."

"Green eggs?" asked Deval. "Sounds pretty gross, if you ask me."

Sofia thought for a moment and ran over to the first grade bookshelf. "Maybe the clue means *Green Eggs and Ham.* You know—the book by Dr. Seuss." She found a copy of the story and opened the front cover. Lying inside was a little note. *Congratulations, super sleuth!* it read. *You've answered the first question. Ted Geisel, otherwise known as Dr. Seuss, was the writer of* Green Eggs and Ham. *Now head to the library where you'll find the answer to question two.*

"Nice!" Deval said to Sofia. Then the group bolted to the library, and Eric read the next clue.

"According to this book, yesterday always follows today."

"What could that possibly mean?" Sofia pondered. All of the kids scratched their heads and waited for a burst of inspiration. Deval began pacing through the aisles, skimming the library titles as he went. The scavenger clue didn't seem to make any sense.

⊙ **DAY 1** Character/Plot What is the problem in the story?

_____

_____

_____

_____

_____

⊙ **DAY 4** Synonyms What is a synonym for *sleuth?*

_____

_____

_____

⊙ **DAY 4** Sequence What event happens before the kids arrive in the library?

_____

_____

_____

_____

_____

R2.0 Students read and understand grade-level appropriate material.

"On the Hunt" 337

⊙ **DAY 4** Sequence
What happened after
the students left
the library?

_____

_____

⊙ **DAY 1**
Character/
Plot Underline two
sentences on this
page that help you
to understand
Eric's personality.

_____

_____

⊙ **DAY 1** Greek and
Latin Roots The Latin
root *spec-* means
"look or see." How
does this root help
you to understand
the meaning of
spectacular?

_____

_____

_____

_____

Eric peered into a heavy reference book that was sitting on a podium. "Hey, check it out—Dr. Seuss's name is listed in the dictionary!"

"Wait a second!" Deval shouted. "That's it! When you look up something in a dictionary, *yesterday* comes after *today*. Alphabetical order!" He raced over to where Eric was standing and lifted the front cover of the dictionary. Sure enough, another slip of paper was waiting for them there. *You know your ABCs, detective! Now head to the main office where the answer to your last clue awaits.*

"I can almost feel those movie tickets in my hand right now," Sofia said. Quickly, the team abandoned the library and took off for the main office.

They slowed their steps as they got near Principal Taylor's doorway. "This place gives me the creeps," Eric said.

"That's because the only time you're ever here is when you've gotten in trouble,"

"Teachers shouldn't blame me for talking in class all of the time!" Eric said. "I can't help it. Everyone in my family talks—just look at my parents, and my sisters, and my auntie, and my dog—"

"Later," Sofia said. "We don't have the time. Deval, what's the last clue?"

Deval looked at the paper and read, "You'd think my name would mean 'I sew,' but actually I run the show."

"Oh, that's an easy one!" Eric said.

Sofia and Deval stared in disbelief. "Easy?" they asked. "So what's the answer?"

"Principal Taylor, of course," Eric said. "Get it? Taylor? Tailor?"

Sofia and Eric laughed hysterically. "Who knew your spectacular feat of genius would be inspired by all your visits to the office!" Sofia said. Then all three of them ran to find their principal.

Principal Taylor smiled at the kids when they arrived. "Looks like you've solved my little puzzle," she said.

"And just in time for dinner," Sofia replied. "I'm starving for some pizza!"

© Pearson Education, Inc., 5

School + Home **Home Activity** Your child read a selection and used comprehension and vocabulary skills from Unit 5. Have your child retell the selection, focusing on the sequence of events in the plot.

R2.0 Students read and understand grade-level appropriate material.

Connect Text to Text

Reading Across Texts

Think about the selections "Diamond Discoveries" and "On the Hunt." Complete the Venn diagram below with details that show similarities and differences between the two texts.

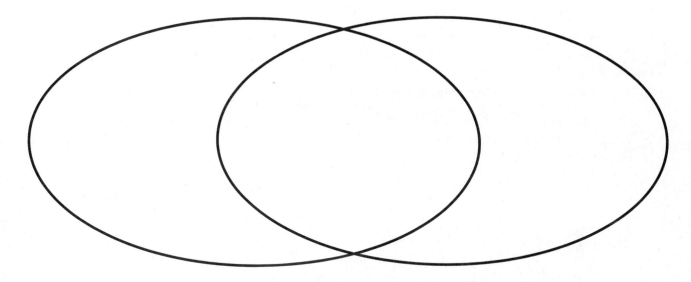

Writing Across Texts

Imagine you are on a quest. What would you be looking for and how would you find it?

_____

_____

_____

_____

_____

_____

_____

_____

_____

Home Activity Your child read two selections this week. Have your child explain to you how they were alike and how they were different.

Summarize Your Learning

> ### Who goes seeking adventure and why?
>
> - *The Skunk Ladder*   • *The Unsinkable Wreck of the R.M.S. Titanic*
> - *Talk with an Astronaut*   • *Journey to the Center of the Earth*
> - *Ghost Towns of the American West*

Think About It!

Think about the selections you read in this unit.

- How were they alike? How were they different?
- Were the selections you read this week similar to others you have read?
- What did you learn?

Write three big ideas about adventure that you learned from this unit.

- _____
- _____
- _____

Question It!

Write three questions about your big ideas.

- _____
- _____
- _____

Talk About It!

Discuss your questions with a partner.

- What questions did your partner have? Were they similar to yours?
  Were they different from yours?
- What things did you and your partner want to know?
- What types of adventures did you want to experience? What types of adventures did you partner want to experience?

© Pearson Education, Inc., 5

Home Activity Your child reviewed and discussed the selections from Unit 5. Have your child describe to you the big ideas about adventure from this unit.

Family Times

Summary

Inside Out

Francisco is the son of migrant workers new to America. He attends an American school and struggles to learn the language. A misunderstanding with a bullying classmate embarrasses him, but he feels better when his drawing wins first prize in a contest. During the year, he studies a caterpillar in the classroom, eventually watching it construct a cocoon and become a butterfly.

Activity

Fitting In Talk to a grandparent or other adult you know who came to America from another country, or who moved from one place to another very different place. Interview the person about his or her experiences trying to "fit in." What was the hardest part? What was the easiest?

Comprehension Skill

Categorize and Classify

To **categorize and classify** is to arrange, describe, or label things based on behaviors, features, or relationships. As you read, you may notice that members of the same categories or classes can be compared to other members using words such as *similarly* and *like* or contrasted with members of different groups using words such as *however*, *unlike*, or *instead*.

Activity

Categorizing Books With a family member, organize your books according to their content, for example, fiction, nonfiction, and reference. Which is your favorite type of book and why? Which category of books shows the most wear?

Lesson Vocabulary

Words to Know

Knowing the meanings of these words is important to reading *Inside Out*. Practice using these words.

Vocabulary Words

caterpillar the wormlike larvae of insects such as butterflies or moths.

cocoon case of silky thread spun by the larvae of various insects, to live in while they are developing into adults

disrespect to show a lack of respect; to be rude

emerge to come into view; come out; come up

migrant a worker, especially a farm worker, who travels from one area to another in search of work

sketched drawn roughly and quickly

unscrewed loosened or taken off by turning

Conventions

Modifiers

Remember to use **modifiers** correctly. A modifier is a word that limits the meaning of another word. Keep modifiers close to the words they modify. Sometimes using modifiers incorrectly changes the meaning of a sentence. For example, *Only Ken visits* has a different meaning from *Ken only visits*. Prepositional phrases should be kept close to the words they modify too. For example: *The gift from France is on the table* has a different meaning than *The gift is on the table from France*.

Activity

Mixed-Up Modifiers With a family member, make a list of seven words or phrases you can use as modifiers. *Tight*, *rich*, and *very rich* are a few examples of modifiers. Then pick a sentence out of a newspaper, magazine, or book. Make a new sentences by inserting as many modifiers as you can from your list into the sentences you choose. How are the meanings of the new sentences similar to the meanings of the original sentences? How are they different?

Practice Tested Spelling Words

Categorize and Classify

- To **categorize and classify** is to arrange, describe, or label things based on behaviors, features, or relationships.
- Members of the same categories or classes may be compared to other members using words such as *similarly* and *like* or contrasted with members of other categories and classes with words such as *however, unlike,* or *instead.*

Directions Read the following passage. Then answer the questions below.

Cocoons are most commonly associated with butterflies or moths, but there are other animals that also spin silk into protective coverings. Whereas butterflies and moths are members of the insect class, spiders belong to the class of eight-legged, mostly land-dwelling creatures, called arachnids, that also includes scorpions and ticks. Spiders are like butterflies or moths because they spin cocoons, but they are unlike them because the cocoons serve different purposes. All spiders spin silk cocoon-like egg sacs within which baby spiders hatch. Some, like the wolf spider, carry their eggs with them. Spiders also use their silk in other ways, such as for building their strong webs, climbing, and wrapping their prey. The larva of the butterfly or moth spins a cocoon around itself as it prepares to enter the final stage of its life. It grows inside the cocoon until it emerges as a winged moth or butterfly.

1. How are spiders alike?

_____

2. What category could be created that includes both spiders and moths?

_____

3. How do wolf spiders take special care of their babies?

_____

_____

4. Name some of the different ways in which spiders use silk.

_____

_____

5. How might the category of cocoons be broken down into two smaller groups?

_____

_____

Home Activity Your child learned what it means to categorize and classify by reading a short passage. Together, read an article in a book, newspaper, or magazine that discusses insects. Create your own categories for them based on how you feel about different insects.

G4R2.2 Use appropriate strategies when reading for different purposes (e.g., full comprehension, location of information, personal enjoyment).

Comprehension 343

Vocabulary

Directions Choose the word from the box that best matches each definition. Write the word on the line.

_____ 1. to show a lack of respect

_____ 2. to come into view

_____ 3. the wormlike larvae of insects such as butterflies and moths

_____ 4. drawn roughly and quickly

_____ 5. worker, especially a farm worker, who travels from one area to another in search of work

Check the Words You Know
____caterpillar
____cocoon
____disrespect
____emerge
____migrant
____sketched
____unscrewed

Directions Choose the word from the box that best fits each sentence below. Write the word on the line.

_____ 6. Farms often use _____ workers, people who travel from place to place looking for work.

_____ 7. I wondered what type of moth could come out of such a protective _____.

_____ 8. She _____ the cap on the pickle jar, after some difficulty.

_____ 9. The explorers _____ pictures in their journals of the plants they discovered.

_____ 10. The gypsy moth _____ is responsible for eating all the leaves of over a millions acres of forests each year.

Write a Journal Entry

On a separate piece of paper, draw and write about a butterfly or moth you have seen outdoors or in a book. Use as many vocabulary words as you can.

 Home Activity Your child identified and used vocabulary words from *Inside Out*. With your child, write a story about how people can change. Use as many vocabulary words as you can.

R1.0 Word Analysis, Fluency, and Systematic Vocabulary Development

© Pearson Education, Inc., 5

Vocabulary • Prefixes

- A **prefix** is added at the beginning of a base word to change its meaning. For example, the prefix *un-* means "the opposite." The prefix *dis-* means "to do the opposite."
- Prefixes do not stand alone in sentences. They usually have their own definitions listed in dictionaries, as well as their origins, such as the Greek or Latin languages.

Directions Read the following passage about Keiko's day at the beach. Then answer the questions below. Use a dictionary to help you.

Keiko was unhappy that she had never been to the beach. She grew up in the mountains and, although she loved climbing to the top of the hills, she felt dissatisfied. Deciding to give her a treat for her birthday, her parents drove several hours with her to the shore. For the first time in her life Keiko played in huge waves. She saw creatures in the sea that were quite dissimilar from animals that lived in the mountains. Although she felt it unlikely she would return to the shore soon, she enjoyed herself like she never had before. Keiko did not want her day at the beach to end.

1. Why are sea animals dissimilar from mountain animals? What does *dissimilar* mean?

_____

_____

2. What does *unlikely* mean? Use a dictionary to help you. Why was it "unlikely" that Keiko would soon return to the shore?

_____

_____

3. Why was Keiko dissatisfied? What word is the opposite of *dissatisfied*?

_____

_____

4. Add prefixes to *pleased* and *excited* so that each new word's meaning will be the opposite of the base word. Use one of these new words in a sentence. Check the word's meaning in a dictionary to be sure of the meaning.

_____

_____

Home Activity Your child learned the meanings of the prefixes *-un* and *-dis*. Look through a newspaper, magazine, or book and make a list of ten new vocabulary words with these prefixes.

G3R1.8 Use knowledge of prefixes (e.g., *un-*, *re-*, *pre-*, *bi-*, *mis-*, *dis-*) and suffixes (e.g., *-er*, *-est*, *-ful*) to determine the meaning of words.

Vocabulary 345

© Pearson Education, Inc., 5

Sequence

Directions Read the following passage. Then answer the questions below.

Paul was planning to bake his mother's birthday cake. He knew his father claimed to hate to cook, but Paul asked him if he wanted to help bake the cake. "No, I'd rather watch the baseball game," his father said. So Paul found a good recipe in a cookbook, made a list of ingredients, and then rode his bike to the supermarket. When he got home, Paul lined up the ingredients on the table in the order he would need them. He put out the flour, sugar, eggs, and milk. Then he turned on his favorite music and put on his mother's apron, singing all the while.

In the living room his father was watching the game and heard Paul making noise out in the kitchen. He looked in to see Paul, flour all over his face, singing and baking. His father had to smile. "It looks like you're having fun. Do you have another apron for me?" Paul's father asked.

1. What did Paul do after his father said he wouldn't help?

_____

_____

2. Did Paul ride his bike to the supermarket before or after he found the recipe?

_____

_____

3. When he got home from the supermarket, what did Paul do with the ingredients?

_____

_____

4. What did Paul do after he put out the flour, sugar, eggs, and milk?

_____

_____

5. Did Paul's father decide to help him bake? How do you know?

_____

_____

_____

© Pearson Education, Inc., 5

Home Activity Your child read a story and determined its sequence of events. With your child, find and read a story that takes place over time and write down the order of events that lead to its conclusion.

R2.2 Analyze text that is organized in sequential or chronological order.

Categorize and Classify

- To **categorize and classify** is to arrange, describe, or label things based on behaviors, features, or relationships.
- Members of the same categories or classes may be compared to other members using words such as *similarly* and *like* or contrasted with members of other categories and classes with words such as *however, unlike,* or *instead.*

Directions Read the following passage. Then answer the questions below.

Paolo was a migrant artist who traveled across the country, drawing pictures of people who attended county fairs. His favorite subjects were children. One day he set up his table under a large maple tree and laid out his art supplies. First, he put his tablets of fine drawing paper on the table. Then he laid out the color pastels. He then set out several charcoal pencils for quick sketches. A couple with a young daughter stopped but said they had no money for a picture. Paolo smiled and said he would draw the little girl without charge. He began to select the colors he would use. When he finished, he gave the beautiful likeness to the grateful parents.

1. What types of art supplies does Paolo use to draw sketches?

_____

2. Name two things that can be classified as "things Paolo uses to draw."

_____

3. Paolo's paper, pencils, and pastels can be put in the category "art supplies." Name three other things you have used that can be put in this category.

_____

4. What kind of people does Paolo like to draw most?

_____

5. What kind of a man do you think Paolo is? Why do you think so?

_____

_____

Home Activity Your child categorized and classified information in a short story. Read a story together and look for examples of categories as they appear.

Name_____

Categorize and Classify

- To **categorize and classify** is to arrange, describe, or label things based on behaviors, features, or relationships.
- Members of the same categories or classes may be compared to other members using words such as *similarly* and *like* or contrasted with members of other categories and classes with words such as *however*, *unlike*, or *instead*.

Directions Read the following passage. Then answer the questions below.

Tommy never wanted to go to the beach. He was always content to stay at home and play video games, except when Laura Jones and her mother invited him for one late summer trip to the seashore. When they got to the beach it was low tide. The wet sand was dotted with a wonderful assortment of shells and stones. Tommy and Laura began to collect them. They first arranged the shells by size, and then they arranged the stones by color. Tommy found some sand dollars and a large piece of silvery driftwood, a tree branch worn smooth by the sea, which was very unlike the delicate and rough-edged shells. When it came time to leave, Tommy carried the driftwood home, hoping to remember one of the greatest days of his life.

1. At what time of year did Laura and Tommy visit the beach?

_____

2. How did Laura and Tommy categorize their shells and stones?

_____

3. How is driftwood different from shells?

_____

_____

4. Do you think sand dollars belong in the category of shells or stones?

_____

5. What things do you like to collect at the beach? Can you put them into categories?

_____

_____

 School + Home **Home Activity** Your child learned what it means to categorize and classify by reading a short passage. Discuss with your child other items, events, people, and places that can be classified into categories.

G4R2.2 Use appropriate strategies when reading for different purposes (e.g., full comprehension, location of information, personal enjoyment).

Follow and Clarify Directions

- Directions are instructions that are given in order, usually in numbered steps.
- Read through all the directions before you begin. Then **follow directions** by doing what is instructed, one step at a time.
- Try to visualize the end result of the directions. If you need to **clarify directions,** reread them, review them, or ask questions.

Directions Use the following directions to answer the questions below.

> **Rhythmic Breathing**
>
> The following directions will help you learn rhythmic breathing for swimming.
>
> 1. Stand in water that is about chest deep.
> 2. Lean forward, and turn your face to one side so that your ear is underwater but your face is just above the water line.
> 3. Breathe in and hold your breath.
> 4. Turn your head so your face is down, and exhale slowly through your mouth.
> 5. Rotate your head back to the start position and inhale again.
> 6. Try performing this action to the right and to the left to see which is more comfortable.
> 7. Then repeat steps 3 through 5 over and over in a regular rhythm.
> 8. Practice until you can do steps 3 through 5 smoothly.

1. What is the purpose of these directions?

_____

2. What is the first step in the directions? What is the last step?

_____

_____

3. To do rhythmic breathing, which steps must be repeated? Why?

_____

_____

4. Why must these steps be done in order?

_____

_____

5. Explain how you were able to visualize the directions. How were you able to clarify directions you didn't understand?

_____

_____

G4W1.3 Use traditional structures for conveying information (e.g., chronological order, cause and effect, similarity and difference, posing and answering a question).

Research and Study Skills 349

Directions Use the following directions to answer the questions below.

Coral Reef Word Puzzle

Follow these directions to complete the coral reef word puzzle.

1. Write down the letters of the word *seal,* the sea mammal that has four flippers, lives in cold water, and eats fish.

2. Next to these four letters, write down the first letter of a word that means the opposite of *push.*

3. Now add the four letters of a word that rhymes with *wrong* and means "the opposite of *short.*"

4. Cross out the letters *a, l,* and *l.*

5. Finally, unscramble the remaining six letters to find the name of something you might find at a coral reef.

---

6. What is the purpose of these directions? What did you do to follow step 1?

_____

_____

7. What is the word you wrote down to complete step 2? What letters do you have after completing step 2?

_____

_____

8. What is the word you wrote down to complete step 3? What letters do you have after completing step 3?

_____

_____

9. What answer do you find for the puzzle after completing steps 4 and 5?

_____

10. Why would it be impossible to solve this word puzzle without following the directions in order?

_____

_____

_____

Home Activity Your child learned about following directions step by step. Talk about a simple recipe for one of your child's favorite foods. Work together to follow the directions for making the recipe step by step.

G4W1.3 Use traditional structures for conveying information (e.g., chronological order, cause and effect, similarity and difference, posing and answering a question).

Family Times

Summary

The Mystery of Saint Matthew Island

The reindeer herd on Saint Matthew Island had grown to six thousand animals. Suddenly, almost all of the reindeer died. A scientist tries to figure out why. His research rules out the usual causes: predators, disease, and old age. He discovers that the reindeer had starved, and a brutal winter sealed their fate.

Activity

Survival Strategies Imagine you and members of your family are scientists studying animals in the wild. Talk with your family about how animals survive. Discuss the different things that can threaten a wild animal's survival, both natural and man-made.

Comprehension Skill

Main Idea and Details

The **main idea** is an important point that has at least one supporting detail. **Details** are smaller pieces of information that tell more about the main idea.

Activity

Zero In Ask members of your family for their opinions about certain animals. For each opinion, or main idea, discuss ideas for supporting details. Make a list of the main ideas and the details that support them.

Lesson Vocabulary

Words to Know

Knowing the meanings of these words is important to reading *The Mystery of Saint Matthew Island*. Practice using these words.

Vocabulary Words

bleached whitened by exposure to sunlight or by use of chemicals

carcasses bodies of dead animals

decay process of rotting

parasites living things that live on or in others, from which they get their food, often harming the others in the process

scrawny having little flesh; lean; thin; skinny

starvation suffering from extreme hunger

suspicions beliefs, feelings, thoughts

tundra a vast, treeless plain in the arctic regions

Grammar

Conjunctions

A **conjunction** is a word that joins words, phrases, or entire sentences. *And, or,* and *but* are conjunctions. You can use conjunctions to join subjects, predicates, and objects. *For example: John and Kathleen; rice or noodles.* Sometimes two sentences about related topics can be combined, using a comma and a conjunction or a subordinating conjunction such as *because, if, then,* or *when. For example: We went to the zoo because we love tigers.*

Activity

Be a Joiner Make a three-column chart. In the first and third columns, write three simple sentences. In the middle column, write *and, or,* and *but.* Cut the paper so there is one sentence on each cut piece of paper. Take turns combining sentences using different conjunctions. Do this by moving the sentences in front of and after each conjunction.

Practice Tested Spelling Words

Main Idea and Details

- The **topic** is the overall subject of a piece of writing. The **main idea** of a selection is the most important idea about the topic of that selection. **Details** are small pieces of information that tell more about the main idea.
- Sometimes the author states the main idea in a single sentence. When the author does not state the main idea, the reader must figure it out.

Directions Read the following passage. Then complete the diagram below.

Plants, just like animals, can become endangered as a result of the actions of human beings. Some plants are threatened after the insects that pollinate the plant die off. For example, one type of milkweed has nearly disappeared because chemicals killed off the butterfly that pollinates the milkweed. In addition, a plant can become endangered when buildings and roads take over the open lands where it grows. Other human activities such as farming and logging can threaten plants too. Finally, human pollution of land and water threatens many types of natural life, including plants. People are often unaware of it, but human activities can have harmful effects on plants and other parts of the natural world.

Main Idea

1.

Details

2.

3.

4.

5.

Home Activity Your child identified the main idea and supporting details of a nonfiction passage. Together, work to identify the main idea and supporting details of individual paragraphs in a magazine article about animals.

R2.3 Discern main ideas and concepts presented in texts, identifying and assessing evidence that supports those ideas.

Comprehension   353

Vocabulary

Directions Choose the word from the box that best matches each definition. Write the word on the line.

_____ **1.** a vast, treeless plain in arctic regions

_____ **2.** living things that live on or in others, from which they get food

_____ **3.** having little flesh; lean; thin

_____ **4.** whitened by exposure to sunlight or the use of chemicals

_____ **5.** beliefs; feelings; thoughts

> ## Check the Words You Know
>
> ___bleached
> ___carcasses
> ___decay
> ___parasites
> ___scrawny
> ___starvation
> ___suspicions
> ___tundra

Directions Choose the word from the box that best matches each clue. Write the word on the line.

_____ **6.** This ground is frozen even in summer.

_____ **7.** Lice and tapeworms are examples of these.

_____ **8.** This is an extreme form of hunger.

_____ **9.** These are dead bodies of animals.

_____ **10.** This is the process of rotting.

Write a Memo

Imagine that you are a zookeeper reporting on illnesses among animals at a zoo. On a separate sheet of paper, write a memo to the zoo's director about what you have observed. Use as many vocabulary words as you can.

© Pearson Education, Inc., 5

 Home Activity Your child identified and used vocabulary words from *The Mystery of Saint Matthew Island*. Together, read a story or nonfiction article. Have him or her point out unfamiliar words. Work together to figure out the meaning of each word by using other words that appear near it.

R1.0 Word Analysis, Fluency, and Systematic Vocabulary Development

Vocabulary · Suffixes

- A **suffix** is a letter or letters added to the end of a base word. Recognizing a suffix will help you figure out the word's meaning.
- In a dictionary, listings for words ending in suffixes are found near their base words.
- The ending *-ed* is added to a verb to make it past tense. The ending *-ing* is added to a verb to make it tell about present or ongoing actions. The endings *-s* and *-es* are added to a singular noun to make it refer to more than one person, place, or thing.

Directions Read the following passage. Then answer the questions below. Use a dictionary to help you.

The pilot flew above the arctic tundra, looking for baby seals. He was checking on the population of seals for a conservation organization. Although hunters were not allowed to kill the seals, some people had suspicions that seals were disappearing. The pilot was strongly hoping he wouldn't find any seal carcasses bleached, or made white, by the sun. As he steered the airplane closer to the frozen ground, he glimpsed a few seals. They did look scrawny, probably because of minor illnesses, but they were alive. Then he saw more and more seals coming into view. The pilot was very pleased.

1. What part of speech is *suspicions*? What meaning does the suffix give the word?

_____

2. How does the suffix in *checking* affect the word's meaning?

_____

3. What is the meaning of *bleached* in the passage? What effect does the suffix have on the word's meaning?

_____

_____

4. How would removing the *-es* suffix in *illnesses* change the meaning of the word?

_____

5. Rewrite the second sentence of the passage to make the action occur in the past.

_____

_____

Home Activity Your child identified and used word suffixes to help determine the meanings of new words in a passage. Work with your child to identify unfamiliar words in another article. Together, identify word suffixes that help you understand the words.

R1.4 Know abstract, derived roots and affixes from Greek and Latin and use this knowledge to analyze the meaning of complex words (e.g., *controversial*).

Sequence

Directions Read the following article. Then answer the questions below.

Before the school was built in 1950, the land on which it stands was a swamp. Back then, the earth was soft, wet, and marshy. Beavers, otters, and turtles slid through the watery land. Cranes, herons, hawks, and egrets swooped overhead or waded in the water.

Then, after the town decided to build the school, the land was filled in. First, truckloads of dirt were added to provide a firm base. Afterward, earth movers were used to shape the land, creating a flat surface with a few low hills. Finally, the school was constructed on top of the newly sculpted land. When the building was finished, no swamp animals or water birds remained. Now students and teachers have taken the place of toads and turtles.

1. According to the article, what was the land like originally? What clues tell you this condition was present before the building of the school?

_____

_____

2. What first lived on the land? Who is there now?

_____

_____

3. What was the first change that was made to the land?

_____

_____

4. What was the next step before the school was constructed?

_____

_____

5. On a separate sheet of paper, explain how clues clarify the sequence of changes described in the second paragraph. How do these clues help you to understand the article?

Home Activity Your child has identified the sequence of changes that a piece of land has undergone. Together, read a newspaper article. Work with your child to make a time line to clarify the sequence of events.

R2.2 Analyze text that is organized in sequential or chronological order.

Main Idea and Details

- The **topic** is the overall subject of a piece of writing. The **main idea** of a selection is the most important idea about the topic of that selection. **Details** are small pieces of information that tell more about the main idea.

Directions Read the following passage. Then answer the questions below.

Sometimes a certain species of animal dies off naturally or through another cause, such as hunting by humans. In these cases, there will be an increase in the number of the animals that the dying species feeds on.

An example of this process can be seen in the relationship among wolves and panthers and deer. Wolves and panthers have largely disappeared from the United States. Consequently, their natural prey, deer, have multiplied. There are more deer in the country now than there were before colonists settled the land centuries ago. Because the deer population has become very large, herds of deer quickly eat up all the food in some areas. Of course, when food is lacking, the animals starve. Human beings can help an area recover its natural balance. In some cases, people introduce natural enemies into an area to control the numbers of the prey animal.

1. In one or two words, what is the topic of this passage?

_____

2. What is the main idea of the passage?

_____

3. What is one important detail that tells more about the main idea?

_____

_____

4. What is another detail that supports the main idea?

_____

_____

5. Identify the text structure used in each paragraph of this article.

_____

_____

Home Activity Your child identified the main idea and supporting details of a nonfiction passage. Together, read a magazine article about another wild animal. Work together to identify the main idea and supporting details of the article.

R2.3 Discern main ideas and concepts presented in texts, identifying and assessing evidence that supports those ideas.

Comprehension **357**

Main Idea and Details

- The **topic** is the overall subject of a piece of writing. The **main idea** of a selection is the most important idea about the topic of that selection. **Details** are small pieces of information that tell more about the main idea.
- Sometimes the author states the main idea in a single sentence. When the author does not state the main idea, the reader must figure it out.

Directions Read the following passage. Then complete the diagram below.

Mari wondered why the numbers of some species swing up or down. Her science teacher explained that environment controls an animal's population size.

"Food, shelter, water, and space all have an effect," Mr. Gonzalez explained. "The animals' numbers are limited by whichever one of these is least available."

"But what about other animals?" Mari asked. "Don't they have an effect too?"

"Yes, that's the other part of the puzzle," said Mr. Gonzalez. "Enemies can cut down an animal's numbers. Some species are reduced because other animals are competing for the same food. Also, if there is a lack of prey for an animal, that animal's numbers will drop."

Main Idea

1. Animal numbers are determined by _____

↓

Details

2. One thing that limits an animal's numbers is availability of _____

3. Also limiting an animal's numbers is lack of _____

4. An animal's numbers will decline if others are _____

5. _____

Home Activity Your child identified the main idea and supporting details of a nonfiction passage. Work with your child to identify the main idea and supporting details of individual paragraphs in a magazine article about wild animals.

R2.3 Discern main ideas and concepts presented in texts, identifying and assessing evidence that supports those ideas.

Time Line

- A **time line** is a chart that shows a sequence of events. Usually a time line uses a bar divided into periods of time to show the order of events. Some time lines are read left to right, and others are read top to bottom.

- You can use a time line to show the time order of events in a nonfiction text. A time line can also show the order of events in a work of fiction.

- A time line may cover any length of time, such as a day or thousands of years. Pay attention to the title and labels on a time line.

Directions Read the following time line. Then answer the questions below.

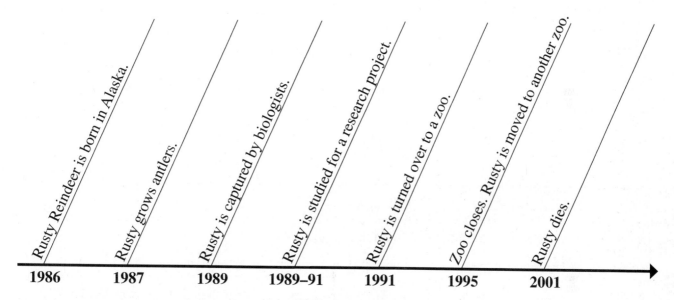

The Life of a Reindeer

1986   1987   1989   1989–91   1991   1995   2001

1. How is this time line organized? What is the topic of this time line?

_____

_____

2. How many years passed between Rusty's birth and his capture?

_____

3. How long was Rusty in zoos?

_____

4. How old was Rusty when he died?

_____

5. The average age of a reindeer in the wild is ten to twelve years. How does the time line help you draw a conclusion about Rusty's life span? Explain.

© Pearson Education, Inc., 5

R2.1 Understand how text features (e.g., format, graphics, sequence, diagrams, illustrations, charts, maps) make information accessible and usable.

Research and Study Skills   359

Name_____

Directions Read the following time line. Then answer the questions.

	History of the Plant That Grew Too Well
1876	Kudzu, a vine from Japan, arrives in U.S.
1900s	Florida farmers begin to feed kudzu to animals.
1930s	U.S. Soil Conservation Service urges use of kudzu to prevent erosion.
1930s	U.S. Civilian Conservation Corps plants kudzu.
1940s	Government pays farmers to plant kudzu.
1940s	Georgia radio personality starts Kudzu Clubs.
1953	Government discourages use of kudzu.
1972	Government declares kudzu a weed.
2004	Kudzu covers 6 million acres in South; people work to eliminate it.

6. What is the topic of this time line? What is the best way to read this time line?

_____

_____

7. Why is a time line appropriate for this topic?

_____

_____

8. When was kudzu first introduced to the United States?

_____

9. How long did it take for the U.S. government to declare kudzu a weed? When was kudzu planted most heavily?

_____

_____

_____

10. What happened with kudzu most recently, according to the time line?

_____

_____

School + Home

Home Activity Your child learned about using time lines as resources. Together, look at a time line in a history book. Ask your child to explain entries and to answer your questions about time order.

R2.1 Understand how text features (e.g., format, graphics, sequence, diagrams, illustrations, charts, maps) make information accessible and usable.

Family Times

King Midas and the Golden Touch

King Midas loves only one thing more than his gold: his daughter. When he is granted a magic wish, he wishes that all he touches turns to gold. He realizes the tragedy of this wish when he turns his daughter to gold. He is overjoyed when he can give up the golden touch and have his daughter back.

Activity

The Wish Game Imagine that you could have one wish granted. What would you wish for? See what your family members would wish for, and make a list. Talk about the consequences of each wish.

Comprehension Skill

Compare and Contrast

Compare and **Contrast** means to tell how two or more things are alike or different. Clue words such as *but*, *like*, *similarly*, and *as* show comparisons. Words such as *but*, *however*, and *instead* show differences.

Activity

Before and After With your family, choose some significant events in your life, such as entering school, starting lessons, making friends, or playing sports. Compare and contrast how things were alike and different for you before and after these milestones.

Lesson Vocabulary

Words to Know

Knowing the meanings of these words is important to reading *King Midas and the Golden Touch*. Practice using these words.

Vocabulary Words

adorn to add beauty to; put ornaments on; decorate

cleanse to make clean

lifeless without life

precious having great value; worth much

realm kingdom

spoonful as much as a spoon can hold

Grammar

Commas

A **comma** is a punctuation mark that indicates a short pause. A comma is used to set off or separate words or groups of words. Use a comma after a person's name when you directly address that person. *For example: Meg, come here.* Use commas to separate three or more words in a series. *For example: The blouse is blue, green, and pink.* Use commas to set off an appositive, which is an explanation placed next to a word. *For example: Our dog, a boxer, is named Pug.* In the example, *a boxer* is an appositive.

Activity

Comma Keeper Look in a newspaper to find sentences that use commas. Make a chart that shows examples of commas used for direct address, series, and appositives.

Practice Tested Spelling Words

Compare and Contrast

- Writers sometimes use **comparison** and **contrast** to organize their writing. Clue words such as *same, also, before, although,* and *however* signal comparisons and contrasts.
- Good readers notice the author's comparisons and contrasts and make their own as they read.

Directions Read the following passage. Then complete the diagram below.

Hillary and her family wanted to move to New York City because it seemed exciting compared to their quiet hometown. They saved money for a year to afford the move. When it was time to move, their friends gave them a big send-off party.

After they moved to New York, they enjoyed the energy of the crowds as they bustled down the streets. They visited museums with amazing collections of art and artifacts. They experimented with new foods from all over the world.

They were unprepared, however, for how expensive everything was. And even though they were surrounded by people, they found it hard to make friends. They were surprised, but sometimes they longed for the peace and quiet of their home town. Over time, they understood that their new home was a mixture of advantages and disadvantages.

| Advantages and Disadvantages of Moving to New York City ||
Advantages	Disadvantages
1.	3.
2.	4.

5. What prior knowledge do you have about the advantages and disadvantages of living in a big city helps you makes comparisons and contrasts?

_____

_____

School + Home **Home Activity** Your child read a short passage and made comparisons and contrasts. After reading a historical article, work with your child to compare and contrast something at two different points in time.

G4R2.1 Identify structural patterns found in informational text (e.g., compare and contrast, cause and effect, sequential or chronological order, proposition and support) to strengthen comprehension.

Comprehension 363

© Pearson Education, Inc., 5

Vocabulary

Directions Choose the word from the box that best matches each definition below. Write the word on the line.

_____ 1. to add beauty to;
put ornaments on

_____ 2. without life

_____ 3. as much as a spoon can hold

_____ 4. kingdom

_____ 5. to make clean

Check the Words You Know

____adorn
____cleanse
____lifeless
____precious
____realm
____spoonful

Directions Fill in the crossword puzzle using the clues below.

DOWN

6. to make pure
7. a king's empire
8. valuable

ACROSS

9. to decorate
10. without life

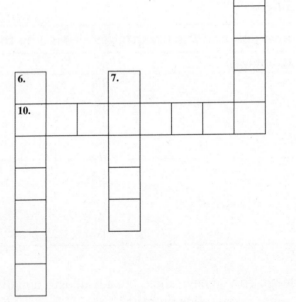

Write a Description

On a separate sheet of paper, write a short description of a king's castle. Use as many vocabulary words as you can.

Home Activity Your child identified and used vocabulary words from *King Midas and the Golden Touch.* Read a myth or fairy tale with your child. Ask your child to point out any of the vocabulary words he or she sees.

R1.0 Word Analysis, Fluency, and Systematic Vocabulary Development

Vocabulary • Suffixes

- A **suffix** is added to the end of a base word to change its meaning or the way it is used in a sentence.
- The suffix *-ful* can mean "full of _____," as in *careful,* or "an amount that fills something," as in *spoonful.* The suffix *-less* means "without," as in *harmless.*
- A dictionary is a book that helps us find the meanings of words we do not know.

Directions Read the following passage. Then answer the questions below. Use a dictionary to help you.

A wealthy king had all he could ask for except the one thing he needed most. His precious daughter was sick and lifeless. He sent out a message to all in his realm that he would give his fortune to anyone who could cure his daughter. In response, a penniless beggar came to the king's castle with a special potion. "If she takes a spoonful, she will improve," he said. Sure enough, with a spoonful she woke up, and with a cupful she was dancing around. As you might guess, the homeless beggar was well rewarded by the joyful king.

1. What is the base word in *lifeless?* How does the suffix help you understand its meaning?

_____

_____

2. What is the base word in *penniless?* How does the suffix help you understand its meaning?

_____

3. What is the base word in *homeless?* How does the suffix help you understand its meaning?

_____

4. Change the word *powerful* so that it has the opposite meaning. Find the meanings of both words in a dictionary.

_____

_____

5. How does the suffix in the word *joyful* help you understand its meaning?

_____

Home Activity Your child identified and used suffixes to understand new words of a passage. Work with your child to identify unfamiliar words in an article. Ask your child if any suffixes can help him or her understand the new words. Confirm the meanings using a dictionary.

R1.4 Know abstract, derived roots and affixes from Greek and Latin and use this knowledge to analyze the meaning of complex words (e.g., *controversial*).

Vocabulary 365

Draw Conclusions

Directions Read the following article. Then answer the questions below.

For months, Meg had been trying to talk her dad into getting a dog. She thought of so many good reasons that finally he gave in. Meg named her new puppy Hap, and she had a lot of fun playing with him all summer.

When her friends would call, she'd say she was too busy. From the time she got up in the morning until the time she went to bed, she was training and chasing Hap. When her friend Callie had a birthday party, Meg said she had to take care of her puppy. She ran home right after swim practice, even though her friends pleaded with her to hang out with them at the pool.

Once school started, though, it was a lot of trouble to run home right after school every day to walk Hap. Meg wanted to be with her friends instead. However, she felt lonely because she wasn't close to her friends anymore. They seemed to have moved on.

1. What conclusion can you draw about Meg based on how she gets her dog? Explain.

_____

_____

2. What conclusion can you draw about Meg during the summer?

_____

_____

3. What is a detail from the story that supports your conclusion?

_____

_____

4. What is another detail from the story that supports your conclusion?

_____

_____

5. What conclusion can you draw about Meg's friends? What details support your conclusion?

_____

_____

Home Activity Your child read a short passage and drew conclusions about its characters. Read a short story to your child. Ask him or her to draw conclusions about the main character.

R2.4 Draw inferences, conclusions, or generalizations about text and support them with textual evidence and prior knowledge.

Compare and Contrast

- Writers sometimes use **comparison** and **contrast** to organize their writing. Clue words such as *same, also, before, although,* and *however* signal comparisons and contrasts.
- Good readers notice the author's comparisons and contrasts and make their own as they read.

Directions Read the following passage. Then answer the questions below.

In every culture, certain qualities are considered precious. But these qualities might not be the same in every culture. Beauty, for example, is valued in many cultures. But what is considered beautiful in one culture may not be beautiful in others. Wealth is also valued in many cultures. But some cultures place a higher value on it than others. In the United States today, youth is greatly valued. Japan, China, and India treat their elders with honor and respect. The oldest members of a family have the highest status.

1. What qualities are being compared and contrasted in the passage?

_____

2. How do attitudes about old age compare in Japan, China, and India?

_____

_____

3. How do attitudes about old age in Japan, China, and India contrast with U.S. attitudes?

_____

_____

4. What is another quality that you might compare and contrast across cultures?

_____

_____

5. How does your prior knowledge about different cultures help you compare and contrast the qualities that those cultures find precious?

_____

_____

_____

Home Activity Your child read a short passage and identified comparisons and contrasts. Read a magazine article about a different culture. Work together with your child to identify some of the culture's values and compare them with your own.

G4R2.1 Identify structural patterns found in informational text (e.g., compare and contrast, cause and effect, sequential or chronological order, proposition and support) to strengthen comprehension.

© Pearson Education, Inc., 5

Compare and Contrast

- Writers sometimes use **comparison** and **contrast** to organize their writing. Clue words such as *same, also, before, although,* and *however* signal comparisons and contrasts.
- Good readers notice the author's comparisons and contrasts and make their own as they read.

Directions Read the following passage. Then complete the diagram below.

White gold and platinum are both metals used to make jewelry. They are both silver or white in color and therefore don't interfere with the color of gemstones. Even though they look similar to most people, they are different metals. White gold is made by mixing gold with other metals. It is very dense and is easily molded into jewelry. To appear truly white rather than gray, white gold is coated with rhodium, another white metal. White gold needs to be recoated after several years for it to continue looking white. Platinum is used for jewelry in almost pure form so it is heavier than white gold. It does not need to be coated to appear white. Platinum is more rare than gold and is two times more expensive than white gold.

Advantages and Disadvantages of Using White Gold for Jewelry Instead of Platinum	
Advantages	**Disadvantages**
White gold is less expensive than platinum.	**3.** White gold is not _____ _____
1. The color of white gold does not interfere _____	**4.** White gold needs to be _____ _____
2. White gold is easily _____ _____	**5.** White gold is less _____ _____

Home Activity Your child read a short passage and made comparisons and contrasts. Read an article about two different time periods or places. Work with your child to compare and contrast the two.

368 Comprehension

G4R2.1 Identify structural patterns found in informational text (e.g., compare and contrast, cause and effect, sequential or chronological order, proposition and support) to strengthen comprehension.

© Pearson Education, Inc., 5

Order Form/Application

Order forms and applications are charts with columns and spaces in which you can write or type. An order form is the means by which a person can purchase merchandise. An application is a form by which a person can apply for a job.

Directions Use this order form from an online catalog to answer the questions below.

GLITTER GOLD ORDER FORM
Click *SUBMIT* when you have completed this form.

Item Number	Item	Quantity	Price
13715	Big Bracelet		$
20166	Big Ring		$ + $5 shipping and handling
		TOTAL PRICE	$

Billing Address

* Name
* Street Address
* City
* State [   ] * ZIP
* Country
  Phone
* E-mail address

Shipping Address
☐ Check this box if same as billing address

* Name
* Street Address
* City
* State [   ] * ZIP
* Country
  Phone

PAYMENT METHOD
* Type of Credit Card _____
* Account Number _____
* Expiration Date _____

Your comments and messages here.

* REQUIRED FIELD

Submit

1. When would you fill out only one of the two address fields shown?

_____

2. If you are buying an item, what information do you need to specify on the order form?

_____

3. If you wish to submit an online order at Glitter Gold, what payment options do you have?

_____

4. How could you send comments to Glitter Gold?

_____

5. If you are ordering from this Web page, what information is optional?

_____

R2.1 Understand how text features (e.g., format, graphics, sequence, diagrams, illustrations, charts, maps) make information accessible and usable.

Name_____

Directions Use this online job application form to answer the questions below.

MIDAS MINING CO. EMPLOYMENT APPLICATION
Click *SUBMIT* when you have completed this form.

PERSONAL INFORMATION

Last Name	First Name	Middle Initial
Address	City	State/ZIP
Phone Number	E-mail Address	Social Security No.
Position Applied For	Full-Time/Part-Time	Date Available to Start

EDUCATION

High School	Address	Graduated
College	Address	Graduated

WORK EXPERIENCE

Current Employer	Address	Duties	Start/End Dates
Employer Name	Address	Duties	Start/End Dates

OTHER SKILLS

REFERENCES

Name	Address	Phone	Relationship

SUBMIT

6. What is the purpose of this form?

_____

7. What is the first piece of information you need to provide on this form?

_____

8. In what section would you say when you could start working?

_____

9. What are three of the five main sections of the application?

_____

10. What directions are given on this form?

_____

Home Activity Your child learned about filling out order forms and applications. Look at an order form or application together. Discuss how to fill it out.

G4W1.7 Use various reference materials (e.g., dictionary, thesaurus, card catalog, encyclopedia, online information) as an aid to writing.

Family Times

Summary

The *Hindenburg*

Hugo Eckener was intent on developing dirigibles, and his *Hindenburg* was the largest one ever. In fact, it was the largest object ever to fly. In 1937, the *Hindenburg* exploded over New Jersey during its tenth transatlantic flight, and thirty-one people died. Instantly, the era of the dirigible ended.

Activity

Surprises Compare notes with your family about unexpected events in the news. Discuss how to plan for the unexpected.

Comprehension Skill

Categorize and Classify

To **categorize and classify** is to arrange, describe, or label things based on behaviors, features, or relationships. As you read, you may notice that members of the same categories or classes may be compared to other members using words such as *similarly* and *like* or contrasted with members of different groups using words such as *however, unlike,* or *instead.*

Activity

Facts You Can Use In a local newspaper, find a list of events that will take place in the near future, such as a circus or a town meeting. With a family member, make a list of those that might be fun for children, those that would be enjoyed by adults, and others that would be fun for the whole family.

Lesson Vocabulary

Words to Know

Knowing the meanings of these words is important to reading *The Hindenburg*. Practice using these words.

Vocabulary Words

criticizing finding fault with; disapproving of; blaming

cruised traveled at the speed at which the vehicle operates best

drenching wetting thoroughly; soaking

era a period of time or history

explosion act of bursting with a loud noise; a blowing up

hydrogen a colorless, odorless gas that burns easily

Conventions

Quotations and Quotation Marks

A **quotation** is the exact words a speaker says. In your writing, put a quotation in **quotation marks.** Use commas to set off the words that introduce a quotation. Also, place the end punctuation or the comma that ends the quotation inside the quotation marks. *For example: Sandy said, "If it rains tomorrow, we can't go to the beach." "I'll keep my fingers crossed then," said Kate.*

Activity

Quote Me Make a chart with two columns. In the left column, write down questions you will ask your family members, such as *Whom do you most admire?* or *What is your biggest strength?* In the right column, record their answers. Be sure to put quotation marks around the words they say.

Practice Tested Spelling Words

_____ _____ _____ _____

_____ _____ _____ _____

_____ _____ _____ _____

_____ _____ _____ _____

Categorize and Classify

- To **categorize and classify** is to arrange, describe, or label things based on behaviors, features, or relationships.
- Members of the same categories or classes may be compared to other members using words such as *similarly* and *like* or contrasted with members of other categories and classes with words such as *however, unlike,* or *instead.*

Directions Read the following passage. Then answer the questions below.

Mike's grandmother, Millie, had never flown in an airplane. In an era when it seemed that everyone traveled by plane, Mike's grandmother never had. She preferred slower ways of traveling, such as by train, bus, or car. For fun, she sometimes enjoyed trips on a cruise ship or on a sailboat. But Millie didn't want to spend all of her vacation time traveling back and forth. She wanted to spend time with her family, so she finally decided to try flying.

As the plane cruised high above the ground, Millie was making new friends and enjoying her view from the little window. When Mike and his family met her at the airport, she told him she now thought that flying was the most comfortable and safest way to travel. She said she wanted to make another trip by plane very soon.

1. Mike's grandmother traveled by airplane. What other categories of travel are mentioned in the story?

_____

2. How many trips had she made by airplane before she visited Mike?

_____

3. If Mike's grandmother had taken a slower form of transportation, what might the result have been?

_____

_____

4. What category of transportation did Millie use for fun?

_____

5. What did Mike's grandmother decide about the category of air travel?

_____

_____

Home Activity Your child categorized and classified information in a short passage. Together, discuss the types of transportation that are available in your area. Categorize them in ways that are important to you based on different reasons and make a list of the types of travel you would do using each.

R2.3 Discern main ideas and concepts presented in texts, identifying and assessing evidence that supports those ideas.

Vocabulary

Directions Choose the word from the box that best matches each definition. Write the word on the line.

_____ 1. finding fault with; disapproving of; blaming

_____ 2. act of bursting with a loud noise; a blowing up

_____ 3. wetting thoroughly; soaking

_____ 4. a period of time or history

_____ 5. traveled at the speed at which the vehicle operates best

Check the Words You Know

___criticizing
___cruised
___drenching
___era
___explosion
___hydrogen

Directions Choose the word from the box that best matches each clue. Write the word on the line.

_____ 6. This is said of extremely heavy rain.

_____ 7. An example of this is the colonial period or the Middle Ages.

_____ 8. A bomb could make this happen.

_____ 9. This element combines with oxygen to make water.

_____ 10. This describes how a ship might have moved along the water.

Write an E-mail Message

On a separate sheet of paper, write an e-mail message you might send from a ship after witnessing the eruption of a volcano. Use as many vocabulary words as you can.

Home Activity Your child identified and used vocabulary words from *The Hindenburg*. Read a story or nonfiction article with your child. Have him or her point out unfamiliar words. Work together to try to figure out the meaning of each word by using other words that appear near it.

R1.0 Word Analysis, Fluency, and Systematic Vocabulary Development

Vocabulary • Unfamiliar Words

- When you see an **unfamiliar word** while reading, use context clues, or words around the unfamiliar word, to figure out its meaning.
- Context clues include definitions, explanations, and synonyms (words that have the same or nearly the same meaning as other words).

Directions Read the following passage. Then answer the questions below.

In the early 1900s, many people were criticizing the Wright brothers for trying to make a flying machine. These people accused the Wright brothers of trying to do something humans were not meant to do. However, the brothers kept working on their invention, even in drenching, soaking rain. In 1903, they finally created an airplane with a propeller and a gas engine. They controlled the speed of the aircraft by increasing or decreasing the spark in the engine. This caused an explosion, or bursting, of fuel that drove the propeller. When they finally got a propeller-driven machine into the air, they cruised at a very slow speed, traveling at only about one mile an hour. Still, the Wright brothers' plane opened up a whole new era of transportation, the age of the airplane.

1. What does *criticizing* mean? What clues help you to determine its meaning?

_____

_____

2. What does *drenching* mean? What clue helps you determine the meaning?

_____

3. What clue helps you to determine the meaning of *explosion*? What does this word mean?

_____

_____

4. What context clue helps you determine the meaning of *cruised*?

_____

5. What does *era* mean? How can you use context clues to determine the meaning?

_____

_____

Home Activity Your child identified and used context clues to understand new words in a nonfiction passage. Work with your child to identify unfamiliar words in another article. Then have him or her find context clues to help with understanding the new words. Confirm the meanings with the glossary in the back of your book or a dictionary.

G3R1.6 Use sentence and word context to find the meaning of unknown words.

Main Idea and Details

Directions Read the following passage. Then answer the questions below.

Rail travel was very popular during the 1920s and 1930s, but later it was replaced by automobiles and airplanes as the leading form of transportation. At the peak of rail travel in 1920, 1.2 billion passengers rode trains. During the 1930s, sleek, streamlined trains were developed, and these grew very popular. During World War II, trains were used extensively to carry soldiers and military equipment. At the end of the war, two-thirds of paying passengers were traveling by train.

However, during the next twenty years, the use of trains fell off. Cars, which had been around since the beginning of the century, became the top choice for going from one place to another. At the same time, the use of airplanes grew for long-distance travel. By the 1950s, more people were traveling by air than by train. Trains were viewed as old-fashioned.

1. In one or two words, what is the topic of this passage?

_____

2. What is the main idea of this passage?

_____

_____

3. What is one detail that supports the main idea?

_____

_____

4. What is another detail that supports the main idea?

_____

_____

5. On a separate sheet of paper, write a summary of this article.

© Pearson Education, Inc., 5

School + Home **Home Activity** Your child identified the main idea and supporting details in a nonfiction passage. Together, read a short nonfiction article about a topic that interests both of you. Work with your child to state the main idea and to identify supporting details.

Categorize and Classify

- To **categorize and classify** is to arrange, describe, or label things based on behaviors, features, or relationships.
- Members of the same categories or classes may be compared to other members using words such as *similarly* and *like* or contrasted with members of other categories and classes with words such as *however*, *unlike*, or *instead*.

Directions Read the following passage. Then answer the questions below.

In preparing for a long car trip, there are a number of things you can do to be sure it is a safe trip. The car should be serviced, meaning tires may need to be inflated and windshield wipers replaced. Fluids, such as engine oil, gasoline, and coolant, may need to be changed or filled.

For safety and comfort, you could pack a first-aid kit and water and snacks. For cold weather, warm clothing and blankets are extra protection. Maps and instructions help drivers navigate. Time passes more quickly for children if they have books or games to play alone or with other children or adults.

Ways to Prepare Before Taking a Trip

1. What fluids does a car use to operate?

_____

2. What kinds of activities are good for children while traveling by car?

_____

3. What kind of protection is good for cold weather?

_____

4. What other safety preparations belong in the category of auto service?

_____

5. What three items could be packed in the car for comfort and safety?

_____

Home Activity Your child learned what it means to categorize and classify by reading a brief article. Together, make a list that categorizes the preparations you make in other areas of your life such as meals, holidays, or household chores.

R2.3 Discern main ideas and concepts presented in texts, identifying and assessing evidence that supports those ideas.

Comprehension 377

© Pearson Education, Inc., 5

Name_____

Categorize and Classify

- To **categorize and classify** is to arrange, describe, or label things based on behaviors, features, or relationships.
- Members of the same categories or classes may be compared to other members using words such as *similarly* and *like* or contrasted with members of other categories and classes with words such as *however, unlike,* or *instead.*

Directions Read the following passage. Then answer the questions below.

Before the invention of air travel, mass transportation over land meant trains. Furnaces that burned coal or wood typically powered the first trains. The heat from the furnaces boiled water, and the steam it produced drove the engines.

As technology progressed, trains evolved. Diesel fuel replaced steam. Cities like San Francisco placed narrow tracks in streets, so trolleys cars could transport passengers up and down hills.

Power came from electrical wires overhead. Electricity also powered the underground subway trains that still rumble on rails below Boston and New York. Some train technology never caught on. Monorails, trains that ride one rail instead of two, though still popular at Disneyland, never became widely used. It seems the public chose to buy automobiles instead of building more rails.

1. What fuels fall into the category "energy sources used in trains"?

_____

2. What class of transportation do personal automobiles compete against?

_____

3. What classification might describe the cities of Boston, New York, and San Francisco?

_____

4. Into what smaller category within the category of trains might monorails fit?

_____

5. What types of transportation do not require coal, wood, or diesel fuel?

_____

 Home Activity Your child learned what it means to categorize and classify by reading a brief article. Together, think about the categories of work that require constant travel. List the types of jobs and the types of transportation that are involved.

R2.3 Discern main ideas and concepts presented in texts, identifying and assessing evidence that supports those ideas.

Map/Globe/Atlas

- A **map** is a drawing of a place that shows where something is or where something happened. You may see different kinds of maps. These include picture maps, road maps, political maps, physical maps, and special-purpose maps. Look carefully at a map's **legend,** or key. It explains any symbols used in the map. It also shows directions as well as a scale of distance.
- An **atlas** is a book of maps.
- A **globe** is a sphere with a map of the world on it. Because the Earth is round, globes give a more accurate picture of the size and shape of the Earth than flat maps do.

Directions Study the following map. Then use the map to answer the questions below.

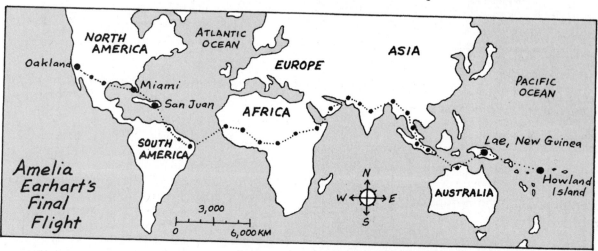

1. On May 20, 1937, Amelia Earhart took off on an airplane flight that she hoped would make her the first person to fly around the world. She began in Oakland, California. What was her last stop in the United States?

_____

2. Where did she land next?

_____

3. About how far was her flight across the United States? How do you know?

_____

_____

4. On which continents did she land along the way to Lae, New Guinea?

_____

5. On July 1, 1937, Amelia Earhart left Lae, New Guinea. What was her next intended stop? How far is this place from New Guinea?

_____

_____

R2.1 Understand how text features (e.g., format, graphics, sequence, diagrams, illustrations, charts, maps) make information accessible and usable.

Directions Study the following map. Then use the map to answer the questions below.

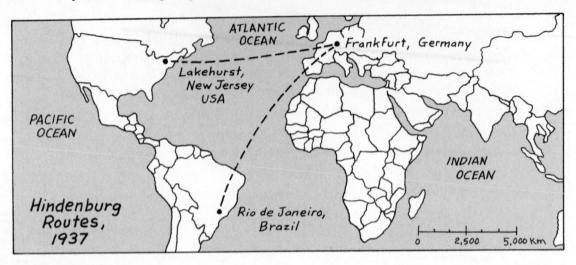

6. The *Hindenburg* was a German airship that flew passengers during the 1930s. What does this map show? How do you know?

_____

_____

7. From what city in Europe did the *Hindenburg* fly? Across what body of water did the *Hindenburg* fly?

_____

_____

8. According to the map, what were the *Hindenburg*'s two destinations in 1937?

_____

_____

9. What was the approximate distance of the route to each of these destinations?

_____

_____

10. Is this map similar to a globe? Which term would you use to describe this map—a road map, a political map that shows the borders of countries, or a physical map that shows elevations and other details of the land?

_____

_____

Home Activity Your child learned about using maps as resources. Look at a road map together. Ask your child to determine distances and plot out routes to destinations you specify.

W1.3 Use organizational features of printed text (e.g., citations, end notes, bibliographic references) to locate relevant information.

Family Times

Summary

Sweet Music in Harlem

C.J. wants to play jazz like Uncle Click, who's being photographed for a magazine. As C.J. tries to find Uncle Click's hat, he gathers lots of people to be in the photo with Click. To cap off the day, Uncle Click gives C.J. a new clarinet, and they even find Click's hat. Click is C.J.'s biggest fan.

Activity

Meeting the Music What kind of music do you like? Talk with your family members about the music each of them likes and why. See if there is any type of music that you all like.

Comprehension Skill

Theme/Setting

• **Theme** is the big idea of a selection.

• **Setting** is the time, place, and environmental conditions in which the events in a story or poem occur.

Activity

Time It With the members of your family, take turns telling your favorite stories. Discuss the stories' themes and settings.

Words to Know

Knowing the meanings of these words is important to reading *Sweet Music in Harlem*. Practice using these words.

Vocabulary Words

bass the largest, lowest sounding stringed instrument in an orchestra or band

clarinet a woodwind instrument, having a mouthpiece with a single reed and played by means of holes and keys

fidgety restless; uneasy

forgetful apt to forget; having a poor memory

jammed made music with other musicians without having practiced

nighttime time between evening and morning

secondhand not new; used already by someone else

Conventions

Punctuation

Use a **semicolon** to join the parts of a compound sentence when no conjunction is used. *For example: Rob pitched; Denise caught.* Use a **colon** to introduce a list. *For example: He played the following sports: baseball, soccer, and tennis.* Use a **hyphen** in compound nouns, such as *great-uncle*, and compound adjectives before a noun, such as *out-of-town guests*. Use **parentheses** for words inserted as a comment. *For example: Ken (a musician) played at the wedding.*

Activity

Wait, Punctuate! Make a chart on a large sheet of paper. Make four boxes in the chart and label them "Semicolons," "Colons," "Hyphens," and "Parentheses." Find a magazine that is OK to cut up. Find sentences that use the four punctuation marks. Cut out the sentences and glue them on the chart.

Practice Tested Spelling Words

Theme/Setting

- **Theme** is the big idea of a selection.
- **Setting** is the time and place the events in a story or poem occur.

Directions Read the following passage. Then answer the questions below.

Will was nervous about playing the clarinet at the school concert. He didn't enjoy being "new" at anything. He liked to feel he was an expert, but learning the clarinet proved to be very different from other things he had tried, like learning to ice skate. In one afternoon Will was flying around the skating rink, but after five months of clarinet lessons, in the drafty school auditorium, he still felt nervous. What if he played at the wrong time or forgot some of the notes? When the time came for his solo, as Will felt the heat of the stage lights, he began to play. Soon he forgot there was anyone watching him. He just felt good about the music. He felt even better when he finished and heard the applause.

1. What is the theme, or big idea, in this story?

_____

_____

2. What was Will trying to do?

_____

_____

3. What is the location, or the setting, of the story?

_____

_____

4. What are the environmental conditions of the setting of the story?

_____

_____

_____

Home Activity Your child learned the meaning of *theme* by reading a short story. Together with your child, write two or more short stories that have the same theme.

R3.4 Understand that *theme* refers to the meaning or moral of a selection and recognize themes (whether implied or stated directly) in sample works.

Vocabulary

Directions Choose the word from the box that best matches each definition below. Write the word on the line.

_____ 1. not new; used already by someone else

_____ 2. made music with other musicians without having practiced

_____ 3. restless; uneasy

_____ 4. the largest, lowest sounding stringed instrument in an orchestra or band

_____ 5. apt to forget; having a poor memory

> ### Check the Words You Know
>
> ____bass
> ____clarinet
> ____fidgety
> ____forgetful
> ____jammed
> ____nighttime
> ____secondhand

Directions Choose the word from the box that best completes each sentence below. Write the word on the line shown to the left.

_____ 6. The trio of jazz musicians _____ together.

_____ 7. They met during the _____ after working all day.

_____ 8. One musician played both a trumpet and a stringed _____.

_____ 9. Another musician played the _____, a favorite woodwind.

_____ 10. The third musician's instrument was an old _____ saxophone.

Write a Review

On a separate sheet of paper, write a review you might compose after you go to a music concert or performance. Use as many vocabulary words as you can.

Home Activity Your child identified and used vocabulary words from *Sweet Music in Harlem*. Read a story or nonfiction article with your child. Have him or her point out unfamiliar words. Work together to try to figure out the meaning of each word by using other words that appear near it.

R1.0 Word Analysis, Fluency, and Systematic Vocabulary Development

© Pearson Education, Inc., 5

Vocabulary · Homographs

- When you are reading, you might see a **homograph**. Homographs are words that are spelled the same but have different meanings and sometimes different pronunciations. For example, *object* can mean both "to protest" and "a thing."
- Use context clues, or words around the unfamiliar word, to figure out its meaning. Context clues include definitions, explanations, and synonyms.
- A dictionary is a book to help you find words you do not know.

Directions Read the following passage about jazz music. Then answer the questions below.

> Jeb played bass in a jazz quartet. Along with his low-sounding stringed instrument, the group also had a clarinet, a trombone, and a piano. Every night when the group jammed, or made music without practicing, they would attract interest. Soon a crowd would gather. Usually they'd get so deeply involved in the music that they'd get forgetful of the time. Before they realized it, instead of nighttime it would be close to daytime.

1. *Bass* can refer to a musical instrument or a fish. What clues help you to determine the meaning in this passage?

_____

_____

2. In this context, is *jam* a noun referring to a fruit spread or a verb referring to playing music without practicing? What clues help you to determine the meaning?

_____

_____

3. Use one of the homographs in the passage twice in a sentence, showing both its meanings.

_____

4. Which meaning of the homograph *close* is used in the last sentence: "shut" or "near to"?

_____

5. *Interest* can mean "a feeling of concern or curiosity" or "money paid for the use of money." How do context clues indicate its meaning in the passage?

_____

_____

Home Activity Your child identified and used context clues to understand homographs in a passage. Work with your child to identify homographs in an article. Then your child can find context clues to help with the understanding of the new words. Confirm the meanings with your child.

R1.3 Understand and explain frequently used synonyms, antonyms, and homographs.

Vocabulary 385

Draw Conclusions

Directions Read the story. Then answer the questions below.

Throughout Harlem, Danielle was known as the little girl with the big horn. Saxophone was her instrument, and she tried to imitate Charlie Parker, John Coltrane, and Kenny Garrett. When she practiced jazz on an old secondhand sax, the neighbors hung out of their windows to listen.

"You have talent," her music teacher told her as she gave her an extra lesson at no charge.

No one had to encourage Danielle.

She practiced any time she had a chance. Then disaster hit. Her saxophone broke. She took it to her uncle, who fixed instruments, but he told her that he could not repair it. The price of a new instrument was way beyond her reach. She was disappointed. The neighbors were also disappointed when the music stopped. A few weeks later, on Danielle's birthday, the neighbors pitched in and presented her with a gift—a secondhand sax! She wrote a song to thank them.

1. How skilled do you think Danielle is at the saxophone? Explain why.

_____

_____

2. What can you tell about the community Danielle lives in? Explain.

_____

_____

3. What do you think Danielle's attitude is toward playing the saxophone?

_____

_____

4. Why do you think the music teacher gives Danielle a free lesson and tells her she has talent?

_____

_____

5. On a separate sheet of paper, explain how you think Danielle feels when she receives the saxophone. What effect do you think the gift will have on her and why?

Home Activity Your child has read a story about playing the saxophone and drawn conclusions about the characters. Read a short story to your child. Challenge him or her to identify the characters' traits and motives.

© Pearson Education, Inc., 5

R2.4 Draw inferences, conclusions, or generalizations about text and support them with textural evidence and prior knowledge.

Theme/Setting

- **Theme** is the big idea of a selection.
- **Setting** is the time and place the events in a story or poem occur.

Directions Read the following passage. Then answer the questions below.

Tamara loved to play the trumpet, and she wanted to play like the jazz greats she heard on the radio. Then one day at the end of the summer her family was invited to a weekend reception at a club in Harlem where Miles Davis, a famous jazz musician, was playing. Overjoyed, she and her family went to the party, bringing her beloved trumpet in case she could get it autographed. The club was small and overcrowded. Tamara waited for what seemed like hours. Finally Miles Davis played and she and all the other club goers fell completely silent and listened to his beautiful music. At the end of his performance Mr. Davis asked if there was anyone in the audience who wanted to come onstage and play with him. And who do you think grabbed her trumpet and jumped up on the stage?

1. What is the location of the story's setting?

_____

2. When does the story take place?

_____

3. What are the environmental conditions of the setting?

_____

_____

4. What is unusual about the setting for the story?

_____

_____

5. What is the theme of the story?

_____

_____

Home Activity Your child learned the meaning of *setting* by reading a short story. Together with your child, choose one room in your house and list all the different activities that it can be used for.

R3.4 Understand that *theme* refers to the meaning or moral of a selection and recognize themes (whether implied or stated directly) in sample works.

Theme/Setting

- **Theme** is the big idea of a selection.
- **Setting** is the time and place the events in a story or poem occur.

Directions Read the following passage. Then answer the questions below.

Three friends got together at Ken's garage. They wanted to play music but didn't have any instruments. "We have a garbage can," said Ken, who held the garbage can upside down and tapped on the side with his drumsticks. "Now the garbage can is a drum," he said. Seeing Ken's drum inspired Jason to rake a big stick along the spokes of his bicycle. "Listen. My bicycle wheel sounds like a strange harp," Jason said. Carin made a cigar box guitar from a box, stick, and wire. Now the three friends had three instruments to play, using cans, boxes, and bicycle wheels. They began to make beautiful, strange music together.

1. What is the setting of this story?

_____

_____

2. What is the theme?

_____

_____

3. What instrument did Ken make?

_____

_____

4. How did Jason use his bike to make music?

_____

_____

5. How did Carin make a guitar?

_____

_____

© Pearson Education, Inc., 5

Home Activity Your child learned the meanings of *theme* and *setting* by reading a short story. Together with your child, read a few short stories with different settings and discuss what types of words authors use to describe settings.

R3.4 Understand that *theme* refers to the meaning or moral of a selection and recognize themes (whether implied or stated directly) in sample works.

Poster/Announcement

- **Posters** and **announcements** announce events. The events may be one time only, or they may be continuing, as with club and organization meetings.
- Usually, posters and announcements answer these questions: Who? What? When? Where? Why?
- To emphasize information, posters and announcements may use color and large type size.
- When you write a poster or announcement, include only important information.

Directions Use this poster to answer the questions.

Who is performing at this event? Who is sponsoring the event?	1.
What is the event? What is the cost?	2.
When is the event?	3.
Where is the event?	4.
Why is the event being held?	5.

R2.1 Understand how text features (e.g., format, graphics, sequence, diagrams, illustrations, charts, maps) make information accessible and usable.

Research and Study Skills 389

Directions Use this announcement to answer the questions.

JOIN TODAY!

Armstrong School
Junior
Jazz Club

This organization is dedicated to
the appreciation of jazz music.
Guest speakers, refreshments, and lots
of music are all part of the fun!

Come and bring your instrument!

Room 201
3:30 p.m. Every Tuesday

---

6. What is the purpose of this announcement?

_____

7. What is the event? Why do you think the event takes place?

_____

_____

8. When and where does the event take place?

_____

9. What does this announcement emphasize? How and why is this emphasis made?

_____

_____

10. On a separate sheet of paper, write an announcement for a school event.

Home Activity Your child learned about reading posters. Point out a poster to your child, and ask him or her how the poster answers these questions about the event it announces: Who? What? When? Where? Why? Talk about how to compose a poster for a school or community event.

W1.3 Use organizational features of printed text (e.g., citations, end notes, bibliographic references) to locate relevant information.

Family Times

Selection Summaries

Week 1 *Inside Out*

The son of migrant workers, Francisco struggles to fit in at school.

Week 2 *The Mystery of Saint Matthew Island*

After the 1,000-member herd of reindeer disappears, a scientist sets out to find out why.

Week 3 *King Midas and the Golden Touch*

When the king gets to wish for anything he wants, his choice leads to despair.

Week 4 *The Hindenburg*

Hugo Eckener built the largest flying object ever, but when the dirigible exploded, an era ended.

Week 5 *Sweet Music in Harlem*

C.J. wants to play jazz like his Uncle Click, who is being photographed for a magazine. The photo shoot leads to unexpected results.

Activity

Where do stories come from? Discuss with a family member how you think the authors of these selections got their ideas.

Comprehension Skills Review

In Unit 6, you learned and used many skills while reading the stories and selections.

- Grouping items by similar traits is called **classifying** or **categorizing** them.
- The **main idea** of a text is what it is mostly about. **Details** support and expand on the main idea.
- When you **compare** two things, you tell how they are alike. When you **contrast** them, you tell how they are different.

- **Theme** is the "big idea" that holds the entire story together. **Setting** is where and when the story takes place.

Activity

Some unexpected developments can be unpleasant, like a sudden storm, or delightful, like a surprise party. Try writing your own story about an expected event, pleasant or not.

Unit Vocabulary Skills

Prefixes

A **prefix** is attached to the front of a word to create a new word.

Activity As you read a selection, list words that begin with prefixes, and check their base words in the dictionary.

Suffixes

A **suffix** is attached to the end of a word to create a new word. Dictionaries often list common suffixes.

Activity When you find a word with a suffix, break off the suffix. How does the suffix change the meaning of the base word?

Unfamiliar Words

When you come across an **unfamiliar word**, use context clues to help you figure out the word's meaning.

Activity As you read, list unfamiliar words and the meanings you devised based on context clues.

Homographs

Homographs are words that are spelled the same but have different meanings or pronunciations.

Activity Brainstorm homographs and try using them in sentences. Use a dictionary to find other homographs.

Unit Spelling Rules

Suffixes -ous, -sion, -ion, -ation

When adding these suffixes, some base words change. A final *e* or *y* may be dropped: *fam<u>ous</u>, furi<u>ous</u>*. Some words have other changes: *deci<u>sion</u>*.

Final Syllable -ant, -ent, -ance, -ence

There is no sound clue to help you decide whether to use an *a* or an *e* in these word endings. The schwa sound in the endings can be spelled in different ways.

Words with ei and ie

Long *e* can be spelled *ei* or *ie*: *beli<u>e</u>ve, rec<u>ei</u>ve*. These are only two of the many ways to spell long *e*.

Compound Words

Some compound words are closed: *keyboard, textbook*. Others are open: *ice cream, a lot*. There are no clues that tell whether a compound word will be open or closed, so it is important to study these words carefully.

Easily Confused Words

Some words are easily confused because they have similar pronunciations and spellings: *quiet, quite*. It is important to study these words and to pay close attention to the way each is spelled and pronounced.

⊙ Prefixes

un	+	certain	=	not certain
dis	+	agree	=	not to agree

A **prefix** is attached to the front of a word to create a new word with a different meaning.

Practice

Read the following sentences. Fill in the blanks with one of the Words to Know. Then choose the definition that best matches the underlined word.

Words To Know
caterpillar
cocoon
disrespect
emerge
migrant
sketched
unscrewed

1. Mrs. Olafsson had always wanted to watch the

   _____ butterflies, but she was <u>unable</u> to see them
   from her home.

   a. not able   b. easily able

2. In her garden, she <u>unexpectedly</u> discovered a _____

   making its _____ on a leafy twig.

   a. in a way that is not expected   b. in a way that is later than expected

3. Afraid her neighbor might damage the cocoon out of _____, she carefully
   <u>unattached</u> the twig and placed it in a jar.

   a. took something off where it was attached   b. attached something again in a new place

4. The leaves she put in the jar having gone <u>uneaten</u>, Mrs. Olafsson _____ the

   butterfly as it began to _____ from the cocoon.

   a. quickly eaten   b. not eaten

5. Mrs. Olafsson wanted the butterfly to stay around, but apparently it <u>disagreed</u>—it took off as soon

   as she _____ the lid of the jar.

   a. did not agree   b. wanted to agree

On Your Own

As you read "The Comet Racer," use what you know about prefixes.

Home Activity Your child studied prefixes. See who can come up with the most words that begin with the prefixes *un-* and *dis-*, using the dictionary to answer any questions.

G3R1.8 Use knowledge of prefixes (e.g., *un-, re-, pre-, bi-, mis-, dis-*) and suffixes (e.g., *-er, -est, -ful*) to determine the meaning of words.

Vocabulary 393

⊙ Categorize and Classify

Grouping items by similar traits is called **classifying** and **categorizing**.

Practice

spider	horse	cat	parakeet	ladybug

Look at the illustrations. Use them to answer the questions below.

1. Which animals would be part of the category "Animals that Fly"?

_____

2. Which animals would be part of the category "Animals People Keep as House Pets"?

_____

3. Which animals would be part of the category "Animals with More Than Four Legs"?

_____

4. Which animals would be part of the category "Animals with Fur"?

_____

On Your Own

Use what you know about categorizing and classifying as you read "The Comet Racer." Write two classifications you read about in this passage.

© Pearson Education, Inc., 5

Home Activity Your child reviewed categorizing and classifying. Together, think of different ways to classify books, music, or games in your home.

Name _____

⊙ Suffixes

carcass	+	-es	=	carcasses
parasite	+	-s	=	parasites
bleach	+	-ed	=	bleached

A **suffix** is attached to the end of a word to create a new word with a new meaning. If you are unsure about the meaning of a word with a suffix, check the dictionary.

Practice

Read the following sentences. Fill in the blanks using the Words to Know. Circle the letter of the meaning of the underlined word. Use a dictionary to help you.

Words To Know

bleached
carcasses
decay
parasites
scrawny
starvation
suspicions
tundra

1. After finding the _____ of two sheep, the farmer

   has his _____ about what caused their <u>deaths</u>.

   a. one sudden death   b. more than one death

2. Because one sheep was noticeably _____, the

   farmer <u>decided</u> that _____ had caused the sheep's

   _____.

   a. is making a decision about something   b. made a decision about something

3. The farmer expressed his <u>concerns</u> about raising sheep to his wife, who had always thought that

   they lived too close to the _____ for the sheep to thrive.

   a. more than one concern   b. one very important concern

4. Because their barn had been _____ by the sun and the cabin was beginning to

   _____, they finally took the sheep and <u>moved</u> south.

   a. will be going somewhere   b. went somewhere

On Your Own

As you read "Dirty Snowballs," look for words that include suffixes, and check their meanings in the dictionary. Make a list of these new words.

Home Activity Your child reviewed suffixes. Together, make a list of words from a book or a magazine article that contain the endings -s, -es, -ed, and -ing. Then write new sentences using those words.

G3R1.8 Use knowledge of prefixes (e.g., *un-, re-, pre-, bi-, mis-, dis-*) and suffixes (e.g., *-er, -est, -ful*) to determine the meaning of words.

⊙ Main Idea

The **main idea** of a text is what it is mostly about. Details support and expand on the main idea.

Despite the cold of the tundra, it is home to a variety of wildlife. Large herbivores, or plant-eaters, such as caribou and musk-ox, live in herds. Smaller plant-eaters, such as mice, shrews, and hares, live here too. The predators of the tundra include wolves, bears, foxes, and wolverines. No matter whether predator or prey, nearly all these animals suffer from the biting insects, such as mosquitoes, black flies, and deer flies.

Practice

Read the passage and answer the questions.

1. What is the main idea of the passage?

_____

_____

2. What details support the main idea?

_____

_____

_____

3. Which of the following sentences would also support the main idea?

   a. Birds such as snowy owls, ducks, and geese also find a home in the tundra.

   b. The tundra becomes very cold during the winter.

On Your Own

Use what you know about main idea as you read "Dirty Snowballs." List details in the passage that support the main idea.

© Pearson Education, Inc., 5

Home Activity Your child reviewed main idea. Together, read a newspaper article and look for the main idea.

R2.3 Discern main ideas and concepts presented in texts, identifying and assessing evidence that supports those ideas.

Name _____

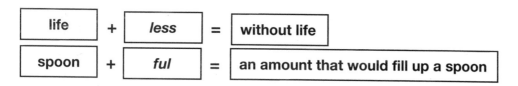

⊙ Suffixes

life	+	*less*	=	without life

spoon	+	*ful*	=	an amount that would fill up a spoon

A **suffix** is attached to the end of a word to create a new word with a new meaning. If you are unsure about the meaning of a word with a suffix, check the dictionary.

Practice

Fill in the blanks with Words to Know. Then circle the letter of the meaning of the underlined word that contains a suffix. Use what you know about the suffixes *-ful* and *-less* to help you.

Words To Know

adorn
cleanse
lifeless
precious
realm
spoonful

1. My mother declared that we were going to spend a <u>peaceful</u>

   afternoon at home, during which we would _____
   every inch of it.

   a. filled with peace   b. without peace

2. After I realized it was <u>hopeless</u> to try to change her mind, she declared that the living room was

   my _____.

   a. having strong hope of success   b. having no hope of success

3. I grabbed a mop and poured a large _____ of detergent in a bucket. I was
   <u>ceaseless</u> in my scrubbing and sweeping, and soon the room was so clean and empty that it

   looked almost _____.

   a. without stopping or ceasing   b. getting ready to stop or cease

4. "Looks like you got a bit carried away," Mom said, as she <u>successfully</u> used a few

   _____ objects to _____ the bare room.

   a. with great success   b. without much success

On Your Own

As you read "The Comet Racer," make a list of words with suffixes. Write sentences for these new words.

Home Activity Your child reviewed suffixes. Together, play a game of adding suffixes to different words to see how their meanings change.

G3R1.8 Use knowledge of prefixes (e.g., *un-, re-, pre-, bi-, mis-, dis-*) and suffixes (e.g., *-er, -est, -ful*) to determine the meaning of words.

Vocabulary   397

© Pearson Education, Inc., 5

☉ Compare and Contrast

When you **compare** two things, you tell how they are alike. When you **contrast** them, you tell how they are different.

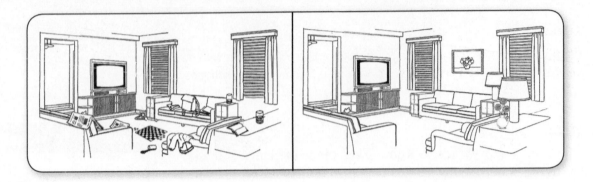

Practice

Look at the pictures. Answer the questions.

1. Describe the room in the first picture. What do you see?

_____

_____

_____

2. Describe the room in the second picture. What do you see?

_____

_____

_____

3. How is the room the same in the both pictures?

_____

_____

4. How is the room different?

_____

_____

_____

On Your Own

Use what you know about compare and contrast as you read "The Comet Racer." Write one thing that compares and one that contrasts in the passage.

Home Activity Your child reviewed comparing and contrasting. Together, compare and contrast two of your family's favorite places.

⊙ Unfamiliar Words

If you encounter an **unfamiliar word** while you are reading, you can use the words and sentences around it, or context clues, to help you figure out the meaning.

Practice

Read the following sentences. Fill in the blanks using the Words to Know. Then circle the letter of the correct definition for each underlined word. Use context clues to help you.

> **Words To Know**
>
> criticizing
> cruised
> drenching
> era
> explosion
> hydrogen

1. After taking off in a downpour, our airplane gained <u>altitude</u> until it

   _____ high above the _____ rain.

   a. depth   b. height   c. speed

2. The gas turbine engines <u>propelled</u> our craft through the air, burning

   jet fuel in a controlled _____.

   a. stored   b. burned   c. moved

3. Although I was secure in the plane, I missed riding in the _____-powered car

   that my father <u>devised</u>.

   a. invented   b. crashed   c. suspended

4. While my aunt was _____ his daydreams, my uncle <u>maintained</u> that his invention

   was the start of a new _____ in transportation.

   a. insisted   b. worried   c. trained

On Your Own

As you read "Dirty Snowballs," list unfamiliar words and their meanings based on context clues. Write sentences using the new words from the passage.

Home Activity Your child reviewed unfamiliar words. Together, check the list of word meanings your child derived from context clues against a print or online dictionary.

G3R1.6 Use sentence and word context to find the meaning of unknown words.

⊙ Categorize and Classify

To **classify** and **categorize** items is to group them by similar traits.

Practice

Look at the illustrations. Use them to answer the questions below.

| Textbook | Mystery | Biography | Picture Book | Fantasy Novel | Nonfiction Book |

1. Which books would you classify as fiction?

_____

_____

2. Would the picture book fit in a category of "Books I Read at School"? Why or why not?

_____

_____

3. Which books would be classified as fact-based books?

_____

_____

4. Which books would be classified as books you might enjoy reading outside of school? Explain your answer.

_____

_____

On Your Own

Use what you know about categorizing and classifying as you read "Dirty Snowballs."

School + Home **Home Activity** Your child reviewed categorizing and classifying. During a library visit, investigate the various ways that books are categorized.

⊙ Homographs

present (adjective):
in attendance

present (verb): to give
something to someone

Homographs are two words that are spelled the same but have different meanings and may have different pronunciations.

Practice

Read the following sentences. Fill in the blanks with one of the Words to Know. Then circle the letter of the correct meaning of the homograph that is underlined in each sentence. Use a dictionary to check your answers.

Words To Know

bass
clarinet
fidgety
forgetful
jammed
nighttime
secondhand

1. Hugh was <u>content</u> with the _____ trumpet and

   _____ that he owned.

   a. happy   b. information

2. He said that he is so _____, he would <u>refuse</u> better instruments out of the worry he would accidentally leave them somewhere.

   a. trash, garbage   b. say no to something

3. At _____, he went to the corner coffeeshop and _____ with other musicians. He wanted to <u>exploit</u> every chance he had to practice.

   a. to take advantage of an opportunity   b. a bold, unusual, daring action

4. The _____ player did not <u>object</u> to Hugh's _____ manner.

   a. a thing   b. speak out against

On Your Own

As you read "The Comet Racer," watch out for words that are homographs, and check their meanings in the dictionary. Write a sentence using the word.

School +Home   **Home Activity** Your child reviewed homographs. With your child, look up a list of homographs online and challenge each other to use each word in a sentence.

🐻 **R1.3** Understand and explain frequently used synonyms, antonyms, and homographs.

⊙ Theme and Setting

Theme is the "big idea" that holds the entire story together. **Setting** is where the story takes place.

Amanda's palms were sweaty and cold. She could not see far out into the auditorium because of the stage lights focused on her and the six other spelling bee finalists. She was the only student from Walnut Hill School who had made it this far. Out in the audience were her classmates and her teacher, Mrs. Mullaney. They were all hoping for her, pulling for her, expecting her to win.

"Number 183," the spelling bee official called. That was Amanda's number. She stepped up to the microphone. "Spell aardvark," said the official.

Amanda said, "A-a-d-v-a-r-k." Her hand flew to her mouth. She was wrong! What would her friends and teachers say?

As she returned to her seat, she heard the audience clapping for her. "Don't worry, Amanda!" someone yelled out. "You did great!" Amanda was relieved. Maybe it didn't matter so much that she hadn't won the spelling bee.

Practice

Read the passage above. Then answer the questions.

1. What is the theme of this story?

_____

_____

2. What does the story tell us about the setting?

_____

_____

3. Write details that would help the reader picture the setting better. Use your imagination.

_____

_____

On Your Own

Use what you know about theme and setting as you read "The Comet Racer." Write about the theme and setting in the passage.

Home Activity Your child reviewed using theme and setting. Talk about the settings of your favorite books or movies. How are they alike? How do they connect to the theme?

R3.4 Understand that *theme* refers to the meaning or moral of a selection and recognize themes (whether implied or stated directly) in sample works.

© Pearson Education, Inc., 5

Dirty Snowballs

Comets have fascinated people for centuries. From Earth, these outer-space bodies look like fuzzy smudges of light in the night sky. But what are comets, and what do we know about them?

A comet is a frozen object in outer space, made of ice and dust. For this reason, some astronomers call them "dirty snowballs." There are three main parts to a comet: the nucleus, the coma, and the tail.

The nucleus is the solid inner part of the comet. It is made up of ice, dust, and gases. It is covered with a black crust that absorbs heat as the comet travels. As the nucleus absorbs the heat of the sun, the ice inside it starts to melt, pressure builds, and the weakest parts of its crust start to rupture, or break up.

Jets of gas shoot out of the weakening nucleus. Each explosion of gas adds to a growing halo of dust and gas that surrounds the nucleus. This halo is called the coma. Together, the coma and the nucleus form the head of the comet. An invisible layer of hydrogen gas surrounds the coma. This is called the hydrogen envelope, and it becomes larger when the comet approaches the sun.

Usually, a comet's nucleus and coma will only be about six miles across. But some are much larger. One famous comet, the Great Comet of 1811, had a coma about as big across as the diameter of the sun!

The comet's tail is also made up of the dust particles and gas molecules that evaporate from the nucleus. The tail is easily visible because the dust particles reflect the sunlight, and it can be millions of miles long. The Great Comet of 1843 had a tail that was more than 150 million miles long.

Comets come into being far outside our solar system, billions or even trillions of miles away from the sun. Scientists think that there are ancient clouds of dust and gas out there that are left over from billions of years ago, when our solar system began.

Most comets never get close enough to Earth for us to see them, even with our most powerful telescopes. But a few do travel close enough for humans to glimpse. Usually comets that can be seen with the naked eye only show up once every five to ten years.

Comets are unpredictable in how they appear to us. Some may linger in the sky for weeks, while others may fade in and out of view in just a few hours. Sometimes one comet will split up into several and continue to move together in the same direction.

© Pearson Education, Inc., 5

⊙ DAY 2 Suffixes
What is the suffix of the word *snowballs?*

_____

What is the suffix of the word *gases?*

_____

⊙ DAY 4 Unfamiliar Words Underline the words in the third paragraph that help you understand the meaning of *rupture.*

⊙ DAY 2 Main Idea and Details Underline the main idea in the fourth paragraph.

⊙ DAY 4 Classify and Categorize What are two types of comets discussed in the article?

_____

_____

_____

_____

_____

R2.0 Students read and understand grade-level appropriate material.

"Dirty Snowballs" 403

⊙ **DAY 2** Main Idea and Details Underline the details in the second paragraph that support the idea that we can't see from Earth how fast comets are moving.

⊙ **DAY 4** Classify and Categorize What types of orbits around the sun can a comet get into?

_____

_____

_____

_____

_____

_____

_____

Remember that comets start out billions of miles away from the sun. When a comet has cruised into our solar system and moves closer to the sun, the dust and ice in the comet heat up and evaporate. This evaporation is what produces the long tails of gas and dust that can be seen from Earth. Comets with extremely long tails can be seen with the naked eye. Those only show up about once every ten years.

Even the comets we can see from Earth are millions of miles away. Because of this, we can't easily see their movement across the sky. This is one way in which comets are very different from meteors, or "shooting stars," which seem to streak across the sky and then disappear. Usually, the only way to tell that a comet is moving is to watch it for several nights. Then you can see that it is moving in relationship to the stars around it.

Sometimes, the Sun's gravity will pull comets into an elliptical orbit. An elliptical orbit is more oval-shaped than circle-shaped. These comets can orbit the Sun for thousands of years. However, other comets orbit too close to the Sun. These comets will melt like an ice cube near a flame. Over thousands of years, the comet will shrink and melt away.

Long ago, people thought comets were bad omens. They thought a comet was a sign that something terrible was about to happen, such as a plague or a war. In our own era, most people don't see comets as messengers of disaster. However, people today continue to be interested in these interstellar snowballs.

One of the most famous comets is Halley's comet. Halley's comet is famous because it returns about every 76 years. Its most recent sighting was in 1985, and it is predicted to return again in 2061. Astronomers have noted every single appearance of Halley's comet since ancient times.

If you ever do see a comet through a telescope or with your naked eye, remember that it was made from the most ancient building blocks of our nebula. The dust and gas that formed that comet is the same dust and gas that formed our own solar system billions of years ago!

© Pearson Education, Inc., 5

School + Home

Home Activity Your child read a selection and used comprehension and vocabulary skills from Unit 6. Have your child point out the main idea and details of each paragraph in the selection. In addition, have your child point out different suffixes and their meanings.

R2.0 Students read and understand grade-level appropriate material.

The Comet Racer

Jaz put on his Black Violet Visor and felt a trickle of sweat run down his back. All around him was the emptiness of space. The electric engine pulse of his ship, the Sorcerer, seemed to match his own frantic heartbeat.

The race master's voice came over Jaz's headset. "Contestants, do you copy?" said the voice. "Comet Kettleboom is approaching at the stargate. Start your engines and line up at the raceway."

Jaz flipped off the idle switch on his dashboard and flew the Sorcerer into its proper lane. Fidgety with excitement, he wondered if he should have had that third glass of Rocketwave Juice an hour earlier.

Back on earth, Jaz knew the immense crowds were cheering for the fourteen different spaceships getting ready to begin. All across the globe, hovering air-screens were projecting images of each ship's location and pilot. Jaz glanced at his own contestant's badge hung around his neck: *Comet Quest Competitor 00904: Jaz Morse. June 1, 2189*

Jaz had worked hard to get to this point. For three years, his precious time had been filled with flight exams, astrophysics lab work, and anti-gravity engineering. When the Comet Quest committee had announced that he would be the fourteenth competitor in the upcoming race, Jaz just knew this was his chance to make history. No single ship had been able to surpass a flying comet—at least, not yet.

The race master's voice jolted Jaz back to reality. "Contestants, do you copy?" There was a brief pause as everyone responded. "All ships on course and ready for velocity activation. Comet Kettleboom 5,000 miles away and counting." Jaz quickly did the calculations in his head. The comet would be here in just over two minutes. He counted to himself as he braced the steering wheel.

"In 10," said the race master, "9... 8... 7... 6... 5... 4... 3... 2... GO!" In the lifeless vacuum of space, fourteen ships bolted forward with a furious burst of blazing heat. Jaz saw Comet Kettleboom flying several hundred miles to his right, as he launched the Sorcerer into action.

The speed gauge on the dashboard registered 15 miles per second, but Jaz knew he was going to have to travel a whole lot faster if he was going to beat that comet. He ramped up the engine core and increased his speed to 20 miles per second. In a few more moments, he was up to 30. *C'mon Sorcerer,* Jaz thought to himself, *I know you're one whizzing wizard of a ship!*

⊙ **DAY 5** Theme/ Setting Underline the words in the first paragraph that help you to know where Jaz is located.

⊙ **DAY 1** Categorize and Classify Would you classify Jaz as an artist, a doctor, or a pilot?

_____

⊙ **DAY 5** Theme/ Setting Describe the setting and its importance to the story.

_____
_____
_____
_____
_____
_____

⊙ **DAY 1** Categorize and Classify What do comets have in common with stars and meteors?

_____
_____
_____

© Pearson Education, Inc., 5

R2.0 Students read and understand grade-level appropriate material.

"The Comet Racer" **405**

⊙ **DAY 5**
Homographs What is the meaning of *lead* in paragraph one?

_____

What is another meaning of *lead*?

_____

⊙ **DAY 3** Compare and Contrast
Compare the Comet Quest race with a running race. Name one similarity and one difference.

_____

_____

_____

_____

_____

_____

_____

⊙ **DAY 3** Suffixes
How does the suffix *-ful* in d*readful* help you to understand the meaning of the word?

_____

_____

_____

⊙ **DAY 1** Prefixes
What is the prefix in *disoriented*?

His on-screen monitors showed his rivals nearby as the comet propelled ahead. Now was the time for Jaz to hit the flash grid core accelerator. With a cool, steady hand and a madly beating heart, Jaz shifted on the accelerator and felt his body push back into his seat. Now he was flying at 40 miles per second—just as fast as Comet Kettleboom. The Sorcerer began to emerge into the lead as the other ships fell behind. "Aces!" Jaz shouted as he sped into the blackness.

Soon he was traveling just under 45 miles per second. He could see the distance shrinking between himself and the racing comet. There it was—that dirty ball of ice just daring him to pass by. "You're mine," Jaz said as he rushed straight ahead.

In the two seconds that followed, Jaz gave one final blast to the thrusters and felt his ship bolt to the front. His heart flip-flopped inside his chest as he called into his headset, "Race master, this is Jaz Morse. I've passed the comet's coma." But no sooner had Jaz made the announcement when he felt his ship give a lurch. A red light suddenly began flashing on his dashboard. Something dreadful was wrong.

Jaz checked his control panel and realized quickly that the dust from the comet had chipped at his ship's outer hull. A mechanism had failed and he was beginning to spin out of control. "Morse to base," Jaz called out. "Requiring immediate assistance." Without a moment to spare, Jaz switched off the flash grid core accelerator. His speed dropped down, but the Sorcerer was still spinning. He cut power to the thrusters and felt his stomach whirling. "C'mon, Sorce!" Jaz yelled. "Please don't fail me now." Madly, he held on to his seat as he tried to pull on the stuck emergency brake.

Just when Jaz thought he'd lose his lunch and his life, he gave one last dramatic pull and felt his ship begin to slow down.

"Race master to Jaz, do you copy? Do you copy?"

Jaz felt a little ill and disoriented as he clutched his contestant's badge. "Did I win?" he groaned into his headset.

"You've won, my boy!" the race master said. "You're the first to fly faster than a speeding comet. Can you make it back to base?"

"Can I move?" would be a better question, Jaz thought to himself. But he straightened in his chair and patted his control panel. "Fine work, Sorcerer. Really fine work."

© Pearson Education, Inc., 5

Home Activity Your child read a selection and used comprehension and vocabulary skills from Unit 6. Have your child retell the selection, comparing and contrasting the plot details and noting the importance of the setting.

R2.0 Students read and understand grade-level appropriate material.

Connect Text to Text

Reading Across Texts

Think about the selections "Dirty Snowballs" and "The Comet Racer." Complete the Venn diagram below with details that show similarities and differences between the two texts.

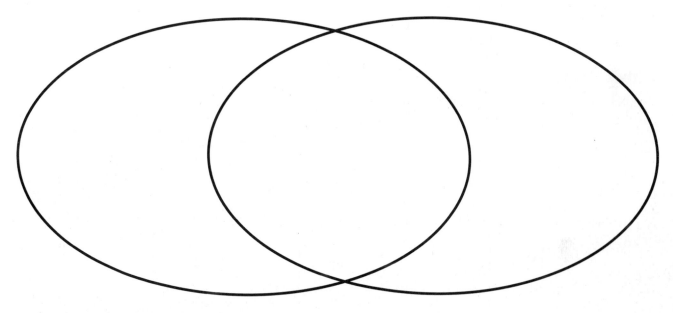

Writing Across Texts

Imagine you are an astronomer who studies comets. What would you tell someone who has never heard of or seen a comet before?

_____

_____

_____

_____

_____

_____

_____

_____

_____

_____

Home Activity Your child read two selections this week. Have your child explain to you how they were alike and how they were different.

Summarize Your Learning

> **What can we learn from encounters with the unexpected?**
>
> • *Inside Out* • *The Mystery of Saint Matthew Island*
> • *King Midas and the Golden Touch* • *The Hindenburg*
> • *Sweet Music in Harlem*

Think About It!

Think about the selections you read in this unit.

- How were they alike? How were they different?
- Were the selections you read this week similar to others you have read?
- What did you learn?

Write three big ideas about adventure that you learned from this unit.

- _____
- _____
- _____

Question It!

Write three questions about your big ideas.

- _____
- _____
- _____

Talk About It!

Discuss your questions with a partner.

- What questions did your partner have? Were they similar to yours?
  Were they different from yours?
- What things did you and your partner want to know?
- Is there ever a way to prepare for an unexpected situation? Why or why not?

Home Activity Your child reviewed and discussed the selections from Unit 6. Have your child describe to you the big ideas about unexpected encounters from this unit.

Section 2

California
Word Study
and Spelling
Practice Book

Contents

© Pearson Education, Inc. 5

Unit 3 Inventors and Artists

Unit 4 Adapting

Spelling Practice Book

Unit 5 Adventurers

Unit 6 The Unexpected

Steps for Spelling New Words

This is one strategy that you can use to learn any new spelling word. It has six steps.

Step 1
Look at the word. **Say** it and listen to the sounds.

Step 2
Spell the word aloud.

Step 3
Think about the spelling. Is there anything special to remember?

Step 4
Picture the word with your eyes shut.

Step 5
Look at the word and **write** it.

Step 6
Cover the word. Picture it and **write** it again. **Check** its spelling. Did you get it right?

Now practice this step-by-step plan on some new spelling words.

Problem Parts

Everybody has words that are hard to spell. When you find such a word, it is a good time to use the Problem Parts strategy.

One of the words you will learn is **fossil**. The word **fossil** has a sound in the middle, but this sound is spelled with not just one *s* but with two. That is tricky! Here are steps to follow in the Problem Parts strategy.

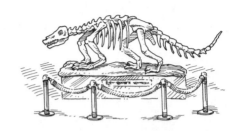

Step 1
Ask yourself which part of the word is giving you a problem.

Step 2
Write the word and underline the problem part.

Step 3
Picture the word. Focus on what the problem part looks like. Sometimes you might want to picture the problem part in large letters to help you.

Now picture the word and see the problem part before you spell it.

Divide and Conquer

Long words can be hard to spell. If you divide them into smaller parts, you can conquer them. Here is how to use the Divide and Conquer strategy.

Compound Words

Divide **compound** words into base words.

Words with Affixes

Divide words with **affixes** into prefixes, suffixes, and base words.

Words with Many Syllables

Divide words with **many syllables** into separate syllables.

Step 1
Say the word slowly and listen for each part or syllable.

Step 2
Use these pictures to help you divide three kinds of long words.

Step 3
Study the word one part or one syllable at a time.

Spelling Practice Book

Meaning Helpers

Even a short word such as *terrain* can be hard to spell—until you discover where it comes from. This is where the Meaning Helper strategy can be used.

Terra is a meaning helper for **terrain** because it helps you remember how to spell the **r** sound with two letters.

The word pairs below are related in meaning.
The **o's** in **photo** help you remember that **photography** has two **o's**.
The sound of **t** in **direct** helps you remember the **t** in **direction**.

Longer Word	Meaning Helper	Clue
photography	photo	photo + graphy
direction	direct	direct + ion

Meaning Helpers can be very useful. Be sure to remember any spelling changes that take place between the two words.

Some words may have a part that gives you problems. You can use
the Memory Tricks strategy to help you with tricky word parts.
Study this example.

Step 1
Ask yourself: Which part of the word gives me trouble?
Then mark the letters that are problems for you.

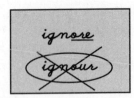

Step 2
Find memory helpers—words or phrases
you already can spell—that have the same
letters.

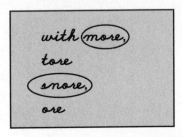

Step 3
Create a memory trick by linking your word with
a memory helper that helps you remember it.

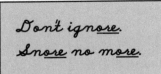

If your memory trick can be made into a picture, think about that picture as
you say the trick to yourself. This can be an extra helper. And silly helpers
are just as good as serious helpers!

Pronouncing for Spelling

We spell some words wrong because we say them wrong. Say a word very carefully to hear all of its sounds. This is called the Pronouncing for Spelling strategy.

Step 1
If a word has silent letters, pronounce them. Don't worry if the word sounds funny.

Step 2
Say the word correctly as you write it.

Sometimes, just saying a word correctly can be helpful. Other times, you may want to use a secret word so you don't forget to include sounds that are not heard.

For example, to remember the **o** in **gasoline** and the spelling of the final syllable, you might secretly say **gas-o-line**, stressing the long **o** and the long **i** in **line**. It won't make sense to anyone else, but you will know that you are using the Pronouncing for Spelling strategy.

Frequently Misspelled Words!

The words below are words that are misspelled the most by students your age. Pay special attention to these frequently misspelled words as you read, write, and spell.

a lot	to	knew
too	when	sometimes
their	didn't	want
there	heard	which
because	then	caught
favorite	we're	let's
that's	everybody	stopped
finally	Mom	TV
our	everyone	beautiful
they're	one	before
it's	went	buy
really	decided	Dad's
different	especially	doesn't
where	getting	everything
again	Halloween	except
until	off	tried
friend	always	and
they	whole	another
you're	happened	clothes
friends	I'm	don't
through	into	excited
were	maybe	outside
believe	said	piece
know	there's	school
something	thought	
probably	upon	
Christmas	usually	

Spelling Practice Book

Short Vowel VCCV, VCV

Generalization Short vowels are often spelled **a:** ch**a**nnel, **e:** m**e**thod, **i:** d**i**stance, **o:** pr**o**blem, **u:** b**u**tter.

Word Sort Sort words by short vowel patterns VCCV or VCV.

VCCV

1. _____

2. _____

3. _____

4. _____

5. _____

6. _____

7. _____

8. _____

9. _____

10. _____

11. _____

12. _____

13. _____

14. _____

15. _____

VCV

16. _____

17. _____

18. _____

19. _____

20. _____

Spelling Words

1. distance
2. method
3. anger
4. problem
5. butter
6. petals
7. enjoy
8. perhaps
9. figure
10. channel

11. admire
12. comedy
13. husband
14. tissue
15. mustard
16. shuttle
17. advance
18. drummer
19. regular
20. denim

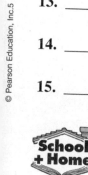

Home Activity Your child is learning about words that have the short vowel sounds *a, e, i, o,* and *u.* Have your child name three words from the list and tell you what the short vowel sound is in each word.

Spelling Practice Book

Short Vowel VCCV, VCV

Spelling Words

distance	method	anger	problem	butter
petals	enjoy	perhaps	figure	channel
admire	comedy	husband	tissue	mustard
shuttle	advance	drummer	regular	denim

Words in Context Complete each sentence with a list word.

1. The _____ keeps the rhythm of the band.

2. Most people _____ the skills of talented artists.

3. Watching a _____ makes people laugh.

4. The _____ bus is the fastest way to get there.

5. I like _____ on my hot dog.

6. Her _____ was forty years old.

7. The shortest _____ between two points is a straight line.

8. The _____ fell off the flower one by one.

9. _____ we can have ice cream after dinner.

10. The skater practiced _____ eights on the ice.

1. _____

2. _____

3. _____

4. _____

5. _____

6. _____

7. _____

8. _____

9. _____

10. _____

Word Meanings Write the list word that has nearly the same meaning.

11. handkerchief

12. canal

13. lard

14. technique

15. like

16. proceed

17. rage

18. jeans

19. usual

20. difficulty

11. _____

12. _____

13. _____

14. _____

15. _____

16. _____

17. _____

18. _____

19. _____

20. _____

Home Activity Your child wrote words that have short vowels. Dictate words and have your child say and spell the word.

2 Unit 1 Week 1

Spelling Practice Book

Short Vowel VCCV, VCV

Proofread a Poster Sarah made a poster for the school fair. Circle seven spelling errors. Find one capitalization error. Write the corrections on the lines.

Come too the village fair!

See the funny comady team show.

Milk a cow and churn some buttar at the farm exhibit.

Sample hot dogs with twenty choices of musterd!

Make tisseu flower bouquets.

Decorate your denim jeans with a special new art method.

Enjoy fifty booths of crafts, fun, and games.

park at the Town Hall parking lot.

Ride the special shuttal bus to the fairgrounds.

Discount tickets are on sale in advanse.

1. _____

2. _____

3. _____

4. _____

5. _____

6. _____

7. _____

8. _____

Spelling Words

distance
method
anger
problem
butter
petals
enjoy
perhaps
figure
channel

admire
comedy
husband
tissue
mustard
shuttle
advance
drummer
regular
denim

Frequently Misspelled Words

and
to
too

Proofread Words Circle the correct spelling of the word.

9. channal   chanel   channel

10. drummer   drumer   drummor

11. metod   methid   method

12. parhaps   perhaps   pirhaps

13. figure   figger   figour

14. petles   petels   petals

15. problam   problem   problim

Home Activity Your child found misspelled list words with VCCV and VCV patterns. Select a list word and ask your child to spell it.

© Pearson Education, Inc. 5

Short Vowel VCCV, VCV

Spelling Words				
distance	method	anger	problem	butter
petals	enjoy	perhaps	figure	channel
admire	comedy	husband	tissue	mustard
shuttle	advance	drummer	regular	denim

Word Search Circle ten hidden list words. Words are down, across, and diagonal. Write the words on the lines.

```
S  M  D  I  S  T  A  N  C  E  D  H
T  H  E  R  P  E  T  A  L  S  R  U
I  M  U  T  E  C  J  L  I  L  U  S
S  X  L  T  H  G  P  Y  Q  Z  M  B
S  K  R  K  T  O  U  B  C  T  M  A
U  X  O  V  A  L  D  L  Q  T  E  N
E  C  H  A  N  N  E  L  A  G  R  D
A  D  M  I  R  E  Z  G  M  R  K  W
```

1. _____
2. _____
3. _____
4. _____
5. _____
6. _____
7. _____
8. _____
9. _____
10. _____

Scramble Unscramble the list words and write them on the lines.

11. cydoem   11. _____

13. stamurd   13. _____

15. medin   15. _____

17. geran   17. _____

19. sahpepr   19. _____

12. gurife   12. _____

14. mepbolr   14. _____

16. ynejo   16. _____

18. teubtr   18. _____

20. vedanac   20. _____

Home Activity Your child has learned to spell longer words with short vowel sounds. Pick two list words and ask your child to use them in a sentence.

© Pearson Education, Inc. 5

Short Vowel VCCV, VCV

Spelling Words				
distance	method	anger	problem	butter
petals	enjoy	perhaps	figure	channel
admire	comedy	husband	tissue	mustard
shuttle	advance	drummer	regular	denim

Alphabetize Write the twelve list words below in alphabetical order.

method	comedy
denim	anger
distance	enjoy
perhaps	advance
admire	figure
channel	regular

1. _____

2. _____

3. _____

4. _____

5. _____

6. _____

7. _____

8. _____

9. _____

10. _____

11. _____

12. _____

Hidden Words Each of these small words can be found inside one of the list words. Write the list word that contains the small words.

13. sue _____

14. rob _____

15. drum _____

16. pet _____

17. ban _____

18. shut _____

19. but _____

20. tar _____

Home Activity Your child has learned to spell longer words with short vowel sounds. Find words with short vowel sounds in a magazine or newspaper and ask your child to spell them.

Long Vowel VCV

Spelling Words				
fever	broken	climate	hotel	basic
vocal	native	silent	labor	spider
label	icon	agent	motive	vital
acorn	item	aroma	legal	solo

Analogies Write the word that completes each comparison.

1. Mouth is to taste as nose is to _____.

2. Loud is to deafening as quiet is to _____.

3. Cold is to chill as hot is to _____.

4. Robin is to bird as black widow is to _____.

5. Two is to duet as one is to _____.

6. Cottage is to house as inn is to _____.

7. Vine is to grape as oak tree is to _____.

8. Smart is to intelligent as lawful is to _____.

9. Friend is to enemy as stranger is to _____.

10. Play is to enjoy as work is to _____.

Word Clues Write the list word that fits each clue.

11. This includes a place's temperatures and rainfall.   _____

12. You'll find one of these sewn into a piece of clothing.   _____

13. You can't use something described as this.   _____

14. An actor or athlete might employ this person.   _____

15. A person who speaks up is described this way.   _____

16. This explains why you did something.   _____

17. This describes something that is absolutely necessary.   _____

18. You can click on one of these on a Web site.   _____

19. This is another word for a thingamajig.   _____

20. This describes something that is not advanced.   _____

Home Activity Your child has learned to spell longer words with long vowel sounds. To practice at home, make up clues about words with long vowel sounds and ask your child to spell them.

Spelling Practice Book

Long Vowel Digraphs

Spelling Words				
coast	feast	speech	wheat	Spain
paint	arrow	needle	charcoal	praise
faint	maintain	crease	groan	breeze
willow	appeal	bowling	complain	sneeze

Word Search Circle ten hidden list words. Words are down, across, and diagonal. Write the words on the lines.

```
F  B  W  S  P  P  A  D  E  Y
N  J  O  I  C  F  A  I  N  T
A  L  A  W  E  R  B  I  P  O
G  Q  W  I  L  L  O  W  N  M
R  T  U  A  E  I  S  U  G  T
O  E  S  P  A  I  N  N  W  Y
A  B  N  P  S  P  E  G  F  T
N  W  H  E  A  T  E  N  O  P
E  K  S  A  I  k  Z  E  N  l
H  E  E  L  C  R  E  A  S  E
```

1. _____   6. _____

2. _____   7. _____

3. _____   8. _____

4. _____   9. _____

5. _____   10. _____

Scramble Unscramble the list words and write them on the lines.

11. elende _____   16. timinana _____

12. worar _____   17. shepec _____

13. sarpie _____   18. larhocca _____

14. zerbee _____   19. stafe _____

15. ascto _____   20. aclimpon _____

Home Activity Your child has learned to spell words with long vowel digraphs. Ask your child to give an example of and spell words with *ea*, *ee*, *ai*, *oa*, and *ow*.

Adding *-ed*, *-ing*

Spelling Words				
supplied	supplying	denied	denying	decided
deciding	included	including	admitted	admitting
occurred	occurring	qualified	qualifying	identified
identifying	delayed	delaying	satisfied	satisfying

Antonyms Write the list word ending in *-ed* that has the opposite or nearly the opposite meaning.

1. unhappy _____

2. on time _____

3. denied _____

4. excluded _____

5. unsure _____

Synonyms Write the list word ending in *-ed* that has the same or nearly the same meaning.

6. happened _____

7. named _____

8. furnished _____

9. confessed _____

10. able; competent _____

Word Clues Write the list word that fits each clue.

11. What a lawbreaker is doing to avoid getting in trouble. _____

12. What an athlete is doing in a regional track meet. _____

13. What trucks full of food are doing at the supermarket. _____

14. What a jury is doing after a trial. _____

15. What an event is doing while it is underway. _____

16. What a detective is attempting by looking at fingerprints. _____

17. What a school is doing when it lets students in. _____

18. What an airline is doing to passengers when running late. _____

19. What a delicious meal is doing for your hunger. _____

20. What you are doing when you put everything in. _____

Home Activity Your child has learned to spell words with *-ed* and *-ing*. To practice at home, name three verbs that describe after-school activities. Ask your child to spell each word with an *-ed* ending and with an *-ing* ending.

© Pearson Education, Inc. 5

Contractions

Spelling Words				
they're	you've	weren't	needn't	there'd
they've	mustn't	what'll	doesn't	hadn't
could've	would've	should've	might've	wouldn't
who've	shouldn't	who'd	this'll	couldn't

Words in Context Complete each sentence with a list word.

1. The students want to raise money, so _____ selling fruit.

2. James had been to big cities, but he _____ ever been to Chicago.

3. I had never met anyone _____ been to Africa.

4. The electricity is out, so _____ we do about dinner?

5. We have practiced for weeks, so _____ be the best school play ever.

6. We'll go to the zoo after lunch since it _____ open until noon on Monday.

7. Several players _____ at the first soccer practice.

8. If there were a big storm, _____ be many people without food and water.

9. You may help chop vegetables, but you _____ cut yourself.

10. It's raining; I knew I _____ brought my umbrella.

11. I just realized I _____ left my spelling book at home.

12. You need to bring a pillow to camp, but you _____ bring a sleeping bag.

13. _____ you like to go swimming?

14. Sophia tried, but she _____ open the jar.

15. The Scotts aren't home; _____ gone to Florida for two weeks.

16. It may rain Saturday, but it _____ affect our plans.

17. Put the dressing on the salad after _____ mixed it well.

18. If I _____ found my cap, I would've worn it to the game.

19. I admire people _____ climbed high mountains.

20. Our team _____ won the game if we'd gotten one more goal.

 Home Activity Your child has learned to spell contractions. Ask your child to give an example of and spell contractions formed with the words *are*, *not*, *have*, and *will*.

© Pearson Education, Inc. 5

Proofread for Spelling Errors

Proofread a Story. Circle twelve spelling mistakes in the story below. Write them correctly.

It was time for the first school ski trip. The bus picked the ski club up right after school. Grace was nervous because she had'nt skied much, but Jody said she shouldnt worry. "It's not a very high mountain, and most kids ski about as well as you do," she said.

On the mountain, Grace was doing fine. Then she accidentally went down a deserted trail. Suddenly it got very rough. She went over a rock, and down she went! Grace tried not to grone as she fell awkwardly in the snow, turning her ankle. Could it be brokon? She could see skiers in the distence, but nobody was nearby. For a moment Grace thought she would fiant. But it was vitel to stay alert and get help. She got her ski off but coudn't stand on her ankle. She saw people at the top of the hill, but no one saw her.

There was only one thing to do. Grace decideed to crawl to the top of the hill. It took all her strength. She had many fears, includeing freezing or being left alone as night fell. Finally she saw someone and called out. Soon about ten people were helping her. They told Grace she was very brave. Luckily she only had a sprain. The next day, she rested all day and thought about what had occured. "Purhaps I will go skiing again sometime," she said. "But I will be careful to ski with a partner."

1. _____   7. _____

2. _____   8. _____

3. _____   9. _____

4. _____   10. _____

5. _____   11. _____

6. _____   12. _____

Spelling Practice Book

Digraphs *th*, *sh*, *ch*, *ph*

Generalization Words can have two consonants together that are pronounced as one sound: **sou**th**ern**, **sh**ovel, **ch**apter, **hy**ph**en**.

Word Sort Sort the list words by digraphs **th**, **sh**, **ch**, and **ph**.

th

1. _____

2. _____

3. _____

4. _____

5. _____

sh

6. _____

7. _____

8. _____

9. _____

10. _____

ch

11. _____

12. _____

13. _____

14. _____

15. _____

16. _____

17. _____

18. _____

ph

19. _____

20. _____

Spelling Words

1. shovel
2. southern
3. northern
4. chapter
5. hyphen
6. chosen
7. establish
8. although
9. challenge
10. approach

11. astonish
12. python
13. shatter
14. ethnic
15. shiver
16. pharmacy
17. charity
18. china
19. attach
20. ostrich

Home Activity Your child is learning about four sounds made with two consonants together, called digraphs. Ask your child to tell you what those four sounds are and give one list word for each sound.

At the Beach
PRACTICE

Digraphs *th*, *sh*, *ch*, *ph*

Spelling Words				
shovel	southern	northern	chapter	hyphen
chosen	establish	although	challenge	approach
astonish	python	shatter	ethnic	shiver
pharmacy	charity	china	attach	ostrich

Word Meanings Write the list word on the line that has the same meaning as the underlined words.

1. We are raising money for a <u>worthy cause</u>.

2. The <u>drugstore</u> filled the prescription for the medicine.

3. The United States is made up of many people from different <u>cultural</u> groups.

4. The restaurant chain wants to <u>set up</u> a diner in the community.

5. We set the table with our best <u>glass</u> dishes.

6. The best way to succeed is to constantly <u>test</u> yourself.

7. The cool breeze sent a <u>quiver</u> down my back.

8. I never would have <u>selected</u> those blue jackets.

9. The plane was on its final <u>move</u> toward the runway.

10. The magic trick was crafted to <u>amaze</u> the unsuspecting audience.

1. _____
2. _____
3. _____
4. _____
5. _____
6. _____
7. _____
8. _____
9. _____
10. _____

Classifying Write the list word that belongs in each group.

11. even if, while, ___

12. cobra, rattler, ___

13. fasten, join, ___

14. spade, scoop, ___

15. episode, part, ___

16. smash, break, ___

17. peacock, swan, ___

18. dash, line, ___

11. _____
12. _____
13. _____
14. _____
15. _____
16. _____
17. _____
18. _____

Home Activity Your child matched list words with synonyms. Name two list words and see if your child can give a synonym for each.

Spelling Practice Book

Digraphs *th, sh, ch, ph*

Proofread a Poster Circle five spelling errors. Find one sentence with a punctuation error. Write the corrections on the lines.

Come to the charaty auction for the
new recreation center.

Help dig the building site. Buy a chance to
shovle some earth.

Bid on and buy, wonderful prizes from around the world!

Challange yourself in contests and games.

Bid on lovely china figures and platters.

Sample delicious northurn and southern cooking!

Time: Saturday, from 9 A.M. to 6 P.M.

Place: The old pharmecy building

1. _____   2. _____

3. _____   4. _____

5. _____

6. _____

_____

Spelling Words
shovel
southern
northern
chapter
hyphen
chosen
establish
although
challenge
approach
astonish
python
shatter
ethnic
shiver
pharmacy
charity
china
attach
ostrich

Proofread Words Circle the correct spelling of the word.

7. The ending of the book will _____ you.
   astonish   astonesh   astonash

8. I need a stapler to _____ the poster to the bulletin board.
   attatch   attach   atach

9. Music is my _____ field of study.
   chosen   chozen   choicen

10. I want to read a _____ a day.
    chaptar   shapter   chapter

11. Numbers, such as sixty-five, are written with a _____.
    hiphen   hyphen   hipfen

12. The _____ in the zoo was 12 feet long.
    pythn   python   pithon

Frequently Misspelled Words
which
they
thought

Home Activity Your child identified misspelled list words. Select words with two different digraph sounds and ask your child to spell them.

© Pearson Education, Inc. 5

Digraphs *th*, *sh*, *ch*, *ph*

Spelling Words				
shovel	southern	northern	chapter	hyphen
chosen	establish	although	challenge	approach
astonish	python	shatter	ethnic	shiver
pharmacy	charity	china	attach	ostrich

Word Search Circle the ten list words below that are hidden in the puzzle. They are across, down, and diagonal. Write the words.

although	chosen	pharmacy	challenge	hyphen
attach	ethnic	approach	establish	southern

```
E   S   T   A   B   L   I   S   H   C   S   A
A   P   H   A   R   M   A   C   Y   H   O   P
T   X   U   Y   I   Y   L   G   J   O   U   P
T   B   Q   Y   P   N   B   N   B   S   T   R
A   C   Q   E   T   H   N   I   C   E   H   O
C   D   L   N   A   D   E   Y   K   N   E   A
H   C   H   A   L   L   E   N   G   E   R   C
G   G   A   L   T   H   O   U   G   H   N   H
```

1. _____
2. _____
3. _____
4. _____
5. _____
6. _____
7. _____
8. _____
9. _____
10. _____

Words in Context Finish the story with list words.

The money we raised at the **(11)** ____ auction will **(12)** ____ you. We were able to **(13)** ____ last year's record amount of $585.00. People bid on items such as an **(14)** ____ egg and a book about snakes with a **(15)** ____ on the cover. One **(16)** ____ cup fetched $25.00! An antique **(17)** ____ brought in $20.00. Auctions are exciting. Each time the gavel sounded, a **(18)** ____ of joy went down my spine.

11. _____
12. _____
13. _____
14. _____
15. _____
16. _____
17. _____
18. _____

Home Activity Your child has learned to read, write, and spell combined consonants, called digraphs. Have your child underline the digraphs in each list word and then say the word.

Spelling Practice Book

Vowel Sounds with *r*

Generalization The vowel sound /ôr/ can be spelled **or** and **ore**: rep**or**t, sn**ore**. The vowel sound /ir/ can be spelled **ear** and **eer**: app**ear**, pion**eer**. The vowel sound /âr/ can be spelled **are** and **air**: sp**are**, ch**air**.

Word Sort Sort words by the way in which the vowel sound with *r* is spelled.

or

1. _____

2. _____

3. _____

4. _____

5. _____

ore

6. _____

7. _____

ear

8. _____

9. _____

eer

10. _____

11. _____

12. _____

13. _____

are

14. _____

15. _____

16. _____

17. _____

18. _____

air

19. _____

20. _____

Home Activity Your child is learning some patterns for spelling vowel sounds with *r*. Have your child read the words aloud and circle the patterns.

© Pearson Education, Inc.5

Name _____

Vowel Sounds with *r*

Spelling Words				
snore	tornado	spare	appear	career
square	report	prepare	pioneer	chair
beware	smear	repair	sword	ignore
order	engineer	resort	volunteer	declare

Words in Context Write the list word to complete each sentence.

1. I _____ loudly when I sleep.

2. Have you heard the saying that the pen is mightier than the _____?

3. The _____ fixed the machine.

4. It was hard to _____ the loud sirens outside.

5. The mayor will _____ a holiday.

6. I have to bring my worn shoes to the shop for _____.

7. We have guests staying in our _____ bedroom.

8. A triangle has three sides; a _____ has four sides.

9. The father told his small child to _____ of traffic.

10. Does the weather _____ forecast rain or sun?

1. _____
2. _____
3. _____
4. _____
5. _____
6. _____
7. _____
8. _____
9. _____
10. _____

Word Groups Write the list word that best completes the group.

11. cyclone, twister, ___

12. show up, materialize, ___

13. job, employment, ___

14. lead the way, be the first, ___

15. get ready, make, ___

16. offer, give aid, ___

17. ask for, send for, ___

18. blur, spread, ___

19. vacation spot, dude ranch, ___

20. seat, bench, ___

11. _____
12. _____
13. _____
14. _____
15. _____
16. _____
17. _____
18. _____
19. _____
20. _____

© Pearson Education, Inc. 5

Home Activity Your child wrote list words with vowel sounds with *r*. Select three words and ask your child what they mean.

Name _____

Vowel Sounds with *r*

Proofread a Story Ramon wrote this story about sharing a room with his brother. Circle six spelling errors. Find one sentence with a punctuation error. Write the corrections on the lines.

> ### My Brother
>
> Our mother asked my brother and me to voluntier to give up our rooms for our visiting grandparents. So, we're sharing the spair attic room, but it's no fun. My brother snores, and it's hard to ignoure it. Just as I was falling asleep, he snored like a tornadoe. That was it I threw my pillow at him. It knocked over the lamp, which hit the chare with a loud pop. This did not apear to disturb him at all. I gave up and slept in the hallway as a last resort.

1. _____   2. _____

3. _____   4. _____

5. _____   6. _____

7. _____

Proofread Words Circle the correct spelling of the word.

8. A _____ is someone who leads the way for others.

   pioneer   pioner   pieneer

9. The knight wore a brightly polished _____ on his hip.

   swoard   sword   sworde

10. The _____ is a wind funnel.

   tornado   tornardo   tornadoe

11. Be careful or you'll _____ the fresh paint.

   smear   smere   smeer

12. I asked the bike shop to _____ my flat tire.

   ripare   repair   repare

Spelling Words

snore
tornado
spare
appear
career
square
report
prepare
pioneer
chair

beware
smear
repair
sword
ignore
order
engineer
resort
volunteer
declare

Frequently Misspelled Words

caught
there's

Home Activity Your child identified misspelled list words in a paragraph. Ask your child to tell you the six patterns used in the list words to spell vowel sounds with *r*.

Spelling Practice Book   Unit 2 Week 3 **37**

© Pearson Education, Inc. 5

Vowel Sounds with *r*

Spelling Words				
snore	tornado	spare	appear	career
square	report	prepare	pioneer	chair
beware	smear	repair	sword	ignore
order	engineer	resort	volunteer	declare

Categorize Write the list word that completes each group.

1. weather, wind, prairie, ___   1. _____

2. interest, study, job, ___   2. _____

3. sleep, nose, exhale, ___   3. _____

4. vacation, travel, hotel, ___   4. _____

5. octagon, hexagon, pentagon, ___   5. _____

6. explorer, frontier, first, ___   6. _____

7. be careful, look out, ___   7. _____

8. spread, blur, smudge, ___   8. _____

9. announce, say, claim, ___   9. _____

10. handle, blade, sheath, ___   10. _____

Word Scramble Unscramble the list words and write them on the lines.

11. e s p r a   11. _____

12. h r c i a   12. _____

13. p e r r i a   13. _____

14. r r d o e   14. _____

15. t v l u n o e r e 15. _____

16. r i e n g e n e   16. _____

17. g r n i o e   17. _____

18. p e a a p r   18. _____

Home Activity Your child has learned to use patterns to spell vowel sounds followed by *r*. Look in a book or magazine with your child and find two other words that use one of these patterns.

© Pearson Education, Inc. 5

Spelling Practice Book

Jane Goodall

SORT

Final Syllables *-en, -an, -el, -le, -il*

Generalization Vowels in final syllables often sound alike even when they are spelled differently: **veter<u>an</u>**, **wood<u>en</u>**, **canc<u>el</u>**, **chuck<u>le</u>**, **foss<u>il</u>**.

Word Sort Sort words by the way in which the final syllable is spelled.

-en

1. _____

2. _____

3. _____

-an

4. _____

5. _____

6. _____

7. _____

-el

8. _____

9. _____

10. _____

11. _____

12. _____

-le

13. _____

14. _____

15. _____

16. _____

17. _____

18. _____

-il

19. _____

20. _____

Spelling Words

1. example
2. level
3. human
4. quarrel
5. scramble
6. evil
7. oxygen
8. wooden
9. double
10. travel

11. cancel
12. chuckle
13. fossil
14. toboggan
15. veteran
16. chisel
17. suburban
18. single
19. sudden
20. beagle

School + Home

Home Activity Your child is learning to spell words with final syllables *-en, -an, -el, -le,* and *-il*. Ask your child to tell you an ending sound and two ways it can be spelled.

Final Syllables *-en, -an, -el, -le, -il*

Spelling Words				
example	level	human	quarrel	scramble
evil	oxygen	wooden	double	travel
cancel	chuckle	fossil	toboggan	veteran
chisel	suburban	single	sudden	beagle

Word Clues Write the list word that matches each clue.

1. a kind of laugh

2. not urban or rural

3. a kind of sled

4. a gas we breathe

5. something made of oak or maple

6. something that has been preserved in stone

7. a small argument

8. two of something

9. only one

10. a kind of hound dog

1. _____

2. _____

3. _____

4. _____

5. _____

6. _____

7. _____

8. _____

9. _____

10. _____

Synonyms Write a list word that has the same meaning as the underlined word.

11. I found a perfect <u>model</u> of my favorite color.

12. Did you <u>mix</u> the eggs for me?

13. The sculptor had to carefully <u>carve</u> the marble bit by bit.

14. One of my goals is to <u>journey</u> around the world.

15. The ground was <u>flat</u> and then it dropped down steeply.

16. The <u>wicked</u> queen tried to poison her enemy.

17. Every <u>person</u> makes a mistake at some time.

18. The politician was <u>an old hand</u> at running elections.

19. I had to <u>call off</u> my dentist appointment today.

20. The storm was <u>swift</u> and unexpected.

11. _____

12. _____

13. _____

14. _____

15. _____

16. _____

17. _____

18. _____

19. _____

20. _____

Home Activity Your child matched list words to meanings. Ask your child to tell you the meaning of three list words.

Jane Goodall

PROOFREAD

Final Syllables *-en, -an, -el, -le, -il*

Proofread a Story Sally wrote this story. There are seven spelling errors and one punctuation error. Circle the errors and write the corrections on the lines.

The Old Woodcarver

We decided to travle to the home of a veteren woodcarver. My dad wanted him to make a tobaggan like the one he owned when he was a child. We drove down a long suburben road. When we got out of the car, a beagel ran from behind the house, followed by the woodcarver. He carried an example of a tiny sled made of metal. "Don't worry," he said with a chuckle, "your sled will be wooden." He pulled a chisle out of his pocket. "Would you like to learn how to carve?" he asked. "I may seem like an old fossel to you," he said. "I'm probably double your father's age, but I'm pretty handy with a chisel."

"Sure," I said, "that's a great idea!

1. _____	2. _____
3. _____	4. _____
5. _____	6. _____
7. _____	

8. _____

Proofread Words Circle the correct spelling of the word.

9.	oxygin	oxygan	oxygen
10.	cancel	cancle	cancil
11.	quarril	quarrel	quarele
12.	evile	eval	evil
13.	human	humen	humin
14.	chukle	chuckle	chuckel
15.	suddin	suddan	sudden
16.	egsample	example	exsampel

Spelling Words

example
level
human
quarrel
scramble
evil
oxygen
wooden
double
travel

cancel
chuckle
fossil
toboggan
veteran
chisel
suburban
single
sudden
beagle

Frequently Misspelled Words

Mom
Dad's
heard

Home Activity Your child identified misspelled words with final syllables *-en, -an, -el, -le, -il*. Ask your child which words are the most difficult for him or her to spell. Have your child spell them.

Jane Goodall

Final Syllables -en, -an, -el, -le, -il

Spelling Words				
example	level	human	quarrel	scramble
evil	oxygen	wooden	double	travel
cancel	chuckle	fossil	toboggan	veteran
chisel	suburban	single	sudden	beagle

Analogies Write the list word that completes each comparison.

1. Hot is to warm as rapid is to ____.

2. Cart is to wagon as sled is to ____.

3. Plate is to dish as argument is to ____.

4. Grin is to smile as laugh is to ____.

5. Silver is to metallic as oak is to ____.

6. Silly is to funny as wicked is to ____.

7. Chair is to seat as mix-up is to ____.

8. Rush is to hurry as ____ is to one.

9. Fun is to enjoyment as ____ is to experienced.

10. Light is to bright as ____ is to even.

1. _____

2. _____

3. _____

4. _____

5. _____

6. _____

7. _____

8. _____

9. _____

10. _____

Word Endings Each word has the final syllable spelled incorrectly. Rewrite the list word with the correctly spelled ending.

11. exampel

12. humen

13. doubel

14. travle

15. cancle

16. fossle

17. chisil

18. suburben

19. beagil

20. oxygan

11. _____

12. _____

13. _____

14. _____

15. _____

16. _____

17. _____

18. _____

19. _____

20. _____

Home Activity Your child has learned to read, write, and spell words with final syllables -en, -an, -el, -le, -il. Take turns saying and spelling each word aloud.

Spelling Practice Book

Final Syllables *er, ar, or*

Generalization Words with final syllables **er, ar,** and **or** often sound alike even when they are spelled differently: **dang*er*, doll*ar*, tract*or*.**

Word Sort Sort the list words by the spelling of the final syllable.

-er

1. _____

2. _____

3. _____

4. _____

5. _____

6. _____

7. _____

8. _____

9. _____

10. _____

-ar

11. _____

12. _____

13. _____

14. _____

-or

15. _____

16. _____

17. _____

18. _____

19. _____

20. _____

Spelling Words

1. danger
2. wander
3. tractor
4. dollar
5. harbor
6. eager
7. eraser
8. surrender
9. solar
10. sticker

11. locker
12. helicopter
13. pillar
14. refrigerator
15. caterpillar
16. rumor
17. glimmer
18. linger
19. sensor
20. alligator

© Pearson Education, Inc. 5

School + Home **Home Activity** Your child is learning about final syllables that sound the same but are spelled differently. Ask your child to spell three list words with endings that sound alike but are spelled differently.

Final Syllables *er, ar, or*

Spelling Words				
danger	wander	tractor	dollar	harbor
eager	eraser	surrender	solar	sticker
locker	helicopter	pillar	refrigerator	caterpillar
rumor	glimmer	linger	sensor	alligator

Definitions Write a list word that means the same or almost the same as the word or phrase.

1. spark

2. port

3. sun

4. gossip

5. post

6. peril

7. cooler

8. excited

9. 100 cents

10. roam

1. _____

2. _____

3. _____

4. _____

5. _____

6. _____

7. _____

8. _____

9. _____

10. _____

Missing Words Write the list word that completes the sentence.

11. I have a habit of chewing on my pencil ____.

12. Smart criminals ____ when spotted.

13. The farmer drove the ____ across the field.

14. I store my schoolbooks in my ____.

15. The ____ floated silently across the swampy water.

16. The ____ became a beautiful butterfly.

17. She pulled the price ____ off the package.

18. The news ____ flew over the accident scene.

19. I like to ____ in my room instead of watching television downstairs.

20. The motion ____ turns on the light when anyone is near.

11. _____

12. _____

13. _____

14. _____

15. _____

16. _____

17. _____

18. _____

19. _____

20. _____

© Pearson Education, Inc. 5

School + Home **Home Activity** Your child wrote words with final syllables *er, ar,* and *or*. Select three list words and ask your child to define them.

Final Syllables *er, ar, or*

Proofread a Sign There are seven spelling errors and one capitalization error. Circle the errors and write the corrections on the lines.

welcome to the Wildlife and Alligater Preserve

- Admission is one dollar for an all-day parking pass.
- You can rent an all-day locker for your convenience.
- Helicoptor rides are available to see the harber from the air.
- To preserve the ecology, stay on the path. Do not wandar off.
- There is no dangor. Animals stay behind a motion senser fence.
- Linger over lunch on our beautiful terrace.
- Do not forget to surrendar your parking pass at the gate when leaving.

Spelling Words
danger
wander
tractor
dollar
harbor
eager
eraser
surrender
solar
sticker
locker
helicopter
pillar
refrigerator
caterpillar
rumor
glimmer
linger
sensor
alligator

1. _____   2. _____

3. _____   4. _____

5. _____   6. _____

7. _____   8. _____

Proofread Words Circle the word that is spelled correctly.

9. doller   dollar   dollor

10. erasor   eraser   erasar

11. stickar   sticker   stickor

12. soler   solar   solor

13. helicoptor   helicoptar   helicopter

14. tracter   tractar   tractor

15. rumer   rumor   rumar

Frequently Misspelled Words
another
we're

Home Activity Your child identified misspelled words with *er, ar,* and *or* endings. Select three list words and ask your child to spell them.

Final Syllables *er, ar, or*

Spelling Words				
danger	wander	tractor	dollar	harbor
eager	eraser	surrender	solar	sticker
locker	helicopter	pillar	refrigerator	caterpillar
rumor	glimmer	linger	sensor	alligator

Word Scramble Riddle Unscramble each list word and then write the numbered letters on the lines below to answer the riddle.

Riddle: What's the answer to "See you later, alligator!"?

1. RRNDSEURE — — — — — — — — —
                                18

2. ARERSE — — — — — —
                      6

3. EOERRIRRFAGT — — — — — — — — — — — —
                     4   2

4. RAERPCTALIL — — — — — — — — — — —
                     3

5. LEMMGRI — — — — — — —
            11

6. LOLDAR — — — — — —
           5

7. PALIRL — — — — — —
                  14

8. EINGLR — — — — — —
          19

9. RLAITALGO — — — — — — — — —
              20   10

10. CISKTRE — — — — — —
               13

11. OSRAL — — — — —
              7

12. LCERKO — — — — — —
            15

13. NGDREA — — — — — —
             1   21

14. UMRRO — — — — —
             17

15. RNEWAD — — — — — —
          8

16. ATOCRTR — — — — — —
               16

17. HRRABO — — — — — —
          9

18. AGREE — — — — —
          12

— —
1 2 3   4 5 6   7   8 9 10 11 12 13 14 15 16 17 18 19 20 21

Home Activity Your child has learned to spell words with final syllables *er, ar,* and *or*. Look through a book or magazine with your child and find four other words with the same endings.

Digraphs *th*, *sh*, *ch*, *ph*

Spelling Words				
shovel	hyphen	challenge	shatter	charity
southern	chosen	approach	ethnic	china
northern	establish	astonish	shiver	attach
chapter	although	python	pharmacy	ostrich

Alphabetize Write the ten list words below in alphabetical order.

ethnic	python
ostrich	charity
hyphen	although
chapter	establish
northern	southern

1. _____

2. _____

3. _____

4. _____

5. _____

6. _____

7. _____

8. _____

9. _____

10. _____

Synonyms Write the list word that has the same, or nearly the same, meaning.

11. surprise _____

12. dare _____

13. shake _____

14. pottery _____

15. picked _____

16. drugstore _____

17. break _____

18. fasten _____

19. dig _____

20. near _____

Home Activity Your child has been learning to spell words with the digraphs *th*, *sh*, *ch*, and *ph*. Ask your child to give an example of a word with each digraph and spell it.

Irregular Plurals

Spelling Words				
staffs	ourselves	pants	scissors	loaves
volcanoes	chiefs	buffaloes	flamingos	beliefs
echoes	shelves	quizzes	sheriffs	dominoes
thieves	measles	avocados	chefs	pianos

Analogies Write the word that completes each comparison.

1. Doctors are to hospitals as _____ are to restaurants.

2. Arms are to shirts as legs are to _____.

3. Drawers are to chests as _____ are to closets.

4. Articles are to essays as tests are to _____.

5. Storm is to tornado as disease is to _____.

6. Knives are to meat as _____ are to paper.

7. Ants are to insects as _____ are to birds.

8. Strings are to violins as keys are to _____.

9. Potatoes are to soups as _____ are to salads.

10. Ice is to cubes as bread is to _____.

Word Clues Write the list word that fits each clue.

11. These animals roamed all over the West. _____

12. These are often black rectangles with white dots. _____

13. You might hear these in a huge canyon. _____

14. These people enforce the law. _____

15. These people may steal from you. _____

16. You don't want to be close when these erupt. _____

17. These are in charge of tribes or companies. _____

18. People have these about topics such as politics. _____

19. Organizations such as schools have these. _____

20. We use this word to describe us. _____

Home Activity Your child has been learning to spell words with irregular plurals. Locate three words with irregular plurals in a newspaper. Say the singular forms of the words and ask your child to spell the plurals.

Vowel Sounds with *r*

Spelling Words				
snore	tornado	spare	appear	career
square	report	prepare	pioneer	chair
beware	smear	repair	sword	ignore
order	engineer	resort	volunteer	declare

Word Search Circle ten hidden list words. Words are down, across, and diagonal. Write the words on the lines.

```
F  V  W  P  P  R  R  E  S  O
S  W  O  R  D  E  E  N  N  R
M  L  A  L  E  S  P  G  P  E
E  Q  W  I  U  L  O  I  S  P
A  R  I  A  T  N  R  N  N  T
R  E  S  O  R  T  T  E  O  Y
A  T  E  P  O  R  D  E  R  B
W  O  H  S  Q  U  A  R  E  E
T  R  S  A  I  P  Z  E  N  R
Z  B  E  W  A  R  E  A  S  E
```

1. _____   6. _____

2. _____   7. _____

3. _____   8. _____

4. _____   9. _____

5. _____   10. _____

Synonyms Write the list word that has the same, or nearly the same, meaning.

11. twister _____   16. fix _____

12. ready _____   17. overlook _____

13. occupation _____   18. seem _____

14. announce _____   19. extra _____

15. seat _____   20. pathfinder _____

Home Activity Your child has been learning to spell words containing vowel sounds with *r*. Select three words from your child's spelling list and make up a sentence with him or her. Ask your child to write the sentence.

Final Syllables *-en, -an, -el, -le, -il*

Spelling Words				
example	level	human	quarrel	scramble
evil	oxygen	wooden	double	travel
cancel	chuckle	fossil	toboggan	veteran
chisel	suburban	single	sudden	beagle

Words in Context Write the word to complete each sentence.

1. I _____ when I hear an amusing joke.

2. You must _____ your appointment if you can't make it.

3. Breathe deeply to get plenty of _____.

4. Sailing is a(n) _____ of a water sport.

5. Molly's _____ is a friendly, cheerful dog.

6. The boys went down the snowy hill on a(n) _____.

7. A sculptor uses a(n) _____ to shape marble.

8. The scientist found a(n) _____ of a dinosaur in the ground.

9. People can _____ in cars, trains, and planes.

10. Baseball players use a(n) _____ bat.

11. Shall we fry, poach, or _____ the eggs?

12. Monkeys have some seemingly _____ characteristics.

Antonyms Write the list word that has the opposite, or nearly the opposite, meaning.

13. newcomer _____

14. agree _____

15. rural _____

16. married _____

17. good _____

18. uneven _____

19. gradual _____

20. single _____

 Home Activity Your child has been learning to spell words with the final syllables *-en, -an, -el, -le,* and *-il*. To practice at home, dictate a word with each ending. Ask your child to spell the word and provide a synonym or antonym for it.

Final Syllables *-er, -ar, -or*

Spelling Words				
danger	wander	tractor	dollar	harbor
eager	eraser	surrender	solar	sticker
locker	helicopter	pillar	refrigerator	caterpillar
rumor	glimmer	linger	sensor	alligator

Analogies Write the word that completes each comparison.

1. Hot is to oven as cool is to _____.

2. Page is to book as penny is to _____.

3. Flower is to bud as butterfly is to _____.

4. Moon is to lunar as sun is to _____.

5. Clothes are to closet as books are to _____.

6. Walk is to stroll as roam is to _____.

7. Patio is to yard as port is to _____.

8. Fingernail is to finger as _____ is to pencil.

9. Fact is to fiction as truth is to _____.

10. Sail is to ship as fly is to _____.

Hidden Words Each of these small words can be found inside one of the list words. Write the list word that contains the small words.

11. in _____

12. tick _____

13. act _____

14. me _____

15. all _____

16. end _____

17. ill _____

18. so _____

19. an _____

20. age _____

Home Activity Your child has been learning to spell words with the final syllables *-er*, *-ar*, and *-or*. Choose a word with each ending from your child's spelling list. Ask your child to spell the word and use it in a sentence.

Proofread for Spelling Errors

Proofread a Newspaper Article. Circle twelve spelling mistakes in the newspaper article below. Write them correctly.

Everyone in our community was shocked when the tornadoe ripped through Springfield this week. Several houses were seriously damaged, and a few were totally destroyed. Allthough Cherry Hill was never in dainger from the storm, everyone wanted to help the people of Springfield.

The fifth-grade classes at Cherry Hill School voted to help the storm victims clean up on Saturday. One volenteer, Lee King, said, "I was eeger to help any way I could, so I grabbed a shovle and went to Springfield with my friends."

The helpers worked on many tasks. They sorted through people's possessions and found valuable papers and pictures. They put ruined books and broken chinna in trash bags. One helper said, "You can't repare everything in one day, and you can't ignoar people facing a chalenge." Some people served sandwiches and cold drinks to the tired storm victims. As fifth-grader Keesha Jackson observed, "We found out that your life can change all of a suddon. Maybe next time my family and I will need help ourselfs."

1. _____   7. _____

2. _____   8. _____

3. _____   9. _____

4. _____   10. _____

5. _____   11. _____

6. _____   12. _____

Schwa

Generalization In many words, the schwa in an unaccented syllable gives no clue to its spelling: **jew<u>e</u>l**, **fact<u>o</u>ry**, **g<u>a</u>rage**, **tropic<u>a</u>l**.

Word Sort Sort the list words by words you know how to spell and words you are learning to spell.

Spelling Words

1. jewel
2. kingdom
3. gasoline
4. factory
5. garage
6. tropical
7. pajamas
8. estimate
9. tomorrow
10. humidity

11. Chicago
12. bulletin
13. carnival
14. illustrate
15. elegant
16. census
17. terrific
18. celebrate
19. operate
20. celery

**words I know
how to spell**

1. _____
2. _____
3. _____
4. _____
5. _____
6. _____
7. _____
8. _____
9. _____
10. _____

**words I am
learning to spell**

11. _____
12. _____
13. _____
14. _____
15. _____
16. _____
17. _____
18. _____
19. _____
20. _____

School + Home **Home Activity** Your child is learning about the sound of schwa. Name three words from the list and ask your child to tell you which sound in each word is the schwa.

Schwa

Spelling Words				
jewel	kingdom	gasoline	factory	garage
tropical	pajamas	estimate	tomorrow	humidity
Chicago	bulletin	carnival	illustrate	elegant
census	terrific	celebrate	operate	celery

Word Clues Write the list word that fits each clue.

1. This may have rides, contests, costumes, and parades.
   1. _____

2. This type of place has palm trees and year-round warm weather.
   2. _____

3. This is a type of board for special announcements.
   3. _____

4. This is what you do at birthdays, anniversaries, and holidays.
   4. _____

5. This is a time that is not yesterday or today.
   5. _____

6. This is where royalty lives and rules.
   6. _____

7. This green vegetable has long, crisp stalks.
   7. _____

8. This is anything with fancy, classic style.
   8. _____

9. This is what you do when you draw pictures.
   9. _____

10. This is a kind of nightwear.
   10. _____

Words in Context Write the list word that best completes each sentence.

11. The national _____ is a counting of everyone who lives in the U.S.
   11. _____

12. Can you _____ the number of students in your school?
   12. _____

13. Our car needs to go to the _____ for an oil change.
   13. _____

14. We'll need to fill the tank with _____.
   14. _____

15. That _____ makes parts for lawnmowers.
   15. _____

16. Air conditioning is used in places with lots of heat and _____.
   16. _____

17. The doctor had to _____ on me to remove my appendix.
   17. _____

18. A diamond is a valuable and precious _____.
   18. _____

19. The largest city in Illinois is _____.
   19. _____

20. That was one _____ roller coaster ride!
   20. _____

Home Activity Your child wrote words with the schwa sound. Ask your child to spell three list words, telling you where the schwa sound is in each word.

Spelling Practice Book

Schwa

Proofread a Letter Laura wrote this letter to her aunt. Circle six spelling errors. Write the words correctly. Find one punctuation error. Write the sentence correctly.

Dear Aunt Betty,
Next week we will celabrate at the carnaval. We've been busy decorating a float. Our theme will be the city of Chicago. The city has many eligant buildings. We want to illestrate this on our float. We were a little off on our estamate of how long it would take to complete it. It probly won't be easy, to get this beautiful, decorated platform out of the garage. Even so, we are looking forward to a terrific day!

1. _____   2. _____

3. _____   4. _____

5. _____   6. _____

7. _____

_____

Spelling Words

jewel
kingdom
gasoline
factory
garage
tropical
pajamas
estimate
tomorrow
humidity

Chicago
bulletin
carnival
illustrate
elegant
census
terrific
celebrate
operate
celery

Proofread Words Circle the correct spelling of the list word.

8. We moved to a _____ climate this winter.

    tropecal   tropical   troppicle

9. The _____ made everyone feel very sticky when they went outside.

    humidity   humiduty   humidety

10. My favorite _____ have feet in them.

    pajammas   pajamers   pajamas

11. The _____ shows that the population of our town has doubled.

    sensus   census   censis

12. The weather _____ says that snow is on the way!

    bullatin   bulliten   bulletin

Frequently Misspelled Words

Christmas
beautiful
probably

Home Activity Your child identified misspelled words with schwas. Have your child tell you the three hardest words and then spell the words aloud.

Schwa

Spelling Words

jewel	kingdom	gasoline	factory	garage
tropical	pajamas	estimate	tomorrow	humidity
Chicago	bulletin	carnival	illustrate	elegant
census	terrific	celebrate	operate	celery

Categorize Write the list word that completes each group.

1. New York, Los Angeles, Boston, ____

2. car, mechanic, car lift, ____

3. assembly line, plant, workshop, ____

4. diamond, sapphire, ruby, ____

5. chic, classic, smart, ____

6. counting, poll, survey, ____

7. stalk, vegetable, green, ____

8. draw, explain, show, ____

9. guess, approximate, ____

10. run, control, drive, ____

1. _____

2. _____

3. _____

4. _____

5. _____

6. _____

7. _____

8. _____

9. _____

10. _____

Words in Context Write the list word that completes each sentence.

11. The ____ has rides, games, and performers.

12. It's not the heat, it's the ____.

13. Do not put off for ____ what you can do today.

14. A ____ is ruled by a king or queen.

15. Before I go to bed, I change into my ____.

16. We ____ Flag Day on June 14.

17. Florida has a ____ climate.

18. That was a ____ skateboard move!

19. A news ____ cut in on our television show.

20. Most cars are still powered by ____ fuel.

11. _____

12. _____

13. _____

14. _____

15. _____

16. _____

17. _____

18. _____

19. _____

20. _____

Home Activity Your child has learned to read, write, and spell words with schwa sounds. Take turns saying and spelling each word aloud.

Spelling Practice Book

Compound Words

Generalization A compound word is smaller words joined together. Keep all the letters when spelling compounds: **water + proof = waterproof.**

Word Sort Sort the list words by words you know how to spell and words you are learning to spell. Write every word.

words I know how to spell	words I am learning to spell
1. _____	11. _____
2. _____	12. _____
3. _____	13. _____
4. _____	14. _____
5. _____	15. _____
6. _____	16. _____
7. _____	17. _____
8. _____	18. _____
9. _____	19. _____
10. _____	20. _____

Spelling Words

1. waterproof
2. teaspoon
3. grasshopper
4. homesick
5. barefoot
6. courthouse
7. earthquake
8. rowboat
9. scrapbook
10. countryside

11. lightweight
12. fishhook
13. spotlight
14. blindfold
15. whirlpool
16. tablespoon
17. greenhouse
18. postcard
19. hummingbird
20. thumbtack

Home Activity Your child is learning about compound words. Help your child draw a line to separate the two words that make up each compound word.

Compound Words

Spelling Words				
waterproof	teaspoon	grasshopper	homesick	barefoot
courthouse	earthquake	rowboat	scrapbook	countryside
lightweight	fishhook	spotlight	blindfold	whirlpool
tablespoon	greenhouse	postcard	hummingbird	thumbtack

Complete the Sentence Write the list word that best completes the sentence.

1. Do you know that three teaspoons equal one ____?

2. The ____ is a place where justice is tested every day.

3. The ant stored food while the ____ played.

4. When you're away for a while, it is common to feel ____.

5. The hum from a ____ comes from its rapidly beating wings.

6. Some people wear a ____ to sleep on an airplane.

7. The ____ is full of exotic plants.

8. The circle of light on the stage was from the ____.

9. I like to walk ____ in the wet sand.

10. The ____ was full of old news clippings and photos.

1. _____
2. _____
3. _____
4. _____
5. _____
6. _____
7. _____
8. _____
9. _____
10. _____

Definitions Answer each clue with a list word. Write it on the line.

11. hills, trees, and lakes

12. not heavy at all

13. carries a message

14. hang something with it

15. stays dry

16. shaking ground

17. boat with oars

18. worm holder

19. one-third of a tablespoon

20. circling water

11. _____
12. _____
13. _____
14. _____
15. _____
16. _____
17. _____
18. _____
19. _____
20. _____

School + Home **Home Activity** Your child used the meaning of list words to write them in sentences and match them with synonyms. Ask your child to tell you what a compound word is and give three examples.

Compound Words

Proofread a Letter Halie wrote a letter home from camp. There are seven spelling errors and one capitalization error. Circle the errors and write the corrections on the lines.

Dear Mom and Dad,

I'm not crying or homsick. This paper got a little wet because I'm in a rowboat. I have a fish hook on the line. The countryside around camp is awesome. We run around bearfoot most days. My Counselor is the nature teacher. Yesterday, everybody saw a hummbird. The camp has a greenhouse where all the vegetables we eat are grown. Thanks for the waterproff slicker. It's litewait and will keep me dry. You sent a really beautiful postcard of the Grand Canyon. I used a thumtack to hang it on my bunk wall!

Write soon,
Halie

1. _____   2. _____

3. _____   4. _____

5. _____   6. _____

7. _____

8. _____

Proofread Words Correct the spelling of the list words. Write the words correctly on the lines.

9. Meet me on the steps of the <u>corthouse</u>.   9. _____

10. My <u>scapebook</u> is full of pictures and mementos. 10. _____

11. Performers love to be in the <u>spotelite</u>.   11. _____

12. The bathwater went down the drain in a little <u>wirlpool</u>.   12. _____

13. Pictures fell off the wall during the <u>erthkwake</u>. 13. _____

14. I folded my scarf into a <u>blindefold</u>.   14. _____

15. A <u>grasshoper</u> has long, strong legs.   15. _____

Spelling Words

waterproof
teaspoon
grasshopper
homesick
barefoot
courthouse
earthquake
rowboat
scrapbook
countryside

lightweight
fishhook
spotlight
blindfold
whirlpool
tablespoon
greenhouse
postcard
hummingbird
thumbtack

Frequently Misspelled Words

something
everybody
everyone

School + Home   **Home Activity** Your child identified misspelled compound words. Ask your child to spell three of the compound words for you.

Compound Words

Spelling Words				
waterproof	teaspoon	grasshopper	homesick	barefoot
courthouse	earthquake	rowboat	scrapbook	countryside
lightweight	fishhook	spotlight	blindfold	whirlpool
tablespoon	greenhouse	postcard	hummingbird	thumbtack

Mixed-Up Words Draw a line to connect the words to make a list word. Then write the list word on the line.

1. earth   weight   1. _____

2. bare   proof   2. _____

3. table   hook   3. _____

4. country   spoon   4. _____

5. fish   fold   5. _____

6. light   tack   6. _____

7. grass   side   7. _____

8. water   foot   8. _____

9. blind   hopper   9. _____

10. thumb   quake   10. _____

Word Scramble Unscramble the words and write them on the lines.

11. thsoueourc   11. _____

12. looplirhw   12. _____

13. stapoone   13. _____

14. regensehou   14. _____

15. mirdmibungh   15. _____

16. watboor   16. _____

17. mecksiho   17. _____

18. dracstop   18. _____

Home Activity Your child has learned to read, write, and spell compound words. Look in other books to find three other compound words.

Consonant Sounds /j/, /ks/, /sk/, and /s/

Generalization The sound /j/ can be spelled **g**, **j**, and **dge**: <u>g</u>inger, <u>j</u>ournal, do<u>dge</u>. The sound /ks/ can be spelled **x**: e<u>x</u>cuse. The sound /sk/ can be spelled **sch**: <u>sch</u>edule. The sound /s/ can be spelled **sc**: <u>sc</u>ene.

Word Sort Sort words by the spelling of the consonant sounds.

Spelling Words

1. excuse
2. scene
3. muscle
4. explore
5. pledge
6. journal
7. science
8. schedule
9. gigantic
10. scheme

11. Japan
12. excellent
13. exclaim
14. fascinate
15. ginger
16. scholar
17. scent
18. dodge
19. smudge
20. schooner

g

1. _____

2. _____

dge

3. _____

4. _____

5. _____

x

6. _____

7. _____

8. _____

9. _____

j

10. _____

11. _____

sch

12. _____

13. _____

14. _____

15. _____

sc

16. _____

17. _____

18. _____

19. _____

20. _____

Home Activity Your child is learning to spell words with consonant sounds /j/, /ks/, /sk/, and /s/. Have your child name one list word with each of these sounds.

Consonant Sounds /j/, /ks/, /sk/, and /s/

Spelling Words				
excuse	scene	muscle	explore	pledge
journal	science	schedule	gigantic	scheme
Japan	excellent	exclaim	fascinate	ginger
scholar	scent	dodge	smudge	schooner

Classify Write the list word that best completes the group.

1. plan, plot, _____

2. avoid, elude, sidestep, _____

3. diary, log, magazine, _____

4. setting, landscape, _____

5. aroma, perfume, odor, _____

6. captivate, interest, _____

7. bone, skin, _____

8. yacht, kayak, _____

9. outstanding, brilliant, _____

10. basil, oregano, _____

1. _____

2. _____

3. _____

4. _____

5. _____

6. _____

7. _____

8. _____

9. _____

10. _____

Words in Context Write the list word that completes each sentence.

11. Tokyo is the largest city in _____.

12. Cry out and _____ mean the same thing.

13. A _____ enjoys learning and studying.

14. The bad weather is my _____ for being late today.

15. Astronauts _____ outer space.

16. I'll add the meeting to my _____.

17. I made a donation _____ to the local charity.

18. My _____ book contains many experiments.

19. The _____ on the wall is from finger paint.

20. The redwood trees in California are _____.

11. _____

12. _____

13. _____

14. _____

15. _____

16. _____

17. _____

18. _____

19. _____

20. _____

Home Activity Your child wrote words with special spellings for certain consonant sounds. Have your child pick the five most difficult words for him or her. Go over the spelling of these words with your child.

Consonant Sounds /j/, /ks/, /sk/, and /s/

Proofread a Travel Poster There are seven spelling errors and one
punctuation error. Circle the errors and write the corrections on the lines.

Spelling Words

excuse
scene
muscle
explore
pledge
journal
science
schedule
gigantic
scheme

Japan
excellent
exclaim
fascinate
ginger
scholar
scent
dodge
smudge
schooner

1. _____   2. _____

3. _____   4. _____

5. _____   6. _____

7. _____

8. _____

Proofread Words Circle the correct spelling of the list words.

9. plege	pleje	pledge
10. sceme	scheme	skeme
11. smudge	smuge	smuje
12. mussle	muscel	muscle
13. dodje	dodge	dogde
14. journal	journle	jurnal
15. jigantic	gidgantic	gigantic
16. skooner	schooner	scooner

Frequently Misspelled Words

except
excited
school

Home Activity Your child identified misspelled list words. Review the *sch* and *sc* words and their
pronunciation with your child.

Consonant Sounds /j/, /ks/, /sk/, and /s/

Spelling Words				
excuse	scene	muscle	explore	pledge
journal	science	schedule	gigantic	scheme
Japan	excellent	exclaim	fascinate	ginger
scholar	scent	dodge	smudge	schooner

Crossword Puzzle Use the clues to find the list words. Write each letter in a box.

Across
1. promise
4. timetable
5. smear
6. spice
7. log
8. avoid
9. boat

Down
2. huge
3. a strong ___
4. student
5. plan

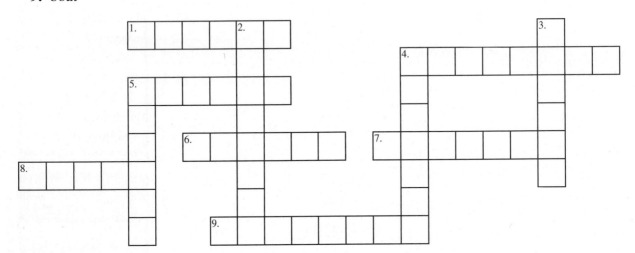

Words in Context Finish the story using list words.

Some foods from **(10)**____ are flavored with **(11)**____. The

(12)____ of the cooking is delicious. The tasty foods will surely

(13)____ your taste buds. It is a great experience to **(14)**____ the

foods of different countries.

10. _____
11. _____
12. _____
13. _____
14. _____

School + Home

Home Activity Your child has learned to read, write, and spell words with consonant sounds spelled in special ways. Take turns spelling aloud the list words with your child.

One Consonant or Two

Generalization Many words have two consonants that stand for the same sound: <u>add</u>re<u>ss</u>, <u>committee</u>.

Word Sort Sort the list words by words you know how to spell and words you are learning to spell. Write every word.

Spelling Words

1. address
2. college
3. mirror
4. recess
5. committee
6. collect
7. Mississippi
8. immediate
9. command
10. appreciate

11. announce
12. possess
13. Tennessee
14. gallop
15. opponent
16. barricade
17. broccoli
18. accomplish
19. allowance
20. zucchini

words I know how to spell

1. _____
2. _____
3. _____
4. _____
5. _____
6. _____
7. _____
8. _____
9. _____
10. _____

words I am learning to spell

11. _____
12. _____
13. _____
14. _____
15. _____
16. _____
17. _____
18. _____
19. _____
20. _____

Home Activity Your child is learning about words with double consonants. Have your child circle the double consonants in each list word.

© Pearson Education, Inc. 5

One Consonant or Two

Spelling Words				
address	college	mirror	recess	committee
collect	Mississippi	immediate	command	appreciate
announce	possess	Tennessee	gallop	opponent
barricade	broccoli	accomplish	allowance	zucchini

Words in Context Write the list word on the line that best completes the sentence.

1. The vegetable _____ looks like little trees.

2. It was hard to cross the street because of the police _____.

3. The capital of _____ is Nashville.

4. Do you plan on going to _____ after high school?

5. "Faster, faster," he urged the horse as it began to _____.

6. He looked in the _____ to comb his hair.

7. The _____ River is the second-longest river in the United States.

8. Our class has _____ after lunch.

9. Do you get a weekly _____ for doing chores?

10. I need your telephone number and _____ for our records.

1. _____

2. _____

3. _____

4. _____

5. _____

6. _____

7. _____

8. _____

9. _____

10. _____

Antonyms Write the list word that has the opposite or nearly the opposite meaning.

11. scatter

12. delayed

13. obey

14. disregard

15. remove

11. _____

12. _____

13. _____

14. _____

15. _____

Synonyms Write the list word that has the same or almost the same meaning as the word.

16. declare

17. group

18. foe

19. summer squash

20. succeed

16. _____

17. _____

18. _____

19. _____

20. _____

School + Home **Home Activity** Your child wrote words with double consonants. Take turns saying and spelling the list words aloud.

One Consonant or Two

Proofread a Newspaper Article Circle six misspelled words. Write the words correctly. Find one capitalization error. Write the sentence correctly.

> Something odd hapenned in the colledge dining room. Some students wanted brocoli at every meal. Their opponents wanted zuchinni. A commitee was formed. They decided to take a vote. No one expected an immediat result. The committee had something surprising to announce. most of the students preferred carrots!

Spelling Words

address
college
mirror
recess
committee
collect
Mississippi
immediate
command
appreciate

announce
possess
Tennessee
gallop
opponent
barricade
broccoli
accomplish
allowance
zucchini

1. _____   2. _____

3. _____   4. _____

5. _____   6. _____

7. _____

Proofread Words Circle the correct spelling of the list words.

8. Memphis and Nashville are cities in _____.

   Tenessee   Tennese   Tennessee

9. Most students love _____ after being inside.

   recess   reccess   recces

10. I _____ a collection of old comic books.

   posess   possess   posses

11. The settlers used a wooden plank to _____ the door.

   barricade   barricad   bariccade

12. I am hoping to _____ a lot this school year.

   acomplish   accomplish   accommplish

13. The bathroom _____ was foggy because of the steam from the shower.

   mirrer   miror   mirror

14. I will _____ the winner at the end of the game.

   announce   anounce   anounnce

Frequently Misspelled Words

different
happened

Home Activity Your child identified misspelled list words. Have your child tell you the three most difficult list words and then spell them to you.

One Consonant or Two

Spelling Words				
address	college	mirror	recess	committee
collect	Mississippi	immediate	command	appreciate
announce	possess	Tennessee	gallop	opponent
barricade	broccoli	accomplish	allowance	zucchini

Double Puzzle Unscramble the words. Write the numbered letters in the boxes below to find the answer to the riddle.

Riddle: What is the name of a dark, rich chocolate dessert?

1. CINUCZIH   __ __ __ __ __ __ __ __₁₆

2. GPLALO   __ __ __ __ __ __₉ __

3. MIRORR   __ __₁ __ __ __ __

4. SADDRSE   __ __₁₄ __ __ __ __₄ __

5. DETIAMIME   __ __ __ __ __₂ __ __ __ __

6. UNOCEANN   __ __ __ __₁₃ __ __ __₁₇ __

7. SSNEEEENT   __ __ __ __ __₆ __ __ __

8. POICSHCALM   __ __ __ __ __₁₅ __ __₅ __₇ __

9. BDCIERARA   __ __ __ __₈ __ __ __ __

10. TAIARPECEP   __ __₁₀ __ __ __ __ __ __ __

11. PSESSSO   __ __ __ __ __ __₃ __

12. EIOETTCMM   __ __ __ __₁₂ __₁₁ __ __ __ __

__ __ __ __ __ __ __ __ __ __ __   __ __ __   __ __ __
1   2   3   4   5   6   7   8   9   10   11   12   13   14   15   16   17

Synonyms Write the list word that has the same or nearly the same meaning.

13. foe _____

14. higher education _____

15. green vegetable _____

16. order _____

17. payment _____

18. gather _____

19. speak to _____

20. time off _____

Home Activity Your child has learned to read, write, and spell words with double consonants. Look at magazines and newspapers with your child and find three other words that have double consonants.

Prefixes *un-, de-, dis-*

Generalization When prefixes **un-**, **de-**, or **dis-** are added to words, the base word does not change: <u>uncover</u>, <u>defrost</u>, <u>discourage</u>.

Word Sort Sort the list words by their prefixes.

un-

1. _____

2. _____

3. _____

4. _____

5. _____

6. _____

7. _____

8. _____

de-

9. _____

10. _____

11. _____

12. _____

dis-

13. _____

14. _____

15. _____

16. _____

17. _____

18. _____

19. _____

20. _____

Spelling Words

1. uncover
2. defrost
3. uncomfortable
4. discourage
5. disadvantage
6. unfortunate
7. unfamiliar
8. disability
9. discomfort
10. deodorant

11. unemployed
12. deflate
13. disbelief
14. unpredictable
15. disapprove
16. disappoint
17. unpleasant
18. dehydrated
19. disqualify
20. undecided

Home Activity Your child is learning to spell words with prefixes *un-*, *de-*, and *dis-*. Have your child circle the prefix in each list word.

Prefixes *un-, de-, dis-*

Spelling Words				
uncover	defrost	uncomfortable	discourage	disadvantage
unfortunate	unfamiliar	disability	discomfort	deodorant
unemployed	deflate	disbelief	unpredictable	disapprove
disappoint	unpleasant	dehydrated	disqualify	undecided

Definitions in Context Write the list word that has the same or almost the same meaning as the underlined word or words.

1. Moisture is removed from <u>dried out</u> food.

2. I need to <u>melt</u> the turkey.

3. It was <u>unlucky</u> that I broke my leg.

4. My mother has been <u>out of work</u> since the factory closed.

5. The outcome of the contest was <u>in doubt</u> for months.

6. The player's tardiness was a <u>difficulty</u> for the team.

7. I took a route home from school that was <u>new</u> to me.

8. The roller coaster ride was <u>disagreeable</u> to me.

9. It was <u>painful</u> to sleep on the old, lumpy mattress.

10. The team decided to <u>ban</u> a player for cheating.

1. _____

2. _____

3. _____

4. _____

5. _____

6. _____

7. _____

8. _____

9. _____

10. _____

Antonyms Write the list word that has the opposite or nearly the opposite meaning.

11. ability

12. with odor

13. belief

14. expected

15. please

16. inflate

17. conceal

18. support

19. encourage

20. comfortable

11. _____

12. _____

13. _____

14. _____

15. _____

16. _____

17. _____

18. _____

19. _____

20. _____

Home Activity Your child wrote words with prefixes. Say a prefix and have your child respond with one word from the list that uses that prefix.

Prefixes *un-*, *de-*, *dis-*

Proofread an Article There are seven spelling errors and one capitalization error. Circle the errors and write the corrections on the lines.

A Very Long Race

Many look upon marathon runners with disbeleaf. These athletes run 26 miles in unfamilar cities. They deal with unpredictible and sometimes unplesant weather. Many run with discomfort and some with a disbility. Many runners become dehidrated. Spectators do not disapoint the runners. They give cups of water to all Runners.

1. _____	2. _____
3. _____	4. _____
5. _____	6. _____
7. _____	

8. _____

Spelling Words

uncover
defrost
uncomfortable
discourage
disadvantage
unfortunate
unfamiliar
disability
discomfort
deodorant

unemployed
deflate
disbelief
unpredictable
disapprove
disappoint
unpleasant
dehydrated
disqualify
undecided

Frequently Misspelled Words

until
before

Proofread Words Circle the correct spelling of the list words.

9.	deordorent	deodorant	deoderant
10.	disqualify	disqualyfie	dequalify
11.	uncomfortible	unconfortable	uncomfortable
12.	deflate	deflait	defleat
13.	deapprove	disapprove	disaprove
14.	disadvantadge	disadvantige	disadvantage
15.	undecided	indecided	undecide
16.	discomfrt	discomfort	discomefrt

School + Home

Home Activity Your child identified misspelled list words. Ask your child to name one word for each prefix studied and spell the word.

Prefixes *un-*, *de-*, *dis-*

Spelling Words				
uncover	defrost	uncomfortable	discourage	disadvantage
unfortunate	unfamiliar	disability	discomfort	deodorant
unemployed	deflate	disbelief	unpredictable	disapprove
disappoint	unpleasant	dehydrated	disqualify	undecided

Adding Word Parts Write the list words that contain the words below.

approve   **1.** _____

pleasant   **2.** _____

qualify   **3.** _____

cover   **4.** _____

courage   **5.** _____

odor   **6.** _____

fortunate   **7.** _____

predictable   **8.** _____

advantage   **9.** _____

frost   **10.** _____

Word Search Find ten list words hidden in the puzzle. Words are found down and across. Then write the words.

```
D I S C O U R A G E D N        11. _____
K D E O D O R A N T E D        12. _____
U N D E C I D E D W F E        13. _____
U N P L E A S A N T R F        14. _____
D I S B E L I E F P O L        15. _____
U N F A M I L I A R S A        16. _____
D I S C O M F O R T T T        17. _____
D E H Y D R A T E D Y E        18. _____
                               19. _____
                               20. _____
```

Home Activity Your child has learned to read, write, and spell words with prefixes. Take turns spelling aloud the list words with your child.

Schwa

Spelling Words				
jewel	kingdom	gasoline	factory	garage
tropical	pajamas	estimate	tomorrow	humidity
Chicago	bulletin	carnival	illustrate	elegant
census	terrific	celebrate	operate	celery

Synonyms Write the list word that has the same or nearly the same meaning.

1. great _____

2. festival _____

3. count _____

4. carport _____

5. tasteful _____

6. gem _____

7. rejoice _____

8. nightclothes _____

9. moisture _____

10. guess _____

Scramble Unscramble the list words and write them on the lines.

11. seloaing _____

12. slurtileat _____

13. tublelin _____

14. wormorto _____

15. plorcita _____

16. troycaf _____

17. torapee _____

18. coaCgih _____

19. midkong _____

20. rylcee _____

Home Activity Your child has been learning to spell words with the schwa sound. Ask your child to name three words with this sound and spell them.

Compound Words

Spelling Words				
waterproof	teaspoon	grasshopper	homesick	barefoot
courthouse	earthquake	rowboat	scrapbook	countryside
lightweight	fishhook	spotlight	blindfold	whirlpool
tablespoon	greenhouse	postcard	hummingbird	thumbtack

Analogies Write the word that completes each comparison.

1. Urban is to city as rural is to _____.

2. Short is to tall as heavy weight is to _____.

3. Librarian is to library as judge is to _____.

4. Animal is to zoo as plant is to _____.

5. Snake is to reptile as _____ is to insect.

6. Glue is to tape as nail is to _____.

7. Pedal is to bicycle as oar is to _____.

8. Scarf is to neck as _____ is to eyes.

9. Cup is to china as _____ is to silverware.

10. E-mail is to computer as _____ is to mailbox.

Word Clues Write the list word that fits each clue.

11. This might describe a raincoat and boots. _____

12. Cooks use this to measure ingredients. _____

13. Make this to remember a special trip. _____

14. Don't become an actor if you don't like this. _____

15. You can feed this in your backyard. _____

16. A big one might cause buildings to fall. _____

17. Beware of this when swimming in a big lake or river. _____

18. Going away to summer camp might make you feel like this. _____

19. Walk this way at the beach if you like sand between your toes. _____

20. Put this on the end of your line. _____

Home Activity Your child has learned to spell compound words. Find four compound words in a magazine. Write all the words of the compounds in random order. Ask your child to put the correct words together to make the compound words.

Consonant Sounds /j/, /ks/, /sk/, and /s/

Spelling Words				
excuse	scene	muscle	explore	pledge
journal	science	schedule	gigantic	scheme
Japan	excellent	exclaim	fascinate	ginger
scholar	scent	dodge	smudge	schooner

Word Search Circle ten hidden list words. Words are down, across, and diagonal. Write the words on the lines.

```
F  V  S  C  H  E  D  U  L  E
E  X  C  L  A  I  M  N  N  R
C  D  H  M  G  I  N  G  E  R
K  Q  O  I  U  L  O  I  S  S
E  R  L  D  T  S  S  N  M  C
D  E  A  O  G  T  C  E  U  I
U  X  R  P  O  E  E  L  R  E
L  C  H  E  O  U  N  R  E  N
S  C  H  O  O  N  E  R  N  C
Z  F  A  S  C  I  N  A  T  E
```

1. _____   6. _____

2. _____   7. _____

3. _____   8. _____

4. _____   9. _____

5. _____   10. _____

Hidden Words Each of these small words can be found inside one of the list words. Write the list word that contains the small words.

11. ant _____   16. our _____

12. cell _____   17. aim _____

13. mud _____   18. edge _____

14. use _____   19. hem _____

15. pan _____   20. cent _____

Home Activity Your child has been learning to spell words with various consonant sounds. Ask your child to write two words in which the *sk* sound is spelled in different ways.

One Consonant or Two

Spelling Words

address	college	mirror	recess	committee
collect	Mississippi	immediate	command	appreciate
announce	possess	Tennessee	gallop	opponent
barricade	broccoli	accomplish	allowance	zucchini

Analogies Write the word that completes each comparison.

1. Jog is to run as trot is to _____.

2. Pecan is to nut as _____ is to squash.

3. Speak is to talk as own is to _____.

4. Friend is to enemy as teammate is to _____.

5. Teacher is to school as professor is to _____.

6. President is to company as chairman is to _____.

7. Open is to close as discard is to _____.

8. Car is to automobile as obstacle is to _____.

9. Cut is to scissors as reflect is to _____.

10. Yell is to shout as proclaim is to _____.

Word Clues Write the list word that fits each clue.

11. a break in the school day _____

12. the second-longest river in the United States _____

13. to make an effort and succeed _____

14. your street number and city _____

15. a green vegetable with stalks and florets _____

16. a general's job in the army _____

17. money received each week _____

18. a state that borders Kentucky _____

19. to value and treasure _____

20. happening right now _____

Home Activity Your child has been learning to spell words with double consonants. To practice at home, dictate three words with double consonants. Have your child write them.

Spelling Practice Book

Prefixes *un-*, *de-*, *dis-*

Spelling Words				
uncover	defrost	uncomfortable	discourage	disadvantage
unfortunate	unfamiliar	disability	discomfort	deodorant
unemployed	deflate	disbelief	unpredictable	disapprove
disappoint	unpleasant	dehydrated	disqualify	undecided

Synonyms Write the list word that has the same or nearly the same meaning.

1. jobless _____

2. strange _____

3. handicap _____

4. reject _____

5. uneasiness _____

6. expose _____

7. doubt _____

8. bar _____

9. dried _____

10. changeable _____

Analogies Write the word that completes each comparison.

11. Fix is to break as freeze is to _____.

12. Easy is to difficult as lucky is to _____.

13. Happy is to sad as relaxed is to _____.

14. Soap is to cleanser as antiperspirant is to _____.

15. Mad is to angry as uncertain is to _____.

16. Drain is to pool as _____ is to balloon.

17. Freedom is to liberty as weakness is to _____.

18. Beautiful is to ugly as charming is to _____.

19. Help is to support as frustrate is to _____.

20. Please is to annoy as encourage is to _____.

Home Activity Your child has been learning to spell words with the prefixes *un-*, *de*, and *dis-*. Find three words with these prefixes in a newspaper. Ask your child to spell each word and name a word that means the opposite.

Proofread for Spelling Errors

Proofread a Biography. Circle twelve spelling mistakes in the biography below.
Write them correctly.

If you go to a large art museum, you might see a painting with a simple sene of a mother and a child. Mary Cassatt painted many pictures like this that still fassinate people. Cassatt was an American painter who was born in 1844. She was one of the first American painters to use Impressionism. French artists began this form of painting in the 1860s. They often painted outdoors in the country side. They wanted to paint realistic scenes and eksplore color.

Mary Cassatt went to an art colege in Pennsylvania and then moved to France to learn more about art. She became friends with Edgar Degas, a famous Impressionist painter. In the late 1800s, Cassatt painted pictures to illastrate the everyday lives of women and children. She became known for these elegent paintings.

Cassatt also made prints that were inspired by the art of Jappan. They have flat, simple shapes. Later, Cassatt helped Americans apreciate Impressionist art. Americans were unfarmiliar with the new art form. They were undesided about buying it. Cassatt helped them see that this was an excelent new style. Cassatt died in 1926, having had a great influence on American art.

1. _____
2. _____
3. _____
4. _____
5. _____
6. _____
7. _____
8. _____
9. _____
10. _____
11. _____
12. _____

Words from Many Cultures

Generalization Many words in English come from other languages and may have unexpected spellings: k<u>h</u>aki, ball<u>et</u>.

Word Sort Sort the list words by words you know how to spell and words that you are learning to spell. Write every word.

words I know how to spell	words I am learning to spell
1. _____	11. _____
2. _____	12. _____
3. _____	13. _____
4. _____	14. _____
5. _____	15. _____
6. _____	16. _____
7. _____	17. _____
8. _____	18. _____
9. _____	19. _____
10. _____	20. _____

Spelling Words

1. khaki
2. hula
3. banana
4. ballet
5. waltz
6. tomato
7. vanilla
8. canyon
9. yogurt
10. banquet

11. macaroni
12. polka
13. cobra
14. koala
15. barbecue
16. safari
17. buffet
18. stampede
19. karate
20. kiosk

Home Activity Your child is learning to spell words that come from other cultures. Look up each word in the dictionary with your child.

Words from Many Cultures

Spelling Words				
khaki	hula	banana	ballet	waltz
tomato	vanilla	canyon	yogurt	banquet
macaroni	polka	cobra	koala	barbecue
safari	buffet	stampede	karate	kiosk

Word Histories Write a list word for each description.

1. This is French for a table full of different foods.

1. _____

2. Many students practice this Japanese form of self-defense.

2. _____

3. Native Americans introduced this fruit to the settlers.

3. _____

4. This is a Turkish treat made from milk.

4. _____

5. This Polynesian dance is usually performed in a grass skirt.

5. _____

6. This is a Spanish word for a large group of running buffaloes or horses.

6. _____

7. Although it has a French name, this dance form started in Russia.

7. _____

8. This furry animal has kept its Australian name.

8. _____

9. Soldiers wear this greenish fabric named by the Persians and Hindus so they can't be easily seen.

9. _____

10. This partner dance means "to turn" in German.

10. _____

11. This is an Italian name for a well-known pasta.

11. _____

12. The Spanish and Portuguese used the same name for this yellow fruit.

12. _____

13. A Native American word is used to name this kind of outside cooking.

13. _____

14. This Polish dance is very lively.

14. _____

15. Although this word is Arabic, this type of journey is done in Africa.

15. _____

16. The Spanish named this flavorful type of bean long before there was ice cream.

16. _____

17. This word for a feast or a formal dinner comes from French.

17. _____

18. This is a Spanish word for a very deep valley carved out by a river.

18. _____

19. The name for this hooded, poisonous snake comes from the Portuguese.

19. _____

20. This is a Turkish word for a newsstand.

20. _____

© Pearson Education, Inc.5

Home Activity Your child wrote words from other cultures. Go over the pronunciation of the French words *buffet* and *ballet*. Remind your child that in French *-et* in these words is pronounced as long *a*.

Words from Many Cultures

Proofread a Poster Circle the seven spelling errors in the school poster. Write the words correctly. Write the last sentence, using correct punctuation.

Our New After-School Programs

Learn to Dance
- poka and Texas two-step
- ballet (with tutus and toe shoes)
- walts and other ballroom dances
- hula and dances of the Pacific

Learn Martial Arts
- karatie • judo • kung fu

Learn How to Cook
- barbecue sauces
- tomatoe salads
- homemade yogurt
- macaronie and cheese and other pastas
- bananana cream pie and other desserts

Sign up at the kyosk outside the office.
Bring a permission form from your parents?

Spelling Words
khaki
hula
banana
ballet
waltz
tomato
vanilla
canyon
yogurt
banquet
macaroni
polka
cobra
koala
barbecue
safari
buffet
stampede
karate
kiosk

1. _____   2. _____

3. _____   4. _____

5. _____   6. _____

7. _____

8. _____

Frequently Misspelled Words
our
again

Proofread Words Circle the correct spelling of the list word. Write the word.

9. The frightened cattle started to ____.

9. _____

    stamped   stampede   stampeed

10. I love the assortment of foods on the restaurant ____.

10. _____

    buffet   buffay   buffee

Home Activity Your child identified misspelled list words. Say a list word and spell it incorrectly. Ask your child to spell the word correctly.

Words from Many Cultures

Spelling Words				
khaki	hula	banana	ballet	waltz
tomato	vanilla	canyon	yogurt	banquet
macaroni	polka	cobra	koala	barbecue
safari	buffet	stampede	karate	kiosk

Words in Context Write list words to complete the menu.

1. Welcome to the 5th Grade ____.

2. Eat all you want at the ____!

1st Course Appetizer

3. green salad with ____

4. cucumber with ____ dressing

2nd Course Entrée

5. chicken served fresh from the ____

6. ____ and cheese

3rd Course Dessert

7. ____ split sundae

Your choice of

8. ____, chocolate, or strawberry ice cream

1. _____
2. _____
3. _____
4. _____
5. _____
6. _____
7. _____
8. _____

Word Search Find ten list words hidden in the puzzle. Words are down, across, and diagonal. Write the words on the lines.

```
S  S  C  S  S  F  S  J  K  D  A  L
T  T  J  O  K  L  S  Y  O  M  T  K
B  K  A  I  B  Q  S  Y  A  N  J  H
A  X  A  M  E  R  W  R  L  H  H  A
L  H  S  R  P  S  A  F  A  R  I  K
L  N  U  U  A  E  W  A  L  T  Z  I
E  B  D  L  P  T  D  K  I  O  S  K
T  V  H  L  A  T  E  E  L  J  U  H
```

9. _____
10. _____
11. _____
12. _____
13. _____
14. _____
15. _____
16. _____
17. _____
18. _____

Home Activity Your child has learned to read, write, and spell words from other cultures. Take turns spelling the list words.

Prefixes *over-*, *under-*, *sub-*, *super-*, *out-*

Generalization When the prefixes **over-**, **under-**, **sub-**, **super-**, and **out-** are added to words, the base word stays the same: <u>over</u>look, <u>under</u>line, <u>sub</u>way, <u>super</u>market, <u>out</u>let.

Word Sort Sort words by their prefixes.

over-

1. _____

2. _____

3. _____

4. _____

under-

5. _____

6. _____

7. _____

8. _____

sub-

9. _____

10. _____

11. _____

12. _____

13. _____

super-

14. _____

15. _____

16. _____

17. _____

out-

18. _____

19. _____

20. _____

Spelling Words

1. overlook
2. underline
3. subway
4. subset
5. supermarket
6. outlet
7. underground
8. overboard
9. undercurrent
10. superstar

11. overtime
12. supersonic
13. submarine
14. undercover
15. overcast
16. outfield
17. output
18. supernatural
19. subdivision
20. subhead

© Pearson Education, Inc., 5

School + Home

Home Activity Your child is learning about prefixes. Have your child tell you the five prefixes used in the list words.

Prefixes *over-*, *under-*, *sub-*, *super-*, *out-*

Spelling Words				
overlook	underline	subway	subset	supermarket
outlet	underground	overboard	undercurrent	superstar
overtime	supersonic	submarine	undercover	overcast
outfield	output	supernatural	subdivision	subhead

Classifying Write the list word that belongs in each group.

1. city, trains, underground, ____

2. sky, clouds, gray, ____

3. diamond, mound, infield, ____

4. police officer, disguise, ____

5. grocery, bakery, butcher, ____

6. daydream, forget, omit, ____

7. highlight, line, ____

8. plane, jet engine, speed of sound, ____

9. work, extra hours, ____

10. performer, actor, singer, ____

1. _____

2. _____

3. _____

4. _____

5. _____

6. _____

7. _____

8. _____

9. _____

10. _____

Definitions Write the list word that fits each definition.

11. This is part of a community.

12. This is the result of production.

13. This means eerie and ghostly.

14. This is a small part of a larger group.

15. This means beneath the earth.

16. This is a vessel that travels underwater.

17. This comes under a heading.

18. This is a pull under the waves.

19. This means falling off a ship.

20. This can be a store that offers discounts.

11. _____

12. _____

13. _____

14. _____

15. _____

16. _____

17. _____

18. _____

19. _____

20. _____

Home Activity Your child wrote words with prefixes. Ask your child to name four words and tell you how the prefixes in each word affect its meaning.

Prefixes *over-*, *under-*, *sub-*, *super-*, *out-*

Proofread a Paragraph Circle six spelling errors. Write the words correctly. Find one punctuation error and write the sentence using the correct punctuation.

If you had a choice, would you want to break the sound barrier in a super sonic jet? Is cruising beneath the surface of the sea in a sub marine more your style? What about riding underground on a large sub way system? Would you rather stay all night in a deserted house waiting for something super natural to happen? Do you like sports. Perhaps you'd really rather be playing ball in the out field? Fortunately, one doesn't have to be a super star to do any of these things.

1. _____   2. _____

3. _____   4. _____

5. _____   6. _____

7. _____

Spelling Words

overlook
underline
subway
subset
supermarket
outlet
underground
overboard
undercurrent
superstar

overtime
supersonic
submarine
undercover
overcast
outfield
output
supernatural
subdivision
subhead

Proofread Words Circle the word that is spelled correctly.

8. submarine	submareen	submarein
9. subdivsion	subdivison	subdivision
10. subersonic	supersonic	supresonic
11. underline	undeline	undrline
12. outfeild	outfeeld	outfield
13. overcast	overcas	ovrcast
14. overlok	overlook	ovarlock
15. suparmarkit	suprmarkat	supermarket
16. overboard	overbored	ovarboard

Frequently Misspelled Words

outside
because

Home Activity Your child identified misspelled list words. Ask your child to tell you which three words are most difficult and then have your child spell them with you.

Prefixes *over-*, *under-*, *sub-*, *super-*, *out-*

Spelling Words				
overlook	underline	subway	subset	supermarket
outlet	underground	overboard	undercurrent	superstar
overtime	supersonic	submarine	undercover	overcast
outfield	output	supernatural	subdivision	subhead

Complete the Word Add a prefix to each word to make a list word.
Write the complete word on the line.

1. ___way

2. ___put

3. ___natural

4. ___market

5. ___line

6. ___head

7. ___division

8. ___current

1. _____

2. _____

3. _____

4. _____

5. _____

6. _____

7. _____

8. _____

Word Search Find and circle ten list words hidden in the puzzle. Words are down, across, and diagonal. Write the words on the lines.

U	S	D	L	T	J	J	I	G	O	S	S
R	N	J	D	Z	D	F	F	H	V	U	U
T	O	D	S	X	O	W	Y	O	E	B	B
G	O	V	E	R	L	O	O	K	R	M	H
S	U	P	E	R	S	T	A	R	B	A	E
B	T	Q	A	R	C	P	C	T	O	R	A
B	P	K	D	N	C	O	L	K	A	I	D
S	U	B	S	E	T	A	V	W	R	N	H
L	T	X	E	A	J	Y	S	E	D	E	V
S	U	B	W	A	Y	B	P	T	R	O	L

9. _____

10. _____

11. _____

12. _____

13. _____

14. _____

15. _____

16. _____

17. _____

18. _____

Home Activity Your child has learned to read, write, and spell words with prefixes. See if you can recombine prefixes and list words to make other words such as *outline*.

Homophones

Generalization A homophone is a word that sounds exactly like another word but has a different spelling and meaning: **cent**, **sent**.

Word Sort Sort the list words by words you know how to spell and words that you are learning to spell. Write every word.

Spelling Words
1. cent
2. sent
3. scent
4. threw
5. through
6. weather
7. whether
8. their
9. there
10. they're
11. chili
12. chilly
13. tide
14. tied
15. pale
16. pail
17. aloud
18. allowed
19. course
20. coarse

**words I know
how to spell**

1. _____

2. _____

3. _____

4. _____

5. _____

6. _____

7. _____

8. _____

9. _____

10. _____

**words I am
learning to spell**

11. _____

12. _____

13. _____

14. _____

15. _____

16. _____

17. _____

18. _____

19. _____

20. _____

School + Home

Home Activity Your child is learning about homophones. Ask your child to look at the word, say it, and then spell it.

Homophones

Spelling Words				
cent	sent	scent	threw	through
weather	whether	their	there	they're
chili	chilly	tide	tied	pale
pail	aloud	allowed	course	coarse

Words in Context Write homophones to complete the sentences.

On a **(1)**____ day, hot, spicy **(2)**____ with cheese really tastes good.

1. _____   2. _____

We made sure the boats were **(3)**____ down securely against the rising **(4)**____.

3. _____   4. _____

The **(5)**____ will determine **(6)**____ or not we play the game.

5. _____   6. _____

I **(7)**____ away for that special one- **(8)**____ offer for my favorite perfume **(9)**____.

7. _____   8. _____   9. _____

Speaking **(10)**____ is not **(11)**____ in the library.

10. _____   11. _____

You **(12)**____ the ball so far that it went **(13)**____ the window!

12. _____   13. _____

(14)____ starting **(15)**____ lemonade business over **(16)**____ near the bakery.

14. _____   15. _____   16. _____

The golf **(17)**____ is designed to be challenging. It has sand, water traps, woods, and smooth and **(18)**____ grass.

17. _____   18. _____

The **(19)**____ child carried the **(20)**____ onto the beach.

19. _____   20. _____

Home Activity Your child learned to use homophones in context. Ask your child to make up other sentences using list words.

© Pearson Education, Inc. 5

Homophones

Proofread an Ad Circle six spelling errors. Write the words correctly. Find one capitalization error. Write the sentence correctly.

> On a chilly day, shout allowed for our delicious chilly! It will warm you through and threw! Ask about our ninety-nine sent special. If the whether is bad, call us. We Deliver for free! Of course, their is no finer tasting treat!

1. _____   2. _____

3. _____   4. _____

5. _____   6. _____

7. _____

Proofread Words Circle the correct spelling of the list word. Write the word.

8. Burlap is a ____ fabric.

    corse   cuarse   coarse

8. _____

9. I think ____ going on a class trip tomorrow.

    they're   their   they'ar

9. _____

10. Sky blue is a ____ color.

    pail   pale   paile

10. _____

11. Your perfume has a lovely ____.

    scent   cent   sent

11. _____

12. I am not sure ____ I can go.

    wheather   whether   weather

12. _____

13. The sailor ____ down the ship's hatch.

    tide   teid   tied

13. _____

14. The candy cost one ____.

    scent   cent   sent

14. _____

15. The score was even and the game was ____.

    tide   teid   tied

15. _____

Spelling Words

cent
sent
scent
threw
through
weather
whether
their
there
they're

chili
chilly
tide
tied
pale
pail
aloud
allowed
course
coarse

Frequently Misspelled Words

their
there
they're

Home Activity Your child identified misspelled and misused homophones. Say a homophone in a sentence and have your child spell it.

Homophones

Spelling Words				
cent	sent	scent	threw	through
weather	whether	their	there	they're
chili	chilly	tide	tied	pale
pail	aloud	allowed	course	coarse

Word Search Circle ten list words that are hidden in the puzzle.
Write each word you find.

```
B  T  J  A  H  Z  T  Z  C  Q  I  D
L  W  H  E  T  H  E  R  O  E  M  Y
T  X  F  R  U  Y  P  O  U  G  N  C
H  M  C  Q  O  Z  F  S  R  N  J  T
E  I  T  L  A  U  R  M  S  V  B  E
R  Z  A  H  B  T  G  A  E  G  E  M
E  W  I  V  E  L  S  H  B  R  H  A
U  P  Y  K  A  I  T  D  P  A  I  L
T  I  E  D  H  Y  R  O  M  K  E  O
D  L  R  L  A  I  L  N  E  D  X  U
H  Q  Y  J  S  O  E  R  Y  A  G  D
W  K  G  D  C  H  I  L  L  Y  N  T
```

1. _____
2. _____
3. _____
4. _____
5. _____
6. _____
7. _____
8. _____
9. _____
10. _____

Words in Context Write a list word to complete each sentence.

11. I'm worried because ____ late getting here.

12. The pitcher ____ the ball over the plate.

13. We had ____ with our hot dog.

14. The ____ was perfect for the beach.

15. The boy needs sunscreen on his ____ skin.

16. Swimming is not ____ when the lifeguard is off duty.

17. She ____ her classmate a party invitation.

18. The rose had a wonderful ____.

19. We looked for seashells when the ____ was out.

20. The ____ fabric was itchy.

11. _____
12. _____
13. _____
14. _____
15. _____
16. _____
17. _____
18. _____
19. _____
20. _____

School + Home **Home Activity** Your child has learned to read, write, and spell homophones. Say a homophone and spell it. Ask your child to say and spell the other homophone or homophones.

Spelling Practice Book

Suffixes *-ible*, *-able*

Generalization When adding the suffix **-ible** or **-able**, there is no sound clue to help you decide which form to use: **flex<u>ible</u>, agree<u>able</u>**.

Word Sort Sort the list words by their suffixes.

-ible	**-able**
1. _____	7. _____
2. _____	8. _____
3. _____	9. _____
4. _____	10. _____
5. _____	11. _____
6. _____	12. _____
	13. _____
	14. _____
	15. _____
	16. _____
	17. _____
	18. _____
	19. _____
	20. _____

Spelling Words

1. sensible
2. washable
3. available
4. agreeable
5. fashionable
6. valuable
7. flexible
8. reasonable
9. favorable
10. breakable

11. convertible
12. forgettable
13. laughable
14. sociable
15. allowable
16. divisible
17. hospitable
18. reversible
19. responsible
20. tolerable

© Pearson Education, Inc. 5

School + Home

Home Activity Your child is learning about the suffixes *-ible* and *-able*. Say and spell the list words with your child.

Suffixes *-ible*, *-able*

Spelling Words				
sensible	washable	available	agreeable	fashionable
valuable	flexible	reasonable	favorable	breakable
convertible	forgettable	laughable	sociable	allowable
divisible	hospitable	reversible	responsible	tolerable

Synonyms Write the list word that has the same or nearly the same meaning.

1. in style
   1. _____

2. bendable
   2. _____

3. welcoming
   3. _____

4. ridiculous
   4. _____

5. car with top down
   5. _____

6. positive
   6. _____

7. permissible
   7. _____

8. able to turn inside out
   8. _____

9. can be cleaned
   9. _____

10. accountable
    10. _____

Antonyms Write the list word that has the opposite or nearly the opposite meaning.

11. memorable
    11. _____

12. unfriendly
    12. _____

13. disagreeable
    13. _____

14. unreasonable
    14. _____

15. unbreakable
    15. _____

16. unavailable
    16. _____

17. intolerable
    17. _____

18. can't be divided
    18. _____

19. foolish
    19. _____

20. worthless
    20. _____

Home Activity Your child used meanings to select list words that were synonyms and antonyms. Have your child tell you the meaning of three list words and spell the words.

Suffixes *-ible*, *-able*

Proofread an Article Find five spelling errors and one capitalization error in the article. Circle the errors and write the corrections on the lines.

> ### Fashion Sense
>
> Store buyers are responsible for ordering fashionible clothing customers will like. Last year, mrs. Clark, the store buyer, ordered dozens of reversible sweaters. The sweaters were washible, availible in a variety of colors, and sold at a reasonible price. When the sweaters sold out quickly, the buyer knew she had made a sensable choice.

1. _____   2. _____

3. _____   4. _____

5. _____   6. _____

Proofread Words Circle the correct spelling of the list word.

7. The gymnast is as _____ as a rubber band.

   flexable   flexibel   flexible

8. Porcelain china is delicate and _____.

   breakable   brakeable   breakible

9. Be _____ to your guests when they visit.

   hospital   hospitable   hospitible

10. I'd love to have a car with a _____ top.

   convertible   convertable   convertibel

11. Sixty-three is _____ by seven.

   dividable   divisable   divisible

12. Eat three _____ and balanced meals every day.

   sensible   sensable   senseable

Spelling Words

sensible
washable
available
agreeable
fashionable
valuable
flexible
reasonable
favorable
breakable

convertible
forgettable
laughable
sociable
allowable
divisible
hospitable
reversible
responsible
tolerable

Frequently Misspelled Words

when
then
went

Home Activity Your child identified misspelled list words. Ask your child to spell three list words that end in *-ible* and three list words that end in *-able*.

Suffixes *-ible*, *-able*

Spelling Words				
sensible	washable	available	agreeable	fashionable
valuable	flexible	reasonable	favorable	breakable
convertible	forgettable	laughable	sociable	allowable
divisible	hospitable	reversible	responsible	tolerable

Crossword Puzzle Use clues to find the list words. Write each letter in a box.

Across

6. friendly
7. levelheaded
8. silly
9. welcoming
10. positive

Down

1. stylish
2. bearable
3. unmemorable
4. precious
5. bendable

Definitions Write the list word that fits the definition.

11. anything that can be cleaned with soap and water   11. _____

12. separable into equal parts   12. _____

13. able to obtain   13. _____

14. fragile and delicate   14. _____

Home Activity Your child has learned to read, write, and spell words with suffixes. Have your child pick out the five hardest words to review with you.

Spelling Practice Book

Negative Prefixes

Generalization When adding prefixes **il-**, **in-**, **im-**, and **ir-**, make no change in the base word: **il**legal, **in**visible, **im**possible, **ir**regular. All of the prefixes mean "not."

Word Sort Sort the list words by their prefixes.

il-

1. _____
2. _____
3. _____

in-

4. _____
5. _____
6. _____
7. _____
8. _____
9. _____
10. _____
11. _____

im-

12. _____
13. _____
14. _____
15. _____
16. _____
17. _____

ir-

18. _____
19. _____
20. _____

Spelling Words

1. invisible
2. illiterate
3. irregular
4. irresistible
5. impossible
6. informal
7. illegal
8. impatient
9. independent
10. incorrect

11. inactive
12. imperfect
13. impolite
14. immature
15. illogical
16. indefinite
17. inappropriate
18. immobile
19. irresponsible
20. inexpensive

School + Home

Home Activity Your child is learning about prefixes that mean "not." Have your child tell you four prefixes that mean "not."

Negative Prefixes

Spelling Words				
invisible	illiterate	irregular	irresistible	impossible
informal	illegal	impatient	independent	incorrect
inactive	imperfect	impolite	immature	illogical
indefinite	inappropriate	immobile	irresponsible	inexpensive

Missing Words Write the missing list word.

1. If you learn to read, you are not ____.

2. If you have good manners, you'll rarely be ____.

3. If you earn a living, you can be ____.

4. If you have a "can do" attitude, little is ____.

5. If you're always trustworthy, you are never ____.

6. If you always follow the law, then you never do anything ____.

7. If you're always right, then you're never ____.

8. If you always act responsibly, then you are not ____.

9. If you set an exact time to meet, it is not ____.

10. If something always makes sense, it is not ____.

1. _____

2. _____

3. _____

4. _____

5. _____

6. _____

7. _____

8. _____

9. _____

10. _____

Classifying Write the list word that completes the group.

11. cheap, reasonable, low-cost, ____

12. flawed, faulty, defective, ____

13. restless, fidgety, ____

14. unseen, faint, ____

15. casual, relaxed, ____

16. idle, quiet, immobile, ____

17. out of place, unsuitable, ____

18. stationary, motionless, ____

19. tempting, appealing, enticing, ____

20. uneven, lopsided, ____

11. _____

12. _____

13. _____

14. _____

15. _____

16. _____

17. _____

18. _____

19. _____

20. _____

© Pearson Education, Inc. 5

School + Home

Home Activity Your child wrote words with prefixes. Ask your child to spell one word for each of the four negative prefixes.

Negative Prefixes

Proofread a Speech Circle six spelling errors in the toymaker's speech.
Write the words correctly. Write the run-on sentence as two sentences.

"I want to create an irresistable toy for children. It will make the user innvisible. I need five independent teams to work on this. As always, I am impashent to get this project started! We do not have an indefinute amount of time. I'm hoping to have this toy on the market by the end of the year. Does anyone have any questions? Does anyone think this task is ilogical or inpossible to do? Do we all agree this can be done let's get to work!"

1. _____   2. _____

3. _____   4. _____

5. _____   6. _____

7. _____

_____

Spelling Words

invisible
illiterate
irregular
irresistible
impossible
informal
illegal
impatient
independent
incorrect

inactive
imperfect
impolite
immature
illogical
indefinite
inappropriate
immobile
irresponsible
inexpensive

Proofread Words Circle the word that is spelled correctly.

8. irresistible   unresistable   ilresistable

9. ilexpensive   imexpensive   inexpensive

10. inmature   immature   imature

11. imperfect   ilperfect   unperfect

12. imdependent   independent   ildependent

13. imactive   innactive   inactive

14. impolite   inpolite   unpolite

15. illiterate   iliterate   inliterate

16. imappropriate   inappropriate   inapropriate

Frequently Misspelled Words

through
always

Home Activity Your child identified misspelled list words. Take turns spelling list words that begin with the four prefixes studied.

Spelling Practice Book

Negative Prefixes

Spelling Words				
invisible	illiterate	irregular	irresistible	impossible
informal	illegal	impatient	independent	incorrect
inactive	imperfect	impolite	immature	illogical
indefinite	inappropriate	immobile	irresponsible	inexpensive

Complete the Word Add a prefix to each word to make a list word. Write the word.

1. ___appropriate
2. ___correct
3. ___definite
4. ___formal
5. ___legal
6. ___logical
7. ___mature
8. ___patient
9. ___perfect
10. ___regular

1. _____
2. _____
3. _____
4. _____
5. _____
6. _____
7. _____
8. _____
9. _____
10. _____

Double Puzzle Unscramble each word. Write one letter on each line. Write the numbered letters to find the answer to the question.

What is the date when the United States celebrates its independence?

11. ALRGIERUR _ _ _ _ _ _ _ _ _
                    3

12. MALFIRON _ _ _ _ _ _ _ _
                1   9

13. TOCNRRIEC _ _ _ _ _ _ _ _ _
                    4

14. CRMEPIFET _ _ _ _ _ _ _ _ _
                        7   5

15. PEIMILTO _ _ _ _ _ _ _ _
                    2

16. MIEARMTU _ _ _ _ _ _ _ _
                        8

17. OCLILGLAI _ _ _ _ _ _ _ _ _
                6

_ _ _ _ _ **h** _ _ **J** _ _ **y**
1 2 3 4 5   6 7   8 9

Home Activity Your child has learned to read, write, and spell words with prefixes. Take turns using list words in sentences that you say aloud. Ask your child to spell aloud the list word that is used in each sentence.

Spelling Practice Book

Words from Many Cultures

Spelling Words				
khaki	waltz	yogurt	cobra	buffet
hula	tomato	banquet	koala	stampede
banana	vanilla	macaroni	barbecue	karate
ballet	canyon	polka	safari	kiosk

Alphabetize Write the ten list words below in alphabetical order.

kiosk	stampede
safari	buffet
koala	polka
banquet	karate
ballet	khaki

1. _____

2. _____

3. _____

4. _____

5. _____

6. _____

7. _____

8. _____

9. _____

10. _____

Classifying Write the list word that belongs in each group.

11. lettuce, carrots, onion, _____

12. dance, ballroom, elegant, _____

13. rattlesnake, boa constrictor, _____

14. spaghetti, noodles, pasta, _____

15. gorge, valley, ravine, _____

16. Hawaii, dance, grass skirt, _____

17. milk, creamy, fruit, _____

18. fruit, yellow, plant, _____

19. chocolate, strawberry, _____

20. food, outdoors, grill, _____

Home Activity Your child has learned to spell words that come from a variety of cultures. With your child, look up several of the words in a dictionary and discuss what the dictionary says about the words' origins.

© Pearson Education, inc.5

Prefixes *over-*, *under-*, *sub-*, *super-*, *out-*

Spelling Words				
overlook	supermarket	undercurrent	submarine	output
underline	outlet	superstar	undercover	supernatural
subway	underground	overtime	overcast	subdivision
subset	overboard	supersonic	outfield	subhead

Analogies Write the list word that completes each comparison.

1. Light is to heavy as sunny is to _____.

2. Title is to subtitle as head is to _____.

3. Sky is to airplane as ocean is to _____.

4. Carpenter is to house as baseball player is to _____.

5. Shoes are to shoe store as food is to _____.

6. Building is to outside as ship is to _____.

7. Street is to bus as underground is to _____.

8. Strong is to athlete as famous is to _____.

9. Comedian is to funny as ghost is to _____.

10. Store is to mall as house is to _____.

Synonyms Write the list word that has the same, or nearly the same, meaning.

11. underscore _____

12. secret _____

13. category _____

14. extra _____

15. production _____

16. hint _____

17. buried _____

18. socket _____

19. fast _____

20. forget _____

Home Activity Your child has completed analogies containing words with prefixes. Ask your child to make up two analogies containing words from the list and explain how the analogies work.

Homophones

Spelling Words				
cent	through	there	tide	aloud
sent	weather	they're	tied	allowed
scent	whether	chili	pale	course
threw	their	chilly	pail	coarse

Crossword Puzzle Use the clues to find the list words. Write each letter in a box.

Across
2. gave permission
6. not here
7. fastened
8. pitched
9. place to play golf

Down
1. said so it could be heard
3. if
4. finished
5. smell
7. belonging to them

Classifying Write the list word that belongs in each group.

10. rain, snow, tornado, _____

11. cold, icy, frosty, _____

12. rough, thick, _____

13. taco, spaghetti, soup, _____

14. bucket, container, jug, _____

15. nickel, dime, quarter, _____

16. you're, we're, _____

17. white, colorless, sickly, _____

18. ocean, waves, high, low, _____

19. letter, mailed, transmitted, _____

Home Activity Your child has learned to spell homophones. Ask your child to find some of the list words in a newspaper or magazine. Then ask your child to spell one or more homophones for each word and use them in sentences.

Suffixes *-ible*, *-able*

Spelling Words				
sensible	fashionable	favorable	laughable	hospitable
washable	valuable	breakable	sociable	reversible
available	flexible	convertible	allowable	responsible
agreeable	reasonable	forgettable	divisible	tolerable

Words in Context Complete each sentence with a list word.

1. Be careful with that vase because it is _____.

2. It is hot in the desert, but the dry air makes it _____.

3. Jim's mom was _____ and invited us to stay for dinner.

4. You can wear the jacket with that side in or out because it is _____.

5. A(n) _____ car is not practical in a cold climate.

6. Anita didn't go to the party because she was not feeling _____.

7. Gold and silver are _____ metals.

8. The critic liked the movie, so he gave it a(n) _____ review.

9. Is that number _____ by ten?

10. It's all right to get your uniform muddy because it is _____.

11. The magician's tricks were so obvious they were _____.

12. The soccer team took care not to make any plays that were not _____.

13. Lizzy often wears new styles because she likes to be _____.

14. I can't recall the story's characters because they were _____.

15. The Henrys asked Carla to baby-sit, but she was not _____ that day.

16. Unlike the unpleasant dog next door, our pet is always _____.

17. Who is _____ for setting the table?

18. It is _____ to wear sturdy shoes on a long hike.

19. If you work on the problem, you will think of a(n) _____ answer.

20. Rubber is used for many items because it is _____.

Home Activity Your child has learned to spell words with the suffixes *-ible* and *-able*. Ask your child to make up several sentences containing list words and to spell each list word used.

Spelling Practice Book

Negative Prefixes

Spelling Words				
invisible	impossible	independent	impolite	inappropriate
illiterate	informal	incorrect	immature	immobile
irregular	illegal	inactive	illogical	irresponsible
irresistible	impatient	imperfect	indefinite	inexpensive

Synonyms Write the list word that has the same, or nearly the same, meaning.

1. restless _____

2. cheap _____

3. rude _____

4. motionless _____

5. casual _____

6. vague _____

7. uneven _____

8. lazy _____

9. separate _____

10. fascinating _____

Antonyms Write the list word that has the opposite, or nearly the opposite, meaning.

11. lawful _____

12. experienced _____

13. excellent _____

14. reasonable _____

15. accurate _____

16. educated _____

17. suitable _____

18. likely _____

19. noticeable _____

20. dependable _____

Home Activity Your child has written synonyms and antonyms for words with negative prefixes. Name several list words. Ask your child to spell each word and to name a synonym and/or antonym for each.

Proofread for Spelling Errors

Proofread a Science Report.   Circle twelve spelling mistakes in the science report below. Write them correctly.

With its brown fur, pail tummy, and round ears, the koalla is an irresistable animal. It lives only in parts of Australia. It is a marsupial. A baby koala is very imature when it is born. Then it lives in a pouch on its mother for six months while it grows.

One of the most unusual features of the koala is its diet. You could not buy this animal's meal at the super market. It eats only leaves from eucalyptus trees. The name koala comes from a native Australian word meaning "no water." Koalas get all their water from the leaves. It may seem impossable to have such a limited diet. But koalas have adapted to their diet in many ways. If their is a drought, they will drink some water. Other features also help them. They have sharp front teeth that help them pull leaves off trees. There back teeth help them cut the leaves.

The leaves that koalas eat do not have much nutrition. Koalas adapt by being very unactive. They may sleep for 20 hours a day! They digest their meals slowly. This helps them get all the availible energy from their food. Theyre sociabel animals, though. They live in groups.

1. _____

2. _____

3. _____

4. _____

5. _____

6. _____

7. _____

8. _____

9. _____

10. _____

11. _____

12. _____

Multisyllabic Words

Generalization When spelling words with many syllables, look carefully at each word part.

Word Sort Sort the list words by words you know how to spell and words that you are learning to spell. Write every word.

words I know how to spell	words I am learning to spell
1. _____	11. _____
2. _____	12. _____
3. _____	13. _____
4. _____	14. _____
5. _____	15. _____
6. _____	16. _____
7. _____	17. _____
8. _____	18. _____
9. _____	19. _____
10. _____	20. _____

Spelling Words

1. elementary
2. vehicle
3. miniature
4. probability
5. definition
6. substitute
7. variety
8. literature
9. elevator
10. Pennsylvania

11. ravioli
12. cafeteria
13. mosaic
14. tuxedo
15. meteorite
16. fascination
17. cylinder
18. intermediate
19. centennial
20. curiosity

Home Activity Your child is learning about words with many syllables. Have your child say each word very slowly, pausing in between each syllable.

Multisyllabic Words

Spelling Words				
elementary	vehicle	miniature	probability	definition
substitute	variety	literature	elevator	Pennsylvania
ravioli	cafeteria	mosaic	tuxedo	meteorite
fascination	cylinder	intermediate	centennial	curiosity

Words in Context Write the list word that best completes each sentence.

1. I'm having lunch in the ____ today.

2. Did you know that cheese ____ is on the menu?

3. Eating a ____ of foods keeps you heathy.

4. Next year our town is 100 years old, so we'll have a ____ celebration.

5. The astronauts drove a lunar ____ on the moon.

6. The colorful ____ on the table top is made of tiny tiles.

7. A shooting star is really a falling ____.

8. The capital of ____ is Harrisburg.

9. The levels of swimming at my camp are beginner, ____, and advanced.

10. Books, poetry, and short stories are all types of ____.

11. Let's take the ____ to the tenth floor.

12. We had a ____ teacher for one week.

13. He had a ____ with all types of model trains.

1. _____

2. _____

3. _____

4. _____

5. _____

6. _____

7. _____

8. _____

9. _____

10. _____

11. _____

12. _____

13. _____

Synonyms Write the list word that has the same or almost the same meaning as the word or phrase.

14. tube

15. tiny

16. basic

17. meaning

18. desire to know

19. formal suit

20. likelihood

14. _____

15. _____

16. _____

17. _____

18. _____

19. _____

20. _____

Home Activity Your child wrote list words containing many syllables. Have your child draw a line between syllables. Use a dictionary to help you.

© Pearson Education, Inc. 5

Multisyllabic Words

Proofread an Article Circle six spelling errors. Write the words correctly.
Find one capitalization error and write the sentence correctly.

Fictional Detectives

Literture has its share of famous detectives. writers
have created an enormous variaty of detectives. All have
curiousity about and a fasination with crime. Usually, they
are average people with an especially high probility of
being right in the middle of a crime scene! As one famous
detective said, "It's elamentry, my dear Watson!"

---

1. _____   2. _____

3. _____   4. _____

5. _____   6. _____

7. _____

_____

Proofread Words Circle the word that is spelled correctly.

8. A _____ looks like a rock.

   metorit   meteoright   meteorite

9. I made a _____ out of glass tile.

   mosaic   mosesic   mosiac

10. My 99-year-old grandfather will have his _____ birthday next year.

   centenial   centennial   cintennial

11. William Penn was the founder of _____.

   Pennsylvania   Pennysylvania   Pennysalvenia

12. The tour _____ can go on land and water.

   veacle   vehicle   vehical

13. A soup can is a _____.

   cylindar   cylander   cylinder

14. My dog is a _____ poodle.

   miniature   miniture   miniatur

Spelling Words
elementary
vehicle
miniature
probability
definition
substitute
variety
literature
elevator
Pennsylvania
ravioli
cafeteria
mosaic
tuxedo
meteorite
fascination
cylinder
intermediate
centennial
curiosity

Frequently Misspelled Words
usually
especially

Home Activity Your child identified misspelled multisyllabic words. Ask your child to select four list words and tell you how many syllables are in each word.

Multisyllabic Words

Spelling Words				
elementary	vehicle	miniature	probability	definition
substitute	variety	literature	elevator	Pennsylvania
ravioli	cafeteria	mosaic	tuxedo	meteorite
fascination	cylinder	intermediate	centennial	curiosity

Classifying Write the word that completes the group.

1. Philadelphia, Liberty Bell, ____

2. interest, attraction, appeal, ____

3. car, bus, truck, ____

4. text, poetry, novels, ____

5. dining room, mess hall, ____

6. assortment, selection, ____

7. shooting star, moon rock, ____

8. tiles, grout, pattern, ____

9. hundred, anniversary ____

10. tube, can, ____

1. _____

2. _____

3. _____

4. _____

5. _____

6. _____

7. _____

8. _____

9. _____

10. _____

Word Search Find ten list words that are hidden in the puzzle. Words are across, down, up, backward, and diagonal. Write the words on the lines.

```
I  L  C  C  E  X  E  I  P  R  M  S
E  N  X  V  D  T  L  C  R  O  I  T
T  E  T  K  H  O  A  F  O  T  N  G
U  C  V  E  I  E  D  F  B  A  I  E
T  D  M  V  R  X  K  V  A  V  A  N
I  O  A  J  M  M  G  Q  B  E  T  U
T  R  T  E  T  U  E  B  I  L  U  T
S  T  U  X  E  D  O  D  L  E  R  C
B  T  N  O  I  T  I  N  I  F  E  D
U  Z  E  L  E  M  E  N  T  A  R  Y
S  N  F  L  G  C  P  E  Y  N  T  Z
C  P  Y  T  I  S  O  I  R  U  C  E
```

11. _____

12. _____

13. _____

14. _____

15. _____

16. _____

17. _____

18. _____

19. _____

20. _____

Home Activity Your child has learned to read, write, and spell multisyllabic words. Take turns using the words in a sentence.

Unusual Spellings

Generalization Some words have letters you don't hear: **doub̲t**. In some words the sound you hear gives no clue to its spelling: **an̲x̲ious**.

Word Sort Sort the list words by words you know how to spell and words that you are learning to spell. Write every word.

words I know how to spell	words I am learning to spell
1. _____	11. _____
2. _____	12. _____
3. _____	13. _____
4. _____	14. _____
5. _____	15. _____
6. _____	16. _____
7. _____	17. _____
8. _____	18. _____
9. _____	19. _____
10. _____	20. _____

Spelling Words

1. league
2. sergeant
3. yacht
4. doubt
5. fatigue
6. debt
7. blood
8. vague
9. anxious
10. foreign

11. bargain
12. condemn
13. intrigue
14. villain
15. cantaloupe
16. flood
17. depot
18. cordial
19. subtle
20. disguise

Home Activity Your child is learning about words with unusual spellings. Look up pronunciations of six list words in the dictionary with your child.

© Pearson Education, Inc. 5

Unusual Spellings

Spelling Words				
league	sergeant	yacht	doubt	fatigue
debt	blood	vague	anxious	foreign
bargain	condemn	intrigue	villain	cantaloupe
flood	depot	cordial	subtle	disguise

Words in Context Write the list word that best completes each sentence.

1. We picked up the package at the bus _____.

2. Today we are going _____ hunting for a pair of shoes.

3. The _____ gave orders to the new soldiers.

4. I cut my finger and got a spot of _____ on my shirt.

5. Does going to a mystery museum _____ you?

6. The city board decided to _____ that old building.

7. The team is playing for the _____ championship.

8. They felt weariness and _____ after playing hockey.

9. The _____ changes to the room were hard to notice.

10. I have no _____ that she liked her gift.

1. _____

2. _____

3. _____

4. _____

5. _____

6. _____

7. _____

8. _____

9. _____

10. _____

Classifying Complete each group with the best list word.

11. mask, costume, _____

12. overseas, far away, _____

13. boat, ship, _____

14. unclear, hazy, _____

15. friendly, pleasant, _____

16. uneasy, tense, _____

17. owe, loan, _____

18. watermelon, honeydew, _____

19. overflow, downpour, _____

20. scoundrel, thug, _____

11. _____

12. _____

13. _____

14. _____

15. _____

16. _____

17. _____

18. _____

19. _____

20. _____

Home Activity Your child wrote words with unusual spellings. Have your child select the four hardest words and spell them to you.

Unusual Spellings

Proofread an Article Circle six spelling errors. Write the words correctly. Find one punctuation error and write the sentence correctly.

Decorating Ideas

Guests were coming on the weekend, and I was antious to redecorate my TV room. I decided to make some sutle changes. I especially needed to disgise a badly cracked wall. The furniture store had imports from many forin countries. In spite of my vaigue description, the sales staff found a bargain that was just what I wanted! It was a wall hanging with colors of gold, rust, and yellow. I painted my walls a light orange color called canteloupe. I was ready for the weekend

1. _____
2. _____
3. _____
4. _____
5. _____
6. _____
7. _____

Spelling Words

league
sergeant
yacht
doubt
fatigue
debt
blood
vague
anxious
foreign

bargain
condemn
intrigue
villain
cantaloupe
flood
depot
cordial
subtle
disguise

Proofread Words Circle the word that is spelled correctly.

8. The police officer was promoted to ____.

sargent   sargeant   sergeant

9. Spies live lives of mystery and ____.

intrige   intrigue   intreague

10. Most stories feature a ____ and a hero.

villain   villann   villin

11. I would love to spend a week on a ____.

yaht   yact   yacht

12. My new shoes were a real ____.

bargen   bargain   bargian

Frequently Misspelled Words

clothes
TV

Home Activity Your child identified misspelled words with unusual spellings. Select four spelling words and ask your child to use each in a sentence.

Unusual Spellings

Spelling Words				
league	sergeant	yacht	doubt	fatigue
debt	blood	vague	anxious	foreign
bargain	condemn	intrigue	villain	cantaloupe
flood	depot	cordial	subtle	disguise

Word Search Circle the ten list words that are hidden in the puzzle. Write each word you find.

```
L  J  I  B  N  N  Y  T  D  X  T  C
A  U  N  I  M  G  O  A  R  C  O  J
I  P  T  V  S  P  I  M  C  N  B  L
D  U  R  E  E  E  J  E  D  H  O  L
R  T  I  D  K  J  R  E  R  R  T  M
O  E  G  F  R  W  M  G  C  O  R  H
C  L  U  G  S  N  R  X  E  L  F  T
B  K  E  S  U  O  I  X  N  A  Z  D
C  A  N  T  A  L  O  U  P  E  N  E
A  F  L  O  O  D  K  F  G  F  X  T
O  P  B  U  C  S  T  Q  V  Y  D  P
```

anxious	depot
condemn	foreign
flood	yacht
cordial	sergeant
cantaloupe	intrigue

1. _____   2. _____   3. _____   4. _____

5. _____   6. _____   7. _____   8. _____

9. _____   10. _____

Words in Context Write the list word that completes each sentence.

11. If in ____, throw it out.   11. _____

12. Sign up for the park district soccer ____.   12. _____

13. I'm in ____ up to my ears.   13. _____

14. It made my ____ boil.   14. _____

15. I cried a ____ of tears.   15. _____

16. What a ____!   16. _____

Home Activity Your child has learned to read, write, and spell words with unusual spellings. Take turns using the words in sentences and then spell each word.

© Pearson Education, Inc., 5

Name _____

Greek Word Parts

Generalization Many words are formed from the Greek word parts **logy,**
meaning "study of"; **aster,** meaning "star"; **therm,** meaning "heat"; and
sphere, meaning "ball."

Word Sort Sort the list words by their Greek word part.

logy	therm
1. _____	13. _____
2. _____	14. _____
3. _____	15. _____
4. _____	16. _____
5. _____	**sphere**
6. _____	17. _____
7. _____	18. _____
8. _____	19. _____
aster	20. _____
9. _____	
10. _____	
11. _____	
12. _____	

Spelling Words

1. geology
2. thermometer
3. astronaut
4. atmosphere
5. biology
6. thermal
7. disaster
8. meteorology
9. technology
10. hemisphere

11. zoology
12. sociology
13. biosphere
14. thermos
15. asterisk
16. thermostat
17. astronomy
18. spherical
19. ecology
20. mythology

Home Activity Your child is learning about four Greek word parts. Have your child explain what each
Greek word part means.

Talk with an Astronaut

PRACTICE

Greek Word Parts

Spelling Words				
geology	thermometer	astronaut	atmosphere	biology
thermal	disaster	meteorology	technology	hemisphere
zoology	sociology	biosphere	thermos	asterisk
thermostat	astronomy	spherical	ecology	mythology

Classifying Write the list word that best fits in each group.

1. container, vacuum, hot, cold, ____

2. animals, study, science, ____

3. Zeus, Apollo, Athena, ____

4. rocks, minerals, earth ____

5. people, society, civilization ____

6. stars, galaxies, planets, ____

7. weather, forecast, barometer, ____

8. avalanche, tornado, hurricane, ____

1. _____

2. _____

3. _____

4. _____

5. _____

6. _____

7. _____

8. _____

Definitions Write the list word that fits the definition.

9. This instrument is used to measure temperature.

10. This is having to do with heat.

11. This is the study of all living things—plants and animals.

12. This traveler has seen the stars from the space shuttle.

13. Earth is this round shape.

14. This means half of a sphere.

15. This means the use of scientific knowledge to solve practical problems.

16. This is a star-shaped mark used in printing and writing.

17. This dial controls the temperature on the air conditioner and heater.

18. This is a sealed glass dome that has all the features of Earth.

19. This is the study of the relation of living things to their environment and one another.

20. This is the air that surrounds Earth.

9. _____

10. _____

11. _____

12. _____

13. _____

14. _____

15. _____

16. _____

17. _____

18. _____

19. _____

20. _____

Home Activity Your child wrote words that have Greek word parts. Have your child underline the Greek word part in each word.

Spelling Practice Book

Name _____

Greek Word Parts

Proofread a Report Circle six spelling errors in the report. Write the words correctly. Find a punctuation error and write the sentence correctly.

Earth on Earth

What do the desert and the moon have in common! Would you believe that astronots rehearsed the moon landing in the desert? The desert is also home to a huge bioshere where Earth's ecology is re-created inside a sealed glass dome. Eight scientists trained in zology, biology, and geology lived inside of the biosphere for two years. If the experiment was a success, a biosphere could be built on the moon. Space exploration would be easier. The experiment was neither a disastor, nor was it a success. The scientists had trouble controlling the atmospher inside. I think its too soon to build a biosphere in space.

---

1. _____   2. _____

3. _____   4. _____

5. _____   6. _____

7. _____

_____

Proofread Words Circle the word that is spelled correctly.

8. thermastat   thermostat   thermestat

9. asterisk   asterick   asterik

10. thermeter   thermometer   thermameter

11. mytholgly   mytholgy   mythology

12. sherical   sphereical   spherical

13. astronomy   astranamy   astronmy

14. hemasphere   hemisphere   hemosphere

15. biology   biolgy   bilogy

Spelling Words

geology
thermometer
astronaut
atmosphere
biology
thermal
disaster
meteorology
technology
hemisphere

zoology
sociology
biosphere
thermos
asterisk
thermostat
astronomy
spherical
ecology
mythology

Frequently Misspelled Words

I'm
it's
let's

School + Home **Home Activity** Your child identified misspelled list words. Ask your child to spell four words, each with a different Greek word part, and tell you what the words mean.

Greek Word Parts

Spelling Words				
geology	thermometer	astronaut	atmosphere	biology
thermal	disaster	meteorology	technology	hemisphere
zoology	sociology	biosphere	thermos	asterisk
thermostat	astronomy	spherical	ecology	mythology

Double Puzzle Unscramble the list words. Write each letter on a line. Write the numbered letters below to solve the riddle.

Where did the gods and goddesses in Greek mythology live?

1. TEEMTRMEORH   __ __ __ __ __ __ __ __ __ __ __
                                     5

2. TREMOEOOLGY   __ __ __ __ __ __ __ __ __ __ __
                          2

3. HERIEMHESP   __ __ __ __ __ __ __ __ __ __
                              10

4. ZLYGOOO   __ __ __ __ __ __ __
                      7

5. GOOCSOLIY   __ __ __ __ __ __ __ __ __
                                  8

6. OHSRETM   __ __ __ __ __ __ __
                      9

7. HRTSEOMATT   __ __ __ __ __ __ __ __ __ __
                                11

8. OTOSYAMNR   __ __ __ __ __ __ __ __ __
                              4

9. TNURATSOA   __ __ __ __ __ __ __ __ __
                                  3

10. OHPATRMESE   __ __ __ __ __ __ __ __ __ __
                        1

11. YGOELOC   __ __ __ __ __ __ __
                          6

__ __ __ __ __   __ __ __ __ __ __ __
1 2 3 4 5   6 7 8 9 10 3 11

Connect the Words Draw a line from the word part to its Greek word part. Then write the word.

12. dis   stat   12. _____

13. thermo   sphere   13. _____

14. myth   aster   14. _____

15. hemi   ology   15. _____

Home Activity Your child has learned to read, write, and spell words with Greek word parts. Have your child pick out the ten hardest words to review with you.

© Pearson Education, Inc., 5

Latin Roots

Generalization The Latin root **ject** means "throw," **aud** means "hear," **terr** means "land," and **dec** means "ten."

Word Sort Sort the list words by their Latin root.

ject

1. _____

2. _____

3. _____

4. _____

5. _____

aud

6. _____

7. _____

8. _____

9. _____

10. _____

terr

11. _____

12. _____

13. _____

14. _____

15. _____

dec

16. _____

17. _____

18. _____

19. _____

20. _____

Spelling Words

1. project
2. audience
3. decade
4. territory
5. auditorium
6. terrier
7. decimal
8. injection
9. December
10. reject

11. eject
12. terrace
13. audit
14. decimeter
15. audition
16. audible
17. decathlon
18. terrarium
19. dejected
20. terrain

Home Activity Your child is learning about Latin roots. Have your child explain what each Latin root in this lesson means.

Latin Roots

Spelling Words

project	audience	decade	territory	auditorium
terrier	decimal	injection	December	reject
eject	terrace	audit	decimeter	audition
audible	decathlon	terrarium	dejected	terrain

Words in Context Write the list words that complete each sentence.

Her voice was barely **(1)**____ in the large **(2)**____ during her singing **(3)**____.

1. _____   2. _____   3. _____

The plants and dirt spilled all over the **(4)**____ when the excited **(5)**____ knocked over my beautiful glass **(6)**____.

4. _____   5. _____   6. _____

As part of the flu prevention **(7)**____, the doctors and nurses gave every child an **(8)**____.

7. _____   8. _____

When you **(9)**____ someone's friendship, that person usually feels **(10)**____.

9. _____   10. _____

The bank's **(11)**____ found that the amount on my deposit had the **(12)**____ point in the wrong place.

11. _____   12. _____

Word Definitions Write the list word that has the same meaning.

13. a ten-year period   13. _____

14. the twelfth month of the year   14. _____

15. land or region   15. _____

16. natural features of the land   16. _____

17. a competition having ten events   17. _____

18. one-tenth of a meter   18. _____

19. those who view or listen to a performance   19. _____

20. to throw out, drive out, or force out   20. _____

Home Activity Your child wrote words that have Latin roots. Have your child tell you five list words and identify the Latin root in each word. Have your child spell each word.

Spelling Practice Book

Latin Roots

Proofread an Article Circle five spelling errors in the article. Write the words correctly. Find a punctuation error and write the sentence correctly.

I'm Already Tired!

It takes an accomplished athlete to compete in a decathalon. Ten separate competitions cover track and field events. These events take place in a stadium on a variety of surfaces. The audiance watches with great attention. One of these events is the javelin throw. With all his might the athlete hurls the javelin. The groan of the effort is audable to everyone. The javelin competition can be won by as little as a decimetr or centimeter. The loser will, naturally, feel dijected. However with nine other events, anyone might win.

1. _____ 2. _____

3. _____ 4. _____

5. _____

6. _____

_____

Spelling Words

project
audience
decade
territory
auditorium
terrier
decimal
injection
December
reject

eject
terrace
audit
decimeter
audition
audible
decathlon
terrarium
dejected
terrain

Proofread Words Circle the word that is spelled correctly.

7. audiance	audience	audeince
8. terrier	terriar	tierrer
9. ejet	eject	ejecte
10. terrarium	terarium	terrairium
11. injetion	injection	injetson
12. terrain	terraine	teraine
13. decad	deckade	decade
14. terratory	territory	terretory
15. decimle	desimal	decimal

Frequently Misspelled Words

into
upon

Home Activity Your child identified misspelled list words. Ask your child to say five list words, tell the Latin root for each, and then spell and define each word.

© Pearson Education, Inc. 5

Latin Roots

Spelling Words				
project	audience	decade	territory	auditorium
terrier	decimal	injection	December	reject
eject	terrace	audit	decimeter	audition
audible	decathlon	terrarium	dejected	terrain

Alphabetize Put the list words in the box below in alphabetical order.

project	audience	decade	territory	auditorium
terrier	decimal	injection	December	reject

1. _____   6. _____

2. _____   7. _____

3. _____   8. _____

4. _____   9. _____

5. _____   10. _____

Crossword Puzzle Use the clues to find the list words. Write each letter in a box.

Across
2. can be heard
4. throw out
6. type of sport contest
7. balcony

8. a try-out
9. review of money
10. tenth of a meter

Down
1. glass container with plants
3. unhappy
5. the ground

Home Activity Your child has learned to read, write, and spell words with Latin roots. Challenge your child to think of other words that use these Latin roots.

Related Words

Generalization Related words often have parts that are spelled the same but are pronounced differently: m**a**jor, m**a**jority.

Word Sort Sort the list words by words you know how to spell and words that you are learning to spell. Write every word.

words I know how to spell

1. _____

2. _____

3. _____

4. _____

5. _____

6. _____

7. _____

8. _____

9. _____

10. _____

words I am learning to spell

11. _____

12. _____

13. _____

14. _____

15. _____

16. _____

17. _____

18. _____

19. _____

20. _____

Spelling Words

1. politics
2. political
3. major
4. majority
5. equal
6. equation
7. sign
8. signature
9. arrive
10. arrival

11. inspire
12. inspiration
13. human
14. humanity
15. clean
16. cleanse
17. resign
18. resignation
19. unite
20. unity

Home Activity Your child is learning about related words that are spelled similarly but pronounced differently. Review the pairs of words with your child and ask him or her to point out the ways in which the pronunciation of the two words in each pair is different.

Related Words

Spelling Words

politics	political	major	majority	equal
equation	sign	signature	arrive	arrival
inspire	inspiration	human	humanity	clean
cleanse	resign	resignation	unite	unity

Definitions Write the list word that has the same meaning as the word or phrase.

1. notification of leaving a job _____ 2. quit _____

3. same _____ 4. one person _____

5. all people _____ 6. wash thoroughly _____

7. dirt free _____ 8. math sentence _____

Words in Context Write the list words that complete the sentence.

major, majority
The (9)____ of the (10)____ companies in town favored the ruling.

9. _____ 10. _____

inspiration, inspire
I use the (11)____ of other artists to (12)____ me.

11. _____ 12. _____

sign, signature
Your (13)____ is needed, so please (14)____ on this line.

13. _____ 14. _____

unite, unity
In order to have (15)____ we must (16)____ as one.

15. _____ 16. _____

political, politics
(17)____ compromise is the basis of (18)____.

17. _____ 18. _____

arrive, arrival
Check the (19)____ board to see when her plane will (20)____.

19. _____ 20. _____

© Pearson Education, Inc. 5

Home Activity Your child wrote related words that are spelled similarly but pronounced differently. Say list words and have your child say and spell the list word that is related.

Related Words

Proofread an Article Circle five spelling errors and two sentences that need to be combined into one sentence. Write the corrections on the lines.

Politics

The United States government is made up of politicle parties. The parties are rarely equel and in politics the majorety rules. This means the larger group usually wins in the vote. Sometimes, representatives from different parties unite to pass a major law. Policy makers, of course, are humen. They may argue for days. Until they arrive at a consensus or agreement. Because of this, it may take months for a law to reach the President who can then signe or veto it.

1. _____	2. _____
3. _____	4. _____
5. _____	
6. _____	
_____	

Proofread Words Circle the list word that is spelled correctly.

7. clense	cleanse	cleanze
8. sien	sine	sign
9. arrive	arive	arrieve
10. politecs	politics	poletics
11. resignation	resignashun	resignacion
12. inspireation	inspriation	inspiration
13. signeture	signature	signater
14. equation	equashun	equasion
15. humanity	hummanity	humannity
16. unetie	unity	unitey

Spelling Words

politics
political
major
majority
equal
equation
sign
signature
arrive
arrival

inspire
inspiration
human
humanity
clean
cleanse
resign
resignation
unite
unity

Frequently Misspelled Words

finally
whole
want

Home Activity Your child identified misspelled words. Write the first four letters of a list word and have your child write the two related words.

Related Words

Spelling Words				
politics	political	major	majority	equal
equation	sign	signature	arrive	arrival
inspire	inspiration	human	humanity	clean
cleanse	resign	resignation	unite	unity

Word Puzzle Complete each list word. Write one letter on each line. Write numbers in the grid. Then use the grid to answer the question.

A	B	C	D	E	F	G	H	I	J	K	L	M	N	O	P	Q	R	S	T	U	V	W	X	Y	Z
2	8		25		4			7		9		13	22				10	19			26	23			17

1. __ __ **m a** __ **n i t** __
   11 24 13 2 22 7 19 18

2. __ __ __ **i t i** __ **s**
   16 1 15 7 19 7 12 10

3. **m a** __ __ __ **i t** __
   13 2 20 1 5 7 19 18

4. __ __ **s i** __ **n**
   5 14 10 7 21 22

5. __ __ __ **a t i** __ **n**
   14 6 24 2 19 7 1 22

6. __ **n i t** __
   24 22 7 19 18

7. __ __ __ **a n s** __
   12 15 14 2 22 10 14

8. **s i** __ **n a t** __ __ __
   10 7 21 22 2 19 24 5 14

9. **i n s** __ **i** __ __
   7 22 10 16 7 5 14

10. **a** __ __ **i** __ **a** __
    2 5 5 7 3 2 15

11. What awe-inspiring event might we attend on Independence Day?

    __ __ __ __ __ __ __ __ __ __   __ __ __ __ __ __ __
    2   4 7 5 14 26 1 5 9 10   25 7 10 16 15 2 18

Words in Context Write the list word that completes each sentence.

12. A new broom sweeps the floor ____.

12. _____

13. All people are created ____.

13. _____

14. Feelings are a ____ emotion.

14. _____

15. She was the ____ for the painting.

15. _____

16. Please ____ on the dotted line.

16. _____

17. Take care to ____ safely.

17. _____

18. My ____ from this job is effective today.

18. _____

19. The ____ part of the test was easy.

19. _____

20. That country had many ____ parties.

20. _____

Home Activity Your child has learned to read, write, and spell related words that have differences in the way similar spellings are pronounced. Ask your child to use two pairs of related words in sentences.

Multisyllabic Words

Spelling Words				
elementary	definition	elevator	mosaic	cylinder
vehicle	substitute	Pennsylvania	tuxedo	intermediate
miniature	variety	ravioli	meteorite	centennial
probability	literature	cafeteria	fascination	curiosity

Analogies Write the list word that completes each comparison.

1. Store is to shop as lunchroom is to _____.

2. Poodle is to dog as poem is to _____.

3. Building block is to cube as tin can is to _____.

4. Huge is to giant as tiny is to _____.

5. Chicago is to Illinois as Philadelphia is to _____.

6. Silk is to fabric as car is to _____.

7. Apple is to fruit as _____ is to pasta.

8. Pleasant is to nice as basic is to _____.

9. Casual is to jeans as formal is to _____.

10. Beginning is to elementary as middle is to _____.

Alphabetize Write the ten list words below in alphabetical order.

meteorite	elevator
curiosity	definition
probability	substitute
fascination	centennial
mosaic	variety

11. _____   16. _____

12. _____   17. _____

13. _____   18. _____

14. _____   18. _____

15. _____   20. _____

Home Activity Your child has completed analogies for multisyllabic words. Take turns making up analogies for list words and completing them.

Unusual Spellings

Spelling Words				
league	fatigue	anxious	intrigue	depot
sergeant	debt	foreign	villain	cordial
yacht	blood	bargain	cantaloupe	subtle
doubt	vague	condemn	flood	disguise

Word Sort Write the list words that fit into each category.

Words with silent _ue_ at the end

1. _____

2. _____

3. _____

4. _____

Words with silent _b_

5. _____

6. _____

7. _____

Words with a silent final consonant

8. _____

9. _____

Words with _oo_ pronounced /u/

10. _____

11. _____

Synonyms Write the list word that has the same, or nearly the same, meaning.

12. dreading _____

13. discount _____

14. melon _____

15. criminal _____

16. ship _____

17. officer _____

18. hide _____

19. friendly _____

20. strange _____

School + Home

Home Activity Your child has learned to spell words with unusual spellings. Take turns choosing a list word and discussing what is unusual about the way it is spelled.

Greek Word Parts

Spelling Words				
geology	biology	technology	biosphere	astronomy
thermometer	thermal	hemisphere	thermos	spherical
astronaut	disaster	zoology	asterisk	ecology
atmosphere	meteorology	sociology	thermostat	mythology

Words in Context Write the list words that complete the sentences.

While sledding, take a hot drink along in a(n) **(1)** _____ and wear **(2)** _____ clothing.

1. _____   2. _____

Tom collects rocks, so he is studying **(3)** _____; Jackie observes animals, so she is studying **(4)** _____.

3. _____   4. _____

Maria wants to travel in space as a(n) **(5)** _____, so she enjoys the study of the moon and planets in **(6)** _____.

5. _____   6. _____

According to the **(7)** _____ it is only 65 degrees, so turn the **(8)** _____ up.

7. _____   8. _____

In his study of plants and animals in **(9)** _____, Jake learned that all living things exist in a(n) **(10)** _____.

9. _____   10. _____

Carl studies environmental science, or **(11)** _____; he wants to use engineering science, or **(12)** _____, to improve the environment in the western **(13)** _____.

11. _____   12. _____   13. _____

While studying social groups in **(14)** _____, James learned about the gods of Greek **(15)** _____.

14. _____   15. _____

Did you know that the **(16)** _____ symbol comes from the Greek word for star?

16. _____

Synonyms Write the list word that has the same, or nearly the same, meaning.

17. air   _____   19. climatology   _____

18. calamity   _____   20. round   _____

Home Activity Your child has learned to spell words with Greek word parts. Ask your child to organize the list words into groups according to word parts and tell what each word part means.

Latin Roots

Spelling Words				
project	auditorium	December	audit	decathlon
audience	terrier	reject	decimeter	terrarium
decade	decimal	eject	audition	dejected
territory	injection	terrace	audible	terrain

Classifying Write the list word that belongs in each group.

1. race, high jump, long jump, _____

2. patio, deck, _____

3. May, July, October, _____

4. millimeter, centimenter, _____

5. aquarium, greenhouse, _____

6. shot, vaccine, inoculation, _____

7. millennium, century, _____

8. poodle, collie, spaniel, _____

9. theater, playhouse, hall, _____

10. state, country, region, _____

Synonyms Write the list word that has the same, or nearly the same, meaning.

11. sad _____

12. emit _____

13. ground _____

14. tryout _____

15. plan _____

16. onlookers _____

17. discard _____

18. heard _____

19. tens _____

20. check _____

 Home Activity Your child has learned to spell words with Latin roots. Take turns brainstorming a word that has one of the list word roots. Look up each word in the dictionary to confirm it comes from a Latin word.

Spelling Practice Book

Related Words

Spelling Words				
politics	equal	arrive	human	resign
political	equation	arrival	humanity	resignation
major	sign	inspire	clean	unite
majority	signature	inspiration	cleanse	unity

Analogies Write the list word that completes each comparison.

1. Go is to move as quit is to _____.

2. Word is to sentence as number is to _____.

3. Beast is to animal as person is to _____.

4. Few is to many as minority is to _____.

5. Picture is to illustration as autograph is to _____.

6. Stop is to go as leave is to _____.

7. Thrill is to excite as encourage is to _____.

8. Earth is to world as mankind is to _____.

9. Customer is to business as candidate is to _____.

10. Imagination is to inventor as _____ is to artist.

Synonyms Write the list word that has the same, or nearly the same, meaning.

11. wash _____

12. symbol _____

13. retirement _____

14. governmental _____

15. togetherness _____

Antonyms Write the list word that has the opposite, or nearly the opposite, meaning.

16. departure _____

17. minor _____

18. dirty _____

19. divide _____

20. uneven _____

 Home Activity Your child has learned to spell related words. Read several pairs of words from the list. Ask your child to explain how knowing the spelling of one word in the pair can help in spelling the other word.

Proofread for Spelling Errors

Proofread a Science Fiction Story. Circle twelve spelling mistakes in the science fiction story below. Write them correctly.

Roger's space vehickle had been traveling toward Mars for ten days. Far below he saw a tiny green and blue spherecal object: Earth. He also saw millions of pinpoints of light. No matter how far he traveled, the stars did not seem to get closer.

People had first landed on Mars a decaid earlier. Roger was not an astronot. He had been an accountant on Earth. But Earth was crowded. People wanted new places to live and work. When the technolegy for traveling to Mars had been perfected, hundreds of people left for the distant planet. There they could claim a large terratory. Scientists had studied the planet's geolegy. They found minerals that were valuable on Earth. People could get rich by mining the materials and sending them back to Earth. They just needed courage and a spirit of adventure.

Suddenly the surface of Mars was in sight. Roger would arive on the red planet in minutes. But then his spaceship shook wildly. It had been hit by a meterite! Roger could not believe his journey would end in dissaster. He tried desperately to land the ship safely. Finally it crashed on Mars. The impact rattled Roger and the ship. But the ship withstood the crash, and Roger seemed all right too. He looked out the spaceship window. The terain looked barren, and the atmosphear was bleak. But Roger had never been so glad to reach his destination.

1. _____   7. _____

2. _____   8. _____

3. _____   9. _____

4. _____   10. _____

5. _____   11. _____

6. _____   12. _____

Suffixes -ous, -sion, -ion, -ation

Generalization When adding **-ous, -sion, -ion,** and **-ation,** some base words change. A final **e** or **y** may be dropped: **fam<u>ous</u>, fur<u>ious</u>.** Some words have other changes: **dec<u>ision</u>.**

Word Sort Sort the list words by their suffix.

-ous	-ion
1. _____	9. _____
2. _____	10. _____
3. _____	11. _____
4. _____	12. _____
5. _____	**-ation**

-sion	
6. _____	13. _____
7. _____	14. _____
8. _____	15. _____
	16. _____
	17. _____
	18. _____
	19. _____
	20. _____

Spelling Words

1. famous
2. invention
3. election
4. furious
5. imagination
6. education
7. nervous
8. explanation
9. various
10. decision

11. relaxation
12. conversation
13. tension
14. humorous
15. exhibition
16. attraction
17. invasion
18. creation
19. occupation
20. destination

School + Home

Home Activity Your child is learning about suffixes. Have your child tell you the four suffixes studied and spell each for you.

Suffixes *-ous*, *-sion*, *-ion*, *-ation*

Spelling Words				
famous	invention	election	furious	imagination
education	nervous	explanation	various	decision
relaxation	conversation	tension	humorous	exhibition
attraction	invasion	creation	occupation	destination

Synonyms Write the list word that has the same or almost the same meaning as the underlined word or phrase.

1. We will reach our <u>journey's end</u> after four days of traveling.

2. People who are <u>well known</u> are often stopped by fans on the street.

3. Sometimes it's very hard to make a <u>choice</u>.

4. I had a very long <u>talk</u> on the phone with my cousin.

5. The 5th graders had a special <u>art show</u> in the auditorium.

6. I felt <u>worried</u> and had butterflies in my stomach.

7. The army ants launched an <u>attack</u> at our picnic.

8. It takes a lot of <u>creative thoughts</u> to write a story.

9. What was your <u>excuse</u> for being late?

10. Who won that close <u>vote</u> last month?

1. _____

2. _____

3. _____

4. _____

5. _____

6. _____

7. _____

8. _____

9. _____

10. _____

Definitions Write the list word that fits each definition.

11. stretching or a strain

12. a thing that delights

13. something that is created

14. funny and amusing

15. knowledge and skills learned

16. differing from one another

17. condition of being relaxed

18. something made for the first time

19. what someone does to earn a living

20. full of wild, fierce anger

11. _____

12. _____

13. _____

14. _____

15. _____

16. _____

17. _____

18. _____

19. _____

20. _____

© Pearson Education, Inc.5

Home Activity Your child wrote words that have suffixes. Have your child underline the suffix in each word.

Suffixes -ous, -sion, -ion, -ation

Proofread an Essay Circle five spelling errors in the essay. Write the words correctly. Find a sentence with a capitalization error and write the sentence correctly.

Laughing Helps

When I feel nervos or edgy, I call my friend. Having a friendly conversasion really helps. My friend is truly funny and tells humorus stories. I told my friend that she would be famus one day. She laughed and said, "well, I don't want to be a performer. I have to finish my educasion first." Still, I think being a comedian seems like a great occupation for her.

---

1. _____   2. _____

3. _____   4. _____

5. _____

6. _____

Spelling Words

famous
invention
election
furious
imagination
education
nervous
explanation
various
decision

relaxation
conversation
tension
humorous
exhibition
attraction
invasion
creation
occupation
destination

Proofread Words Circle the word that is spelled correctly. Write the word.

7. varius   varous   various   7. _____

8. invension   invention   invensiun   8. _____

9. tention   tensiun   tension   9. _____

10. furious   furyous   furius   10. _____

11. attration   attraction   attracshun   11. _____

12. destinashun destinasion   destination   12. _____

13. relacsation relaxation   relaxasion   13. _____

14. exsibition   exabition   exhibition   14. _____

15. election   elektion   elecsion   15. _____

16. invation   invasion   invashion   16. _____

Frequently Misspelled Words

didn't
said
don't

School + Home

Home Activity Your child identified misspelled list words. Say a suffix and have your child tell you a list word ending in that suffix. Then have your child spell the word.

© Pearson Education, Inc. 5

Suffixes *-ous, -sion, -ion, -ation*

Spelling Words				
famous	invention	election	furious	imagination
education	nervous	explanation	various	decision
relaxation	conversation	tension	humorous	exhibition
attraction	invasion	creation	occupation	destination

Match Suffixes Draw a line from the word or word part to its suffix. Write the word on the line.

attract   ion   **1.** _____

creat   sion   **2.** _____

deci   ous   **3.** _____

exhibit   ion   **4.** _____

furi   ion   **5.** _____

humor   ous   **6.** _____

imagin   ation   **7.** _____

occup   ous   **8.** _____

relax   ation   **9.** _____

vari   ation   **10.** _____

Double Puzzle Unscramble the list words. Use the numbered letters to find the answer to the question.

What is a destination for fun, attractions, and relaxation?

11. ASFUMO   __ __ __ __ __ __
       4

12. ESNVOUR   __ __ __ __ __ __ __
       9

13. ONTNEIS   __ __ __ __ __ __ __
         6

14. CNPAIUCTOO   __ __ __ __ __ __ __ __ __ __
         11   1

15. ESOOTRACNIVN   __ __ __ __ __ __ __ __ __ __ __ __
         13   3

16. XOHNIEBITI   __ __ __ __ __ __ __ __ __ __
     7

17. VINANOIS   __ __ __ __ __ __ __ __
         12   2

18. ARECNTOI   __ __ __ __ __ __ __ __
       8

19. NINVETNIO   __ __ __ __ __ __ __ __ __
         10

20. DEUNCAIOT   __ __ __ __ __ __ __ __ __
       5

__ __ __ __ __ __ __ __ __ __
1   2   3   4   5   6   7   4   8   9   10

__ __ __ **k**
11   12   13

Home Activity Your child has learned to read, write, and spell words with suffixes. Look through books or magazines with your child and try to find four other words with the same endings.

Final Syllable -*ant*, -*ent*, -*ance*, -*ence*

Generalization There is no sound clue to help you decide whether to use an **a** or **e**: import**ant**, intellig**ent**, inst**ance**, experi**ence**.

Word Sort Sort the list words by their ending.

-ant

1. _____

2. _____

3. _____

4. _____

-ent

5. _____

6. _____

7. _____

-ence

8. _____

9. _____

10. _____

11. _____

12. _____

13. _____

14. _____

-ance

15. _____

16. _____

17. _____

18. _____

19. _____

20. _____

Spelling Words

1. important
2. experience
3. ignorant
4. entrance
5. difference
6. instance
7. absence
8. appearance
9. intelligent
10. evidence

11. pollutant
12. clearance
13. confidence
14. conference
15. insurance
16. ambulance
17. hesitant
18. consistent
19. excellence
20. persistent

School + Home

Home Activity Your child is learning about final syllables. Have your child choose and spell a list word for each of the four final syllables being studied.

Final Syllable -*ant*, -*ent*, -*ance*, -*ence*

Spelling Words				
important	experience	ignorant	entrance	difference
instance	absence	appearance	intelligent	evidence
pollutant	clearance	confidence	conference	insurance
ambulance	hesitant	consistent	excellence	persistent

Antonyms Write the list word that has the opposite or almost the opposite meaning of the underlined word or phrase.

1. I was <u>certain</u> to ask for help on my assignment.

2. We thought his <u>presence</u> was the cause of the loss.

3. We had trouble finding the <u>exit</u> to the building.

4. The facts in the case are <u>unimportant</u>.

5. Our students strive for <u>poor quality</u> in all they do.

6. That constant buzzing in the television is a(n) <u>occasional</u> annoyance.

7. A good employee is hard working and <u>inconsistent</u>.

8. It takes a while to develop self-assurance and <u>shyness</u>.

9. Car exhaust is an air <u>cleaner</u>.

10. By human standards, slugs and snails are not <u>stupid</u>.

1. _____

2. _____

3. _____

4. _____

5. _____

6. _____

7. _____

8. _____

9. _____

10. _____

Definitions Write the list word on the line that has the same meaning.

11. anything that shows what is true and what is not

12. a kind of sale

13. financial protection against harm, illness, or loss

14. vehicle that provides transportation to the hospital

15. a change

16. a person or thing serving as an example

17. knowing little or nothing

18. what is seen, done, or lived through

19. a meeting of interested persons to discuss a particular subject

20. the act of coming into sight

11. _____

12. _____

13. _____

14. _____

15. _____

16. _____

17. _____

18. _____

19. _____

20. _____

© Pearson Education, Inc.5

Home Activity Your child wrote words that have syllables ending in -*ant*, -*ent*, -*ance*, -*ence*. Have your child underline the final syllable in each word.

Final Syllable -*ant*, -*ent*, -*ance*, -*ence*

Proofread an Article Circle and write six spelling errors. Circle one capitalization error and write the sentence correctly.

Help Is on the Way

With sirens wailing, the ambulence driver carefully winds through traffic. It takes a lot of confidents to do this important job. In large cities, with persistant traffic, a driver must be extra careful. Still, the Driver must take the fastest route to the emergency room. Time makes all the differants when people need emergency care. All drivers try to get each won of their patients to the emergency room entrance as quickly as possible.

1. _____   2. _____

3. _____   4. _____

5. _____   6. _____

7. _____

_____

Spelling Words
important
experience
ignorant
entrance
difference
instance
absence
appearance
intelligent
evidence
pollutant
clearance
confidence
conference
insurance
ambulance
hesitant
consistent
excellence
persistent

Proofread Words Circle the correct spelling of the list word. Write the word.

8. absense   abcense   absence   8. _____

9. intelligant   intelligent   intellagent   9. _____

10. insurance   insurants   insurence   10. _____

11. pollutent   pollutant   pollutint   11. _____

12. ignorent   ignorint   ignorant   12. _____

13. apperence   appearance   appearants   13. _____

14. important   importent   inportant   14. _____

15. hezitent   hesitent   hesitant   15. _____

Frequently Misspelled Words
off
one
tired

Home Activity Your child identified misspelled list words. Ask your child to name the four words he or she has the most difficulty spelling and spell them for you.

Final Syllable -*ant*, -*ent*, -*ance*, -*ence*

Spelling Words

important	experience	ignorant	entrance	difference
instance	absence	appearance	intelligent	evidence
pollutant	clearance	confidence	conference	insurance
ambulance	hesitant	consistent	excellence	persistent

Alphabetical Order Write the list word that fits in alphabetical order between the two words.

1. amazement/ambush

2. clay/clef

3. igloo/illness

4. herb/hickory

5. above/absorb

6. permit/person

7. cone/confess

8. poll/pomp

9. ewe/exit

10. ill/impress

1. _____

2. _____

3. _____

4. _____

5. _____

6. _____

7. _____

8. _____

9. _____

10. _____

Word Search Circle ten list words that are hidden in the puzzle. Write each word.

```
K L K A D O Q V L H E C E E
G D S V P I T K S O S O X N
F K N B W P F M E O D N P T
S X O A Q M E F U J R F E R
I P H J K G Y A E U X I R A
E V I D E N C E R R P D I N
I N S U R A N C E A E E E C
C O N S I S T E N T N N N E
I N T E L L I G E N T C C V
I N S T A N C E O S A E E E
```

11. _____

12. _____

13. _____

14. _____

15. _____

16. _____

17. _____

18. _____

19. _____

20. _____

Home Activity Your child has learned to read, write, and spell words with final syllable spellings -*ant*, -*ent*, -*ance*, -*ence*. Take turns saying and spelling the words aloud.

Words with *ei* and *ie*

Generalization Long **e** can be spelled **ei** or **ie**: rec<u>ei</u>ve, bel<u>ie</u>ve.

Word Sort Sort the list words by the way the long *e* is spelled.

ei	**ie**
1. _____	10. _____
2. _____	11. _____
3. _____	12. _____
4. _____	13. _____
5. _____	14. _____
6. _____	15. _____
7. _____	16. _____
8. _____	17. _____
9. _____	18. _____
	19. _____
	20. _____

Spelling Words

1. brief
2. believe
3. receive
4. leisure
5. piece
6. relief
7. seize
8. ceiling
9. field
10. neither

11. apiece
12. receipt
13. yield
14. deceive
15. achieve
16. grief
17. niece
18. protein
19. shield
20. conceited

© Pearson Education, Inc. 5

Home Activity Your child is learning long e spellings of *ei* and *ie*. Have your child circle the long *e* spelling in each list word.

Words with *ei* and *ie*

Spelling Words				
brief	believe	receive	leisure	piece
relief	seize	ceiling	field	neither
apiece	receipt	yield	deceive	achieve
grief	niece	protein	shield	conceited

Classifying Write the list word that completes each group.

1. nor, not any, ___

2. give way, move aside, ___

3. sadness, sorrow, ___

4. stuck-up, self-important, ___

5. grab, clutch, ___

6. short, to the point, ___

7. free time, vacation, ___

8. fool, trick, ___

9. ticket, voucher, ___

10. reach, gain, ___

1. _____

2. _____

3. _____

4. _____

5. _____

6. _____

7. _____

8. _____

9. _____

10. _____

Missing Words Write the list word that completes each sentence.

11. Meat, nuts, and cheese all supply ____, a necessary nutrient.

12. My aunt says I'm her favorite ____.

13. We get three presents ____.

14. He looked up and saw water dripping from the ____.

15. I ____ that it's always best to tell the truth.

16. Did you ____ the package you ordered?

17. A police officer's badge is called a ____.

18. The open ____ was grassy and filled with flowers.

19. I need a new ____ of chalk.

20. I feel ____ that I have completed my assignment.

11. _____

12. _____

13. _____

14. _____

15. _____

16. _____

17. _____

18. _____

19. _____

20. _____

© Pearson Education, Inc. 5

Home Activity Your child wrote words that have long *e* spelled *ei* and *ie*. Say a list word and ask your child to tell if the long *e* sound in the word is spelled *ei* or *ie*. Then have your child spell the word.

Spelling Practice Book

Words with *ei* and *ie*

Proofread a Dialogue Circle seven spelling errors. Write the words correctly. Circle one capitalization error and write the sentence correctly.

Ticket Seller: That's $4.00 apeace for the movie.

Amos: Okay! Can we get a receit?

Ticket Seller: You get a piece of the ticket back.

Ari: Did you recieve your change?

Amos: I beleve I did. Let me count.

Ari: It's a relefe that we were on time.

Amos: We're the only ones here. Neither Jonathan nor his freind made it.

Ari: Well, I heard Jonathan's neece was coming too.

Amos: Here they are!

Ari: Get your Ticket! Let's go in!

Spelling Words
brief
believe
receive
leisure
piece
relief
seize
ceiling
field
neither
apiece
receipt
yield
deceive
achieve
grief
niece
protein
shield
conceited

1. _____   2. _____

3. _____   4. _____

5. _____   6. _____

7. _____   8. _____

Proofread Words Circle the correct spelling of the list word. Write each word.

9. They work to ____ greatness.   9. _____

   achieve   acheive   acheave

10. Traffic should ____ to the right.   10. _____

    yeild   yield   yeeld

11. Fish is a good source of ____.   11. _____

    proteen   protien   protein

12. He tried to ____ his neighbor.   12. _____

    decieve   deceive   decive

Frequently Misspelled Words
believe
friend
friends
piece

Home Activity Your child identified misspelled list words. Ask your child to tell you the four list words that are the most difficult to spell. Help your child practice these words.

© Pearson Education, Inc. 5

Words with *ei* and *ie*

Spelling Words

brief	believe	receive	leisure	piece
relief	seize	ceiling	field	neither
apiece	receipt	yield	deceive	achieve
grief	niece	protein	shield	conceited

Crossword Puzzle Use each clue to find the list words. Write one letter in each box.

Across
3. proof of payment
7. sorrow
8. find comfort
9. free time
10. to trick
11. to give way

Down
1. short
2. each
4. badge
5. grab
6. part

Antonyms Write the list word that has the opposite or nearly the opposite meaning.

12. send   12. _____
13. floor   13. _____
14. humble   14. _____
15. both   15. _____
16. fail   16. _____
17. question   17. _____
18. nephew   18. _____
19. forest   19. _____
20. sugar   20. _____

Home Activity Your child has learned to read, write, and spell words with long *e* spellings of *ie* and *ei*. Take turns using the words in sentences.

© Pearson Education, Inc. 5

Compound Words

Generalization Some compound words are closed: **keyboard**, **textbook**. Other compound words are open: **ice cream**, **a lot**.

Word Sort Sort the list words according to whether they are open or closed compound words.

open

1. _____
2. _____
3. _____
4. _____
5. _____
6. _____
7. _____
8. _____
9. _____

closed

10. _____
11. _____
12. _____
13. _____
14. _____
15. _____
16. _____
17. _____
18. _____
19. _____
20. _____

Spelling Words

1. ice cream
2. a lot
3. keyboard
4. fairy tale
5. horseshoe
6. piggy bank
7. textbook
8. guidelines
9. newspaper
10. space shuttle
11. hay fever
12. dead end
13. password
14. teenager
15. skateboard
16. everything
17. barbed wire
18. cartwheel
19. root beer
20. fingerprint

School + Home

Home Activity Your child is learning about open and closed compound words. Ask your child to pick a list word and use it in a sentence.

© Pearson Education, Inc. 5

Compound Words

Spelling Words				
ice cream	a lot	keyboard	fairy tale	horseshoe
piggy bank	textbook	guidelines	newspaper	space shuttle
hay fever	dead end	password	teenager	skateboard
everything	barbed wire	cartwheel	root beer	fingerprint

Word Meanings Write the list word that fits each description.

1. This is a type of soft drink.

2. This is a board with wheels.

3. A person who is in between a child and an adult in age is this.

4. A road that goes nowhere is this.

5. This could be a clue at a crime scene.

6. This is what you do when you turn head over heels.

7. This could make your eyes water and your nose tickle.

8. This is a daily publication.

9. This is something you save money in.

10. This is cold and sweet.

1. _____

2. _____

3. _____

4. _____

5. _____

6. _____

7. _____

8. _____

9. _____

10. _____

Definitions Write a list word to match each definition.

11. plenty

12. an imaginary story

13. a horse's footwear

14. a book one reads for school

15. rules or suggestions

16. an outer space vehicle

17. a secret word

18. all

19. wire with spikes

20. set of keys on a computer

11. _____

12. _____

13. _____

14. _____

15. _____

16. _____

17. _____

18. _____

19. _____

20. _____

Home Activity Your child spelled compound words. Ask your child to pick a list word, spell it, and use it in a sentence.

Compound Words

Proofread a Letter Circle five words that are spelled incorrectly. Write the words on the lines. Find a sentence with incorrect punctuation. Write the sentence correctly.

I am having a lot of fun this summer even with my hayfever. Summer camp is every thing I expected. We get to eat ice cream and drink rootbeer after every meal. Our camp advisor is a teanager named Karen. She has given us a password to use when entering our cabin. She also knows many tricks on her skate board. She has even had an article written about her in the local newspaper? Maybe you can join us next year.

1. _____   2. _____

3. _____   4. _____

5. _____

6. _____

_____

Spelling Words

ice cream
a lot
keyboard
fairy tale
horseshoe
piggy bank
textbook
guidelines
newspaper
space shuttle

hay fever
dead end
password
teenager
skateboard
everything
barbed wire
cartwheel
root beer
fingerprint

Proofread Words Circle the word that is spelled correctly. Write it on the line.

7.	alot	a lot	7. _____
8.	piggybank	piggy bank	8. _____
9.	icecream	ice cream	9. _____
10.	fairy tale	fairytale	10. _____
11.	cartwheel	cart wheel	11. _____
12.	finger print	fingerprint	12. _____
13.	key board	keyboard	13. _____
14.	dead end	deadend	14. _____

Frequently Misspelled Words

sometimes
everything
maybe
a lot

Home Activity Your child identified misspelled words. Say and spell a list word for your child. Make some intentional errors. Have your child spell the word correctly.

Compound Words

Spelling Words				
ice cream	a lot	keyboard	fairy tale	horseshoe
piggy bank	textbook	guidelines	newspaper	space shuttle
hay fever	dead end	password	teenager	skateboard
everything	barbed wire	cartwheel	root beer	fingerprint

Crossword Puzzle Use each clue to find the list words. Write one letter in each box.

Across
2. crime scene clue
5. between child and adult
6. secret phrase
7. all

Down
1. board with wheels
3. daily journal
4. horse's footwear

Classifying Write the list word that belongs in each group.

8. plenty, abundant, ____   8. _____

9. monitor, mouse, ____   9. _____

10. myth, legend, ____   10. _____

11. safe, savings and loan, ____ 11. _____

12. suggestions, recommendations, ____ 12. _____

13. rocket, space station, ____ 13. _____

14. one way, two lane, ____   14. _____

15. picket, chain link, ____   15. _____

Home Activity Your child worked a crossword puzzle and classified words. Ask your child to pick a list word and use it in a sentence.

Spelling Practice Book

Easily Confused Words

Generalization Some words are easily confused because they have similar pronunciations and spellings: **quiet**, **quite**.

Word Sort Sort the list words by words you know how to spell and words you are learning to spell. Write each word.

words I know how to spell	words I am learning to spell
1. _____	11. _____
2. _____	12. _____
3. _____	13. _____
4. _____	14. _____
5. _____	15. _____
6. _____	16. _____
7. _____	17. _____
8. _____	18. _____
9. _____	19. _____
10. _____	20. _____

Spelling Words

1. quiet
2. quite
3. finely
4. finally
5. except
6. accept
7. than
8. then
9. since
10. sense

11. affect
12. effect
13. from
14. form
15. later
16. latter
17. adapt
18. adopt
19. medal
20. metal

School + Home **Home Activity** Your child is learning about easily confused words. Ask your child to say each list word and spell it aloud.

Easily Confused Words

Spelling Words				
quiet	quite	finely	finally	except
accept	than	then	since	sense
affect	effect	from	form	later
latter	adapt	adopt	medal	metal

Definitions Write the list word that means the same as each word or phrase.

1. silent

2. at last

3. receive

4. shape

5. a type of award

1. _____

2. _____

3. _____

4. _____

5. _____

Words in Context Write a list word to finish each sentence.

6. How will this score ___ my grade?

7. I'll see you ___.

8. They plan to ___ a child soon.

9. By ___ we should know the results of the race.

10. My aunt has a good ___ of humor.

11. I think this project is not ___ finished yet.

12. This piano has been very ___ tuned.

13. Everyone was there ___ me.

14. I would rather go to a movie ___ do my homework.

15. I haven't seen her ___ last year.

16. What ___ will this poor test score have on my overall grade?

17. I like to walk home ___ school.

18. I prefer the former choice to the ___.

19. It is important to be able to ___ to new situations.

20. The magnet picked up the ___ pieces.

6. _____

7. _____

8. _____

9. _____

10. _____

11. _____

12. _____

13. _____

14. _____

15. _____

16. _____

17. _____

18. _____

19. _____

20. _____

School + Home   **Home Activity** Your child matched words with definitions and finished sentences. Ask your child to define the word *adapt*.

Easily Confused Words

Proofread a Dialogue Circle six spelling mistakes in the article below. Write them correctly. Find a sentence with a misplaced comma. Write the sentence correctly.

Spelling Words

quiet
quite
finely
finally
except
accept
than
then
since
sense
affect
effect
from
form
later
latter
adapt
adopt
medal
metal

My Brother the Hero

When my brother finely got back form serving overseas, my family was happy and proud. We attended a ceremony where we watched him except a metal. When he stood up to receive his award, we were very quite. Latter we went out to dinner to celebrate his return.

---

1. _____   2. _____

3. _____   4. _____

5. _____   6. _____

7. _____

_____

Proofread Words Circle the word that is spelled correctly. Write it on the line.

Frequently Misspelled Words

where
were

8. axcept   accept   8. _____

9. adupt   adapt   9. _____

10. adoped   adopt   10. _____

11. affect   afect   11. _____

12. except   exsept   12. _____

13. finaly   finally   13. _____

14. sense   sence   14. _____

15. then   thun   15. _____

Home Activity Your child identified misspelled words. Ask your child to pick a list word and use it in a sentence.

Easily Confused Words

Spelling Words				
quiet	quite	finely	finally	except
accept	than	then	since	sense
affect	effect	from	form	later
latter	adapt	adopt	medal	metal

Word Scramble Unscramble each word to write a list word.

1. taapd
2. telam
3. ofrm
4. ratel
5. fftcee
6. neess
7. petcac
8. etqui
9. liynef
10. neth

1. _____
2. _____
3. _____
4. _____
5. _____
6. _____
7. _____
8. _____
9. _____
10. _____

Sound-alike Words Write a list word that sounds like each word listed below.

11. quiet
12. finely
13. accept
14. then
15. sense
16. effect
17. later
18. form
19. metal
20. adapt

11. _____
12. _____
13. _____
14. _____
15. _____
16. _____
17. _____
18. _____
19. _____
20. _____

© Pearson Education, Inc. 5

Home Activity Your child unscrambled words and matched sound-alike words. Ask your child to pick a list word and spell it.

Suffixes -*ous*, -*sion*, -*ion*, -*ation*

Spelling Words				
famous	imagination	various	tension	invasion
invention	education	decision	humorous	creation
election	nervous	relaxation	exhibition	occupation
furious	explanation	conversation	attraction	distination

Antonyms Write the list word that has the opposite, or nearly the opposite, meaning.

1. serious   _____

2. relaxed   _____

3. repulsion   _____

4. unknown   _____

5. destruction   _____

6. calm   _____

7. uncertainty   _____

8. alike   _____

Words in Context Complete each sentence with a list word.

9. Reading, writing, and math are important parts of your _____.

10. The lightbulb was a marvelous _____.

11. Nursing is a helpful _____.

12. In a good _____, everyone has a chance to speak.

13. We saw a(n) _____ of modern art at the museum.

14. Some people play card games for _____.

15. The beach is a popular summer _____.

16. Our picnic was ruined by a(n) _____ of ants.

17. You must use your _____ to write a compelling poem.

18. It is important for citizens to vote in each _____.

19. Stretching a rubber band increases its _____.

20. You must have a good _____ for missing soccer practice.

Home Activity Your child has been learning to spell words with suffixes. Call out some of the list words and ask your child to give a synonym or antonym for each word.

© Pearson Education, Inc. 5

Final Syllable *-ant, -ent, -ance, -ence*

Spelling Words				
important	difference	intelligent	confidence	hesitant
experience	instance	evidence	conference	consistent
ignorant	absence	pollutant	insurance	excellence
entrance	appearance	clearance	ambulance	persistent

Analogies Write the word that completes each comparison.

1. Happiness is to sadness as presence is to _____.

2. Sweet is to sour as educated is to _____.

3. Rose is to flower as smoke is to _____.

4. Trip is to journey as example is to _____.

5. Night is to day as exit is to _____.

6. Pretty is to lovely as smart is to _____.

7. Doctor is to hospital as paramedic is to _____.

8. Heat is to cold as sameness is to _____.

9. Game is to sport as meeting is to _____.

10. Difficult is to easy as insignificant is to _____.

Words in Context Complete each sentence with a list word.

11. The car repairs were paid for by the _____ company.

12. The jury considered the _____ against the man on trial.

13. Bright autumn colors gave the trees a lovely _____.

14. The soccer players liked the referee because his calls were _____.

15. Confronting a bear must be a frightening _____.

16. Because he was shy, Will was _____ to meet people.

17. There was a(n) _____ sale of snow boots at the end of the winter.

18. That baseball player has much _____ in his ability.

19. At the spring assembly, the best students were rewarded for _____.

20. To succeed in your goal, you must be _____.

Home Activity Your child learned to spell words with the final syllables *-ant*, *-ent*, *-ance*, and *-ence*. Ask your child to find an example of a word with each ending in a magazine and then spell each word without looking at the magazine.

Words with *ei* and *ie*

Spelling Words				
brief	piece	field	yield	niece
believe	relief	neither	deceive	protein
receive	seize	apiece	achieve	shield
leisure	ceiling	receipt	grief	conceited

Word Search Circle ten hidden list words. Words are down, across, and diagonal.
Write the words on the lines.

```
R  E  C  E  I  P  T  U  N  E
E  F  C  B  A  I  I  H  I  J
C  B  H  M  G  E  N  E  E  R
P  R  O  T  E  I  N  I  C  N
R  I  L  D  T  S  S  N  E  E
O  E  E  G  Y  I  E  L  D  I
T  F  L  R  O  F  E  I  R  T
E  C  E  I  L  I  N  G  E  H
S  C  Y  E  E  N  E  R  N  E
K  F  A  F  C  F  I  A  T  R
```

1. _____   6. _____

2. _____   7. _____

3. _____   8. _____

4. _____   9. _____

5. _____   10. _____

Synonyms Write the list word that has the same, or nearly the same, meaning.

11. each _____   16. relaxation _____

12. grab _____   17. fool _____

13. succeed _____   18. vain _____

14. meadow _____   19. suppose _____

15. protect _____   20. get _____

School + Home

Home Activity Your child has learned to spell words with long e spellings of *ei* and *ie*. Ask your child to find three sets of rhyming words on the list and spell each word.

© Pearson Education, Inc. 5

Compound Words

Spelling Words				
ice cream	horseshoe	newspaper	password	barbed wire
a lot	piggy bank	space shuttle	teenager	cartwheel
keyboard	textbook	hay fever	skateboard	root beer
fairy tale	guidelines	dead end	everything	fingerprint

Mixed-Up Words Draw a line to connect two words to make a list word. Then write the list word on the line.

1. horse	tale	**1.** _____
2. skate	ager	**2.** _____
3. barbed	shuttle	**3.** _____
4. teen	thing	**4.** _____
5. fairy	wire	**5.** _____
6. every	cream	**6.** _____
7. cart	word	**7.** _____
8. ice	board	**8.** _____
9. space	shoe	**9.** _____
10. pass	wheel	**10.** _____

Words in Context Complete each sentence with a list word.

11. During the spring, Linda's runny nose is caused by _____.

12. Robbie has over fifty dollars in coins in his _____.

13. The thief was caught because he left his _____ on the door of the store.

14. The Clarks' house is on a(n) _____ street, so there is very little traffic.

15. You will be well informed if you read a city _____ each day.

16. The boys drank _____ with their pizza at the party.

17. Many jobs have _____ that employees must follow.

18. There was _____ of snow on the sidewalk, so Sam shoveled it.

19. Study for the history test by reading Chapter 2 in your _____.

20. You will write fast after you learn to type on the computer _____.

Home Activity Your child has learned to spell compound words. Ask your child to give an example of an open compound and a closed compound, spell each one, and use each one in a sentence.

Spelling Practice Book

Easily Confused Words

Spelling Words				
quiet	except	since	from	adapt
quite	accept	sense	form	adopt
finely	than	affect	later	medal
finally	then	effect	latter	metal

Antonyms Write the list word that has the opposite or nearly the opposite meaning.

1. coarsely _____

2. reject _____

3. earlier _____

4. noisy _____

5. now _____

Synonyms Write the list word that has the same or nearly the same meaning.

6. result _____

7. reward _____

8. very _____

9. because _____

10. select _____

Analogies Write the word that completes each comparison.

11. First is to last as former is to _____.

12. Start is to begin as at last is to _____.

13. In is to out as to is to _____.

14. Milk is to drink as iron is to _____.

15. Buy is to purchase as influence is to _____.

16. North is to direction as sight is to _____.

17. Also is to too as but is to _____.

18. Gift is to present as shape is to _____.

19. Work is to labor as change is to _____.

20. Log is to dog as fan is to _____.

Home Activity Your child has learned to spell sound-alike words. Ask your child to name three pairs of list words, spell each word, and explain how they differ in meaning.

© Pearson Education, Inc. 5

Proofread for Spelling Errors

Proofread a Mystery Story. Circle twelve spelling mistakes in the mystery story below. Write them correctly.

When I went to the park that day, I didn't expect to get mixed up in a spy drama. Here's what happened: I live in Washington, D.C., and often walk in a park near my house. It's a popular place, but on that rainy Sunday morning, it was pretty quite. I was walking along admiring the autumn leaves when two men in khaki raincoats stepped in front of me. "What's the pass word?" one said. I was very confused. I finely convinced the men that I had no idea what they meant. "Then why are you carrying a news paper?" the man asked. Well, I'd been reading the sports page, but I didn't think that was against the law. The man said, "I beleive you can help us."

After a short conversasion with me, the men retreated behind the trees. They promised I was in no danger, but I felt nerveous as I waited for the man they had described. Than a small man with blond hair and a beard came down the path. He looked carefully at me and my paper. As he walked past, he murmured softly, "The password is cartwheel." Suddenly the men in raincoats jumped out and handcuffed the man. "What's the password?" they shouted to me. I told them, and they escorted the small man to a dark car waiting nearby.

Well, that was the end of my spying career. Apparently, I'd helped the FBI get importent evidance about a disloyal agent. I didn't get a metal or anything, but I did get a VIP tour of FBI headquarters. I especially enjoyed the finger print department. I think that will be my specialty when I become an agent.

1. _____   7. _____

2. _____   8. _____

3. _____   9. _____

4. _____   10. _____

5. _____   11. _____

6. _____   12. _____

Contractions

Unit 1, Week 5

1. they're
2. you've
3. weren't
4. needn't
5. there'd
6. they've
7. mustn't
8. what'll
9. doesn't
10. hadn't
11. could've
12. would've
13. should've
14. might've
15. wouldn't
16. who've
17. shouldn't
18. who'd
19. this'll
20. couldn't

Adding -ed, -ing

Unit 1, Week 4

1. supplied
2. supplying
3. denied
4. denying
5. decided
6. deciding
7. included
8. including
9. admitted
10. admitting
11. occurred
12. occurring
13. qualified
14. qualifying
15. identified
16. identifying
17. delayed
18. delaying
19. satisfied
20. satisfying

Long Vowel Digraphs

Unit 1, Week 3

1. coast
2. feast
3. speech
4. wheat
5. Spain
6. paint
7. arrow
8. needle
9. charcoal
10. praise
11. faint
12. maintain
13. crease
14. groan
15. breeze
16. willow
17. appeal
18. bowling
19. complain
20. sneeze

Long Vowel VCV

Unit 1, Week 2

1. fever
2. broken
3. climate
4. hotel
5. basic
6. vocal
7. native
8. silent
9. labor
10. spider
11. label
12. icon
13. agent
14. motive
15. vital
16. acorn
17. item
18. aroma
19. legal
20. solo

Short Vowel VCCV, VCV

Unit 1, Week 1

1. distance
2. method
3. anger
4. problem
5. butter
6. petals
7. enjoy
8. perhaps
9. figure
10. channel
11. admire
12. comedy
13. husband
14. tissue
15. mustard
16. shuttle
17. advance
18. drummer
19. regular
20. denim

Final Syllables *er*, *ar*, *or*

Unit 2, Week 5

1. danger
2. wander
3. tractor
4. dollar
5. harbor
6. eager
7. eraser
8. surrender
9. solar
10. sticker
11. locker
12. helicopter
13. pillar
14. refrigerator
15. caterpillar
16. rumor
17. glimmer
18. linger
19. sensor
20. alligator

Final Syllables *-en*, *-an*, *-el*, *-le*, *-il*

Unit 2, Week 4

1. example
2. level
3. human
4. quarrel
5. scramble
6. evil
7. oxygen
8. wooden
9. double
10. travel
11. cancel
12. chuckle
13. fossil
14. toboggan
15. veteran
16. chisel
17. suburban
18. single
19. sudden
20. beagle

Vowel Sounds with *r*

Unit 2, Week 3

1. snore
2. tornado
3. spare
4. appear
5. career
6. square
7. report
8. prepare
9. pioneer
10. chair
11. beware
12. smear
13. repair
14. sword
15. ignore
16. order
17. engineer
18. resort
19. volunteer
20. declare

Irregular Plurals

Unit 2, Week 2

1. staffs
2. ourselves
3. pants
4. scissors
5. loaves
6. volcanoes
7. chiefs
8. buffaloes
9. flamingos
10. beliefs
11. echoes
12. shelves
13. quizzes
14. sheriffs
15. dominoes
16. thieves
17. measles
18. avocados
19. chefs
20. pianos

Digraphs *th*, *sh*, *ch*, *ph*

Unit 2, Week 1

1. shovel
2. southern
3. northern
4. chapter
5. hyphen
6. chosen
7. establish
8. although
9. challenge
10. approach
11. astonish
12. python
13. shatter
14. ethnic
15. shiver
16. pharmacy
17. charity
18. china
19. attach
20. ostrich

Prefixes *un-*, *de-*, *dis-*

Unit 3, Week 5

1. uncover
2. defrost
3. uncomfortable
4. discourage
5. disadvantage
6. unfortunate
7. unfamiliar
8. disability
9. discomfort
10. deodorant
11. unemployed
12. deflate
13. disbelief
14. unpredictable
15. disapprove
16. disappoint
17. unpleasant
18. dehydrated
19. disqualify
20. undecided

One Consonant or Two

Unit 3, Week 4

1. address
2. college
3. mirror
4. recess
5. committee
6. collect
7. Mississippi
8. immediate
9. command
10. appreciate
11. announce
12. possess
13. Tennessee
14. gallop
15. opponent
16. barricade
17. broccoli
18. accomplish
19. allowance
20. zucchini

Consonant Sounds /j/, /ks/, /sk/, and /s/

Unit 3, Week 3

1. excuse
2. scene
3. muscle
4. explore
5. pledge
6. journal
7. science
8. schedule
9. gigantic
10. scheme
11. Japan
12. excellent
13. exclaim
14. fascinate
15. ginger
16. scholar
17. scent
18. dodge
19. smudge
20. schooner

Compound Words

Unit 3, Week 2

1. waterproof
2. teaspoon
3. grasshopper
4. homesick
5. barefoot
6. courthouse
7. earthquake
8. rowboat
9. scrapbook
10. countryside
11. lightweight
12. fishhook
13. spotlight
14. blindfold
15. whirlpool
16. tablespoon
17. greenhouse
18. postcard
19. hummingbird
20. thumbtack

Schwa

Unit 3, Week 1

1. jewel
2. kingdom
3. gasoline
4. factory
5. garage
6. tropical
7. pajamas
8. estimate
9. tomorrow
10. humidity
11. Chicago
12. bulletin
13. carnival
14. illustrate
15. elegant
16. census
17. terrific
18. celebrate
19. operate
20. celery

Negative Prefixes

Unit 4, Week 5

1. invisible
2. illiterate
3. irregular
4. irresistible
5. impossible
6. informal
7. illegal
8. impatient
9. independent
10. incorrect
11. inactive
12. imperfect
13. impolite
14. immature
15. illogical
16. indefinite
17. inappropriate
18. immobile
19. irresponsible
20. inexpensive

Suffixes -ible, -able

Unit 4, Week 4

1. sensible
2. washable
3. available
4. agreeable
5. fashionable
6. valuable
7. flexible
8. reasonable
9. favorable
10. breakable
11. convertible
12. forgettable
13. laughable
14. sociable
15. allowable
16. divisible
17. hospitable
18. reversible
19. responsible
20. tolerable

Homophones

Unit 4, Week 3

1. cent
2. sent
3. scent
4. threw
5. through
6. weather
7. whether
8. their
9. there
10. they're
11. chili
12. chilly
13. tide
14. tied
15. pale
16. pail
17. aloud
18. allowed
19. course
20. coarse

Prefixes over-, under-, sub-, super-, out-

Unit 4, Week 2

1. overlook
2. underline
3. subway
4. subset
5. supermarket
6. outlet
7. underground
8. overboard
9. undercurrent
10. superstar
11. overtime
12. supersonic
13. submarine
14. undercover
15. overcast
16. outfield
17. output
18. supernatural
19. subdivision
20. subhead

Words from Many Cultures

Unit 4, Week 1

1. khaki
2. hula
3. banana
4. ballet
5. waltz
6. tomato
7. vanilla
8. canyon
9. yogurt
10. banquet
11. macaroni
12. polka
13. cobra
14. koala
15. barbecue
16. safari
17. buffet
18. stampede
19. karate
20. kiosk

Related Words

Unit 5, Week 5

1. politics
2. political
3. major
4. majority
5. equal
6. equation
7. sign
8. signature
9. arrive
10. arrival
11. inspire
12. inspiration
13. human
14. humanity
15. clean
16. cleanse
17. resign
18. resignation
19. unite
20. unity

Latin Roots

Unit 5, Week 4

1. project
2. audience
3. decade
4. territory
5. auditorium
6. terrier
7. decimal
8. injection
9. December
10. reject
11. eject
12. terrace
13. audit
14. decimeter
15. audition
16. audible
17. decathlon
18. terrarium
19. dejected
20. terrain

Greek Word Parts

Unit 5, Week 3

1. geology
2. thermometer
3. astronaut
4. atmosphere
5. biology
6. thermal
7. disaster
8. meteorology
9. technology
10. hemisphere
11. zoology
12. sociology
13. biosphere
14. thermos
15. asterisk
16. thermostat
17. astronomy
18. spherical
19. ecology
20. mythology

Unusual Spellings

Unit 5, Week 2

1. league
2. sergeant
3. yacht
4. doubt
5. fatigue
6. debt
7. blood
8. vague
9. anxious
10. foreign
11. bargain
12. condemn
13. intrigue
14. villain
15. cantaloupe
16. flood
17. depot
18. cordial
19. subtle
20. disguise

Multisyllabic Words

Unit 5, Week 1

1. elementary
2. vehicle
3. miniature
4. probability
5. definition
6. substitute
7. variety
8. literature
9. elevator
10. Pennsylvania
11. ravioli
12. cafeteria
13. mosaic
14. tuxedo
15. meteorite
16. fascination
17. cylinder
18. intermediate
19. centennial
20. curiosity

Easily Confused Words

Unit 6, Week 5

1. quiet
2. quite
3. finely
4. finally
5. except
6. accept
7. than
8. then
9. since
10. sense
11. affect
12. effect
13. from
14. form
15. later
16. latter
17. adapt
18. adopt
19. medal
20. metal

Compound Words

Unit 6, Week 4

1. ice cream
2. a lot
3. keyboard
4. fairy tale
5. horseshoe
6. piggy bank
7. textbook
8. guidelines
9. newspaper
10. space shuttle
11. hay fever
12. dead end
13. password
14. teenager
15. skateboard
16. everything
17. barbed wire
18. cartwheel
19. root beer
20. fingerprint

Words with *ei* and *ie*

Unit 6, Week 3

1. brief
2. believe
3. receive
4. leisure
5. piece
6. relief
7. seize
8. ceiling
9. field
10. neither
11. apiece
12. receipt
13. yield
14. deceive
15. achieve
16. grief
17. niece
18. protein
19. shield
20. conceited

Final Syllable -ant, -ent, -ance, -ence

Unit 6, Week 2

1. important
2. experience
3. ignorant
4. entrance
5. difference
6. instance
7. absence
8. appearance
9. intelligent
10. evidence
11. pollutant
12. clearance
13. confidence
14. conference
15. insurance
16. ambulance
17. hesitant
18. consistent
19. excellence
20. persistent

Suffixes -ous, -sion, -ion, -ation

Unit 6, Week 1

1. famous
2. invention
3. election
4. furious
5. imagination
6. education
7. nervous
8. explanation
9. various
10. decision
11. relaxation
12. conversation
13. tension
14. humorous
15. exhibition
16. attraction
17. invasion
18. creation
19. occupation
20. destination

Section 3

California
Grammar
and Writing
Practice Book

Contents

© Pearson Education, Inc. 5

Unit 4 Adapting

Unit 5 Adventurers

Unit 6 The Unexpected

Grammar Cumulative Review

© Pearson Education, Inc.5

Standardized Test Practice

Unit Writing Lessons

Grammar and Writing Practice Book

Writer's Self-Evaluation Checklist

If I want to tell a story, my writing will be narrative. My purpose will be to entertain or inform.

My writing is **narrative.** It has

❑ a beginning, a middle, and an end

❑ characters

❑ a setting

❑ a plot, or story line

If I want to tell my reader about a person, place, or thing, my writing will be **descriptive.** My purpose will be to give my reader a picture of what I am describing. Poetry is often descriptive. Descriptions may appear within other types of writing as well.

My writing is **descriptive.** It will

❑ create a picture of a person, place, or thing

❑ use words that appeal to the senses

❑ offers strong details

If I want to explain something, my writing will be **expository.** My purpose will be to provide information.

When my writing is **expository,** my information will

❑ be arranged in an order that makes sense

❑ include transition words, such as *first, next,* and *last*

❑ be checked for accuracy

If I want to convince people to agree with me about something, my writing will be **persuasive.** Reviews that I write of books or movies will be persuasive. So will a letter to my aunt telling her why she should come visit this summer.

When my writing is **persuasive,** I will

❑ include reasons, facts, and examples to support my ideas

❑ use persuasive words, such as *must* or *best*

❑ organize my ideas in order of importance

Grammar
Lessons

Four Kinds of Sentences and Interjections

Each kind of sentence begins with a capital letter and has a special end mark.

A **declarative sentence** makes a statement. It ends with a period.
The creek goes through dense forests.

An **interrogative sentence** asks a question. It ends with a question mark.
Do you see a red kayak?

An **imperative sentence** gives a command or makes a request. It ends with a period.
The subject (*you*) does not appear, but it is understood.
Look in the marsh.

An **exclamatory sentence** shows strong feeling. It ends with an exclamation mark.
The water is freezing!
What a cold day it is!

An **interjection** is a word or a group of words that expresses strong feeling. It is not a complete sentence.
Oh no! What a mess!

Directions Rewrite each sentence. Make any needed corrections in capitalization and punctuation.

1. the creek is dangerous in winter?

_____

2. he's not breathing.

_____

3. do you know how to perform CPR.

_____

Directions Complete each sentence with words from the box. Then write whether the sentence is *declarative, interrogative, imperative,* or *exclamatory.*

> think I see something!   make boating dangerous.
>
> the opposite shore.   wear life jackets?

4. Strong winds and tides _____

5. Did the boaters _____

6. Drive toward _____

7. Gosh, I _____

Home Activity Your child learned about four kinds of sentences. Have your child write about an event at school using one example of each kind of sentence.

Four Kinds of Sentences and Interjections

Directions Complete each sentence by adding your own words and the correct end punctuation. The label tells what kind of sentence each should be.

1. People in boats and kayaks _____ (declarative)

_____

_____

2. Have you ever _____ (interrogative)

_____

_____

3. Wow! Emergencies _____ (exclamatory)

_____

_____

4. A class in CPR _____ (declarative)

_____

_____

5. Please learn _____ (imperative)

_____

_____

Directions Think about an emergency you saw or were involved in. Write three sentences describing the emergency. Make each sentence a different kind.

_____

_____

_____

_____

Home Activity Your child learned how to use four kinds of sentences in writing. Have your child write about his or her homework routine, including at least one declarative, one interrogative, one imperative, and one exclamatory sentence.

Four Kinds of Sentences and Interjections

Directions Read the paragraph. Mark the letter that identifies what kind of sentence each is.

(1) Would you know what to do in an emergency? (2) My neighbor came home from a soccer game one night. (3) He looked at the house on the corner. (4) Was that smoke coming from the garage? (5) Flames were shooting out of the window! (6) My friend called his neighbors and the fire department. (7) His quick thinking saved the house and the family. (8) Think about how you would react in a situation like this.

1. A declarative
   B interrogative
   C imperative
   D exclamatory

2. A declarative
   B interrogative
   C imperative
   D exclamatory

3. A declarative
   B interrogative
   C imperative
   D exclamatory

4. A declarative
   B interrogative
   C imperative
   D exclamatory

5. A declarative
   B interrogative
   C imperative
   D exclamatory

6. A declarative
   B interrogative
   C imperative
   D exclamatory

7. A declarative
   B interrogative
   C imperative
   D exclamatory

8. A declarative
   B interrogative
   C imperative
   D exclamatory

Directions Circle the letter of the sentence that has correct end punctuation.

9. A Accidents happen unexpectedly!
   B Think about how to handle them!
   C You don't have to be a hero?
   D Just stay calm and get help.

10. A Jon's dad gives first aid!
    B Is he a doctor?
    C Remember the talk he gave!
    D I think he's a firefighter?

Home Activity Your child prepared for taking tests on kinds of sentences. Have your child read part of a story to you and identify each sentence as declarative, interrogative, imperative, or exclamatory.

Four Kinds of Sentences and Interjections

Directions Add the correct end punctuation to each sentence. Then on the line write whether the sentence is *declarative, interrogative, imperative,* or *exclamatory.*

1. Have you ever ridden in a boat _____

2. It's important to know about boat safety _____

3. Be sure to wear a life jacket _____

4. Wow! The water can be dangerous _____

5. Please learn how to swim _____

Directions Underline the mistakes in each sentence. Write the correct letter or punctuation mark above each underline.

6. can you paddle a kayak.

7. kayaks are fun in rivers and lakes!

8. watch out for that waterfall?

9. don't let the boat tip over

10. kayaking takes practice

11. always wear a helmet?

Directions Add your own words to complete each sentence. Write the new sentences. Be sure you use end punctuation correctly.

12. Safety rules for boats _____

_____

13. A ride in a kayak _____

_____

14. Don't _____

_____

15. Would you like _____

_____

Home Activity Your child reviewed four kinds of sentences. For five minutes, write down what you say to each other. Have your child identify each kind of sentence.

Grammar and Writing Practice Book

Name _____

Regular and Irregular Plural Nouns

Plural nouns name more than one person, place, or thing.
- Add *-s* to form the plural of most nouns.
  swing/swings   animal/animals
- Add *-es* to nouns ending in *ch, sh, x, z,* and *ss.*
  fox/foxes   bush/bushes   churc... ...ches
- If a noun ends in a vowel and *y*, add *-s.*
  monkey/monkeys   toy/toys
- If a noun ends in a consonant and *y*, change *y* to *i* and add *-...*
  blueberry/blueberries   pony/ponies   penny/pennies
- Some nouns have **irregular plural** forms. They change spelling.
  woman/women   tooth/teeth   ox/oxen
- For most nouns that end in *f* or *fe*, change *f* to *v* and add *-es.*
  wife/wives   wolf/wolves   thief/thieves
- Some nouns have the same singular and plural forms.
  salmon   trout   sheep

Directions Underline the plural nouns in each sentence.

1. Some seals live on those beaches.

2. The fishermen in boats near shore caught many salmon.

3. You will see crabs, shells, and driftwood near the water.

4. Don't burn your feet on the hot sand.

5. Clumps of seaweed float on the waves.

Directions Cross out each incorrectly spelled plural noun. Write the correct spelling above the word you crossed out.

6. You can find blueberrys on the bushs near those beaches.

7. The skys over the shore were clear, but we saw cloudes in the distance.

8. The four woman prepared the picnic, and the children played with beach toyes.

Home Activity Your child learned about regular and irregular plural nouns. Take a walk and have your child identify people, places, animals, and things in groups. Ask him or her to spell these plural nouns correctly.

Regular and Irregular Plural Nouns

Directions Write a sentence using the plural form of each noun.

1. woman

_____

2. foot

_____

3. monkey

_____

4. deer

_____

5. leaf

_____

Directions Write the paragraph on the lines. Write the plural form of each noun in ( ). Add a word of your own to describe each plural noun. Write your own ending sentence for the paragraph.

It was a beautiful day, and ____ (family) were enjoying the beach. Near the waves, ____ (boy) made ____ (sand castle). By the dunes, some ____ (man) tossed a football. Several ____ (lady) searched for ____ (seashell). Two ____ (baby) put their ____ (toe) in the water.

_____

_____

_____

_____

_____

_____

_____

_____

Home Activity Your child learned how to use plural nouns in writing. Have your child point out plural nouns on packages and labels and explain the rule for forming each plural.

Grammar and Writing Practice Book

Name _____

Regular and Irregular Plural Nouns

Directions Mark the letter of the word that correctly completes each sentence.

1. There are interesting ____ at the beach.
   A creature
   B creatures
   C creaturees
   D creaturies

2. Many____ of tiny fish swim near shore.
   A bunches
   B bunchs
   C bunchies
   D bunch

3. Seashells covered the ____ of animals.
   A body
   B bodys
   C bodies
   D bodyes

4. Some loud ____ fly overhead in autumn.
   A goose
   B gooses
   C goosies
   D geese

5. Tiny ____ play in the sand dunes.
   A mice
   B mouses
   C mousies
   D mouse

6. Other animals live in nearby ____.
   A marsh
   B marshs
   C marshes
   D marshies

7. Insects buzz in the ____.
   A grasss
   B grasseses
   C grasses
   D grassies

8. Many ____ of animals live in the ocean.
   A varietys
   B variety
   C varieteys
   D varieties

9. You might see sharks with sharp ____.
   A tooth
   B tooths
   C toothes
   D teeth

10. Whales live long ____.
    A lifes
    B lives
    C live
    D livies

School-Home CONNECTION

Home Activity Your child prepared for taking tests on regular and irregular plural nouns. Have your child make flash cards with singular and plural forms of nouns on opposite sides. Use the cards to help him or her learn plural forms.

Regular and Irregular Plural Nouns

Directions Write the plural forms of the underlined singular nouns.

1. What <u>activity</u> do you enjoy at the beach?

   _____

2. Some people take <u>blanket</u> and <u>umbrella</u> for sunbathing.

   _____

3. <u>Child</u> and <u>adult</u> can take <u>class</u> in sailing and surfing.

   _____

4. Some people ride <u>horse</u> or <u>pony</u> on the sand.

   _____

Directions Cross out each incorrectly spelled plural noun. Write the correct spelling above the word you crossed out.

5. The sailors' wifes made picnic lunchs for the beach.

6. They served sandwichs, peaches, and tomatos.

7. The antes, flys, and bees did not bother anyone.

8. The women packed colorful glasss and dishs.

Directions Write each sentence. Write the plural forms of the nouns in ( ). Add your own describing word for each plural noun.

9. _____ (country) have _____ (seashore) with _____ (hotel) and _____ (restaurant) nearby.

   _____

   _____

10. _____ (beach) with white sand and _____ (wave) are _____ (place) for _____ (vacation).

    _____

    _____

Home Activity Your child reviewed regular and irregular plural nouns. Ask your child to list things you have in your kitchen and write the plural form for each noun.

Possessive Nouns

A **possessive noun** shows ownership. A **singular possessive noun** shows that one person, place, or thing has or owns something. A **plural possessive noun** shows that more than one person, place, or thing has or owns something.

- To make a singular noun show possession, add an apostrophe (') and -s.
  a bird's song
- To make a plural noun that ends in -s show possession, add an apostrophe (').
  several weeks' work
- To make a plural noun that does not end in -s show possession, add an apostrophe (') and -s.
  the women's papers

Directions Write each noun as a possessive noun. Write *S* if the possessive noun is singular. Write *P* if the possessive noun is plural.

1. friends _____ _____

2. story _____ _____

3. freedom _____ _____

4. mornings _____ _____

5. children _____ _____

6. milk _____ _____

Directions Add an apostrophe (') or an apostrophe (') and -s to make each underlined word possessive. Write the sentence on the line.

7. A diplomat life requires travel.

_____

8. Would democracy followers win the struggle?

_____

Home Activity Your child learned about possessive nouns. Have your child look at some sale ads and make up sentences about them using possessive nouns.

Possessive Nouns

Directions Make each sentence less wordy by replacing the underlined words with a possessive noun phrase. Write the sentence on the line.

1. <u>The pride of a son</u> in his father can inspire him all his life.

   _____

2. <u>The rights of fathers</u> are strong in Japanese society.

   _____

3. <u>The wishes of a father</u> should always be respected by his family.

   _____

4. <u>The status of an elderly relative</u> is highest of all.

   _____

5. What is more, <u>the commands of government officials</u> must be obeyed by all.

   _____

   _____

6. <u>The wants of an individual</u> are less important than <u>the well-being of the nation.</u>

   _____

   _____

Directions Write a paragraph describing some of the traits of people in your family. Use possessive nouns to make your writing smooth and less wordy.

_____

_____

_____

_____

_____

_____

 Home Activity Your child learned how to use possessive nouns in writing. Have your child make labels for the belongings of different family members using possessive nouns.

Possessive Nouns

Directions Mark the letter of the word that correctly completes each sentence.

1. ____ Jews fled from the German soldiers.
   A Polands
   B Poland's
   C Polands'
   D Polands's

2. American ____ efforts helped win the war.
   A soldiers
   B soldier's
   C soldiers'
   D soldiers's

3. A ____ shoes wore out quickly.
   A soldiers
   B soldier's
   C soldiers'
   D soldiers's

4. Success often depended on the ____ food supply.
   A armies
   B armie's
   C armys'
   D army's

5. Soldiers carried several ____ cold rations.
   A days
   B day's
   C days'
   D days's

6. Many ____ stomachs were often empty.
   A refugees
   B refugee's
   C refugees'
   D refugees's

7. A ____ kindness kept them alive another day.
   A strangers
   B stranger's
   C strangers'
   D strangers's

8. Money might be sewn into ____ coat linings.
   A women's
   B woman's
   C womens'
   D womans'

9. Worry haunted the refugee ____ eyes.
   A childrens
   B children's
   C childrens'
   D childrens's

10. ____ stories seemed unbelievable.
    A Survivors
    B Survivor's
    C Survivors'
    D Survivors's

Home Activity Your child prepared for taking tests on possessive nouns. Have your child write several sentences describing a favorite toy or game using possessive nouns (such as *the bear's nose* or *the pieces' shapes*).

Possessive Nouns

Directions Write each sentence. Change the underlined phrase to show possession.

1. The <u>honesty of children</u> is refreshing.

_____

2. The <u>comment of one little boy</u> was especially moving.

_____

3. The <u>eyes of the grown-ups</u> were red from lack of sleep.

_____

4. Did they sleep on the <u>benches of the park</u>?

_____

Directions: Cross out each incorrect possessive noun. Write the correct possessive form above the word you crossed out.

5. Some children held their fathers hands.

6. One little girls' coat was too small for her.

7. The little girl looked warm and happy in Sukios' coat.

8. Small acts of kindness made the outcast's lives better.

Directions Write a paragraph describing a refugee family that the Sugiharas might have helped. Use possessive nouns correctly.

_____

_____

_____

_____

_____

Home Activity Your child reviewed possessive nouns. Ask your child to write sentences telling what he or she appreciates about home, family, school, and friends. Ask your child to try to use a possessive noun in each sentence.

Grammar and Writing Practice Book

Main and Helping Verbs

Directions Mark the letter of the words that correctly identify the underlined word or words in the sentence.

1. People <u>should</u> drive less.
   A helping verb
   B main verb
   C verb phrase
   D not a verb

2. Exhaust fumes <u>are polluting</u> the environment.
   A helping verb
   B main verb
   C verb phrase
   D not a verb

3. Certain chemicals will <u>kill</u> fish.
   A helping verb
   B main verb
   C verb phrase
   D not a verb

4. Runoff from farms <u>may contain</u> these chemicals.
   A helping verb
   B main verb
   C verb phrase
   D not a verb

5. Oil tankers have spilled <u>millions of gallons</u> of oil.
   A helping verb
   B main verb
   C verb phrase
   D not a verb

6. Fish, birds, and mammals <u>are</u> coated with the oil.
   A helping verb
   B main verb
   C verb phrase
   D not a verb

7. Without help they soon <u>will die</u>.
   A helping verb
   B main verb
   C verb phrase
   D not a verb

8. Many towns are putting garbage in <u>landfills</u>.
   A helping verb
   B main verb
   C verb phrase
   D not a verb

9. Plastics <u>do</u> not break down easily.
   A helping verb
   B main verb
   C verb phrase
   D not a verb

10. We are <u>poisoning</u> ourselves slowly.
    A helping verb
    B main verb
    C verb phrase
    D not a verb

Home Activity Your child prepared for taking tests on main and helping verbs and verb phrases. Have your child write sentences about his or her day's activities using verb phrases and point out main and helping verbs.

Main and Helping Verbs

Directions Choose a helping verb from the box to complete each sentence. Write the sentence on the line. Underline the verb phrase.

> could   should   has   was   had   did

1. Jane Goodall _____ studied African animals for decades.

_____

2. She _____ raised in England.

_____

3. Even as a little girl, she _____ always loved animals.

_____

4. In the jungle, Jane _____ watch chimpanzees for hours.

_____

5. She _____ not notice the hours passing.

_____

6. We _____ admire such devotion to animals.

_____

Directions Find the verb phrases. Underline each helping verb. Circle each main verb.

7. A wildlife refuge may provide the only safe habitat for some animals.

8. Many animals have been hunted too much.

9. Scientists have predicted the extinction of some species.

10. Animals in trouble are described as endangered.

11. Many groups are working to protect endangered animals.

12. Without our help, these animals will disappear like the dodo.

Home Activity Your child reviewed main and helping verbs. Ask your child to make up sentences using verb phrases to describe an animal's past, present, and future actions.

Subject-Verb Agreement

The subject and verb in a sentence must **agree,** or work together. A singular subject needs a singular verb. A plural subject needs a plural verb.

Use the following rules for verbs that tell about the present time.

- If the subject is a singular noun or *he, she,* or *it,* add *-s* or *-es* to most verbs.
  The wagon *creaks.* It *lurches* along.

- If the subject is a plural noun or *I, you, we,* or *they,* do not add *-s* or *-es* to the verb.
  The oxen *pull* the wagon. They *strain* uphill.

- For the verb *be,* use *am* and *is* to agree with singular subjects and *are* to agree with plural subjects.
  I *am* hot. Thomas *is* happy. The patriots *are* loyal. We *are* late.

- **A collective noun** names a group, such as *family, team,* and *class.* A collective noun is singular if it refers to a group acting as one: The family *is taking* a vacation. A collective noun is plural if it refers to members of the group acting individually: The family *are arguing* about the destination.

Directions Match each subject with a verb that agrees. Write the letter of the correct verb on the line.

_____ **1.** The colonists   **A.** are training.

_____ **2.** The British king   **B.** is beginning.

_____ **3.** A war   **C.** rebel.

_____ **4.** Troops   **D.** sends his army.

Directions Underline the verb in ( ) that agrees with the subject of each sentence.

5. The American colonies (trade, trades) with England.

6. Two of the colonies' exports (is, are) cotton and indigo.

7. England (tax, taxes) the items imported into the colonies.

8. Tea (is, are) a popular drink in the colonies.

9. The Boston Tea Party (show, shows) the colonists' anger about taxes.

10. Today, Americans (drink, drinks) more coffee than tea.

11. Earlier conflicts (is, are) forgotten.

12. The two countries (consider, considers) themselves close allies.

Home Activity Your child learned about subject-verb agreement. Have your child make up sentences about clothes he or she wears, using both singular subjects (shirt, belt) and plural subjects (socks, shoes) and making sure verbs agree.

Subject-Verb Agreement

Directions Add a verb to complete each sentence. Be sure to use the correct verb form.

1. The Liberty Bell _____ a well-known American symbol.

2. It _____ in the Liberty Bell Center in Philadelphia.

3. Many tourists _____ this site.

4. _____ the bell ever ring?

5. No. A crack _____ up the side of the bell.

6. The main metals in the bell _____ copper and tin.

7. The bell _____ 2,080 pounds.

8. Philadelphia _____ in southeastern Pennsylvania.

9. More than a million and a half people _____ there.

10. Tourists _____ the many historic sites in Philadelphia.

Directions Circle the verb that agrees with each subject. Then write sentences using at least three of the subject-verb pairs.

11.	class	is studying	are studying
12.	historic site	inspire	inspires
13.	teacher	tell	tells
14.	some students	sing	sings
15.	they	is	are
16.	I	feel	feels

_____

_____

_____

_____

_____

Home Activity Your child learned how to write subjects and verbs that agree. Ask your child to make up sentences in the present tense describing favorite animals, first using a singular subject, then a plural subject (dog/dogs, lion/lions, and so on).

Subject-Verb Agreement

Directions Mark the letter of the verb that agrees with the subject in the sentence.

1. Many poems ____.
  A rhyme
  B rhymes
  C rhimes
  D rhiming

2. I ____ the poems of Longfellow.
  A enjoy
  B enjoys
  C enjoies
  D enjoying

3. His work ____ both rhyme and rhythm.
  A use
  B uses
  C using
  D user

4. "The Midnight Ride of Paul Revere" ____ a narrative poem.
  A be called
  B are called
  C is called
  D be

5. Narrative poems ____ a story.
  A telling
  B tells
  C tell
  D telled

6. Poetry ____ vivid word pictures.
  A paint
  B painting
  C painter
  D paints

7. Our class ____ in unison.
  A recite
  B reciting
  C recites
  D recities

8. We ____ to do choral readings.
  A like
  B likes
  C liking
  D be liking

9. It ____ like a song.
  A be
  B being
  C are
  D is

10. The rhyming words ____ good to me.
  A sound
  B sounding
  C sounds
  D soundies

Home Activity Your child prepared for taking tests on subject-verb agreement. Have your child copy some subject and verb pairs from a favorite book and explain why the subjects and verbs agree.

Name _____

Subject-Verb Agreement

Directions Underline the subject of each sentence. Circle the verb in ( ) that agrees with the subject.

1. Paul Revere (is, are) a legendary figure of the Revolutionary War.

2. Americans (love, loves) hearing about his midnight ride.

3. I (imagine, imagines) that night.

4. Three men (ride, rides) from Boston to Concord.

5. Danger (lurk, lurks) around every bend.

6. An English scout (yell, yells) "Stop! Who goes there?"

7. His companions (stop, stops) one of the three riders.

8. One man (go, goes) no farther that night.

9. It (is, are) Paul Revere.

10. Few people (know, knows) that fact.

Directions Add a present tense verb to complete each sentence. Be sure the verb agrees with the subject in number.

11. This portrait _____ a serious man.

12. It _____ a portrait of Paul Revere.

13. Several objects _____ on the table next to him.

14. They _____ a silversmith's tools.

15. The man's right hand _____ his chin thoughtfully.

16. His left hand _____ a silver teapot.

17. Americans still _____ the silver work of Revere.

18. A silver piece by Paul Revere _____ great value today.

Home Activity Your child reviewed subject-verb agreement. Ask your child to read a newspaper or magazine article and point out singular and plural subjects. Have him or her explain why the verbs agree with those subjects.

Grammar and Writing Practice Book

Past, Present, and Future Tenses

The **tense** of a verb shows when something happens. Verbs in the **present tense** show action that happens now. Some present tense singular verbs end with *-s* or *-es*. Most present tense plural verbs do not end with *-s* or *-es*.

An inventor <u>creates</u> a new tool. Inventions <u>serve</u> us well.

Verbs in the **past tense** show action that has already happened. Most verbs in the past tense end in *-ed*.

Not long ago, electronics <u>changed</u> the world.

Verbs in the **future tense** show action that will happen. Add *will* (or *shall*) to most verbs to show the future tense.

Many more inventions <u>will appear</u>.

- Some regular verbs change spelling when *-ed* is added. For verbs ending in *e*, drop the *e* and add *-ed*: *used, celebrated*. For verbs ending in a consonant and *y*, change the *y* to *i* and add *-ed*: *spied, lied*.

- For most one-syllable verbs that end in one vowel followed by one consonant, double the consonant and add *-ed*: *wrapped, patted*.

- Irregular verbs change spelling to form the past tense: *are/were, bring/brought, eat/ate, find/found, fly/flew, go/went, have/had, is/was, make/made, see/saw, sit/sat, take/took, tell/told, think/thought, write/wrote.*

Directions Write the correct present, past, and future tense of each verb.

Verb	Present	Past	Future
1. jump	She _____.	She _____.	She _____.
2. sit	He _____.	He _____.	He _____.
3. worry	We _____.	We _____.	We _____.
4. stop	It _____.	It _____.	It _____.

Directions Rewrite each sentence. Change the underlined verb to the tense in ( ).

5. The Perez twins <u>dream</u> about a new invention. (present)

_____

6. They <u>study</u> the laws of motion. (past)

_____

Home Activity Your child learned about present, past, and future tenses. Have your child read a page in a story aloud, changing past tense verbs to present tense ones or present tense verbs to past tense ones.

Past, Present, and Future Tenses

Directions Underline the verb or verbs that use the wrong tense. Write the correct tense.

1. Last year, Teresa made a fascinating science project. It shows the ice in Antarctica. Teresa demonstrates the ice shrinking. When the projects were judged, Teresa won first place.

   _____

2. We will work on our project next week. I discuss my ideas with my group. It will be interesting to hear everyone's ideas. _____

3. The play is about an amazing invention. It describes a very useful machine. Today's inventors were creative. _____

Directions Replace each underlined verb with the verb in the correct tense. Use the correct tense to make the order of events clear. Write the paragraph.

4. People <u>begin</u> using electrical power in the 1800s. 5. Edison <u>invent</u> the electric light. 6. Today, everyone <u>depend</u> on electricity. 7. People <u>used</u> electricity for work and play. 8. In the future, the demand for electrical power <u>increase</u>.

_____

_____

_____

_____

_____

Directions Pretend that you have created an invention that will change the world. Write a paragraph about how you came up with the invention, what it does, and how it will change the future.

_____

_____

_____

_____

_____

_____

 School-Home CONNECTION

Home Activity Your child learned how to use present, past, and future tenses in writing. With your child, talk about an activity he or she completed, an ongoing activity, and a future activity.

Past, Present, and Future Tenses

Directions Mark the letter of the verb that correctly completes the sentence.

1. Next week, our class _____ a science fair.
   A hold
   B held
   C has held
   D will hold

2. Thirty students _____ projects in the fair.
   A will display
   B displayed
   C had displayed
   D displaying

3. Now we _____ the classroom for the fair.
   A prepared
   B preparing
   C prepares
   D prepare

4. Our teacher _____ a judge in the fair.
   A is
   B was
   C are
   D will be

5. Last year, she also _____ the fair.
   A judge
   B judges
   C judged
   D will judge

6. My parents always _____ I should be a scientist.
   A say
   B says
   C saying
   D will say

7. I was thrilled when I _____ the contest last year.
   A win
   B wins
   C won
   D will win

8. I hope I _____ first place next week.
   A gets
   B got
   C gotten
   D will take

9. I _____ the competition will be stiff.
   A knows
   B know
   C knew
   D will know

10. Right now, I _____ on my project each night.
    A work
    B works
    C worked
    D will working

Home Activity Your child prepared for taking tests on present, past, and future tenses. Have your child explain the present, past, and future tenses of verbs and give examples of each.

Past, Present, and Future Tenses

Directions Identify the tense of each underlined verb. Write *past, present,* or *future.*

1. You <u>will enjoy</u> this book about inventions. _____

2. Inventors <u>create</u> new machines. _____

3. Each machine <u>does</u> a different task. _____

4. In the past, people <u>invented</u> steam engines. _____

5. Later, other people <u>made</u> computers. _____

6. Today, inventors <u>work</u> on new energy sources. _____

7. They <u>think</u> of saving the environment. _____

8. Perhaps they <u>will succeed</u> someday. _____

9. I <u>will invent</u> a bed-making machine. _____

10. It <u>will save</u> me much work. _____

Directions Rewrite each sentence twice. First, change the underlined verb to past tense. Then change it to future tense.

11. The computer <u>is</u> a useful invention.

    Past: _____

    Future: _____

12. We <u>get</u> information on computers.

    Past: _____

    Future: _____

13. Computers <u>make</u> our lives more productive.

    Past: _____

    Future: _____

 Home Activity Your child reviewed past, present, and future tenses. With your child, list verbs that describe what your family does each day. Challenge your child to write the present, past, and future tenses of the verbs and use them in sentences.

Principal Parts of Regular Verbs

A verb's tenses are made from four basic forms. These basic forms are called the verb's **principal parts.**

Present	Present Participle	Past	Past Participle
watch	(am, is, are) watching	watched	(has, have, had) watched
study	(am, is, are) studying	studied	(has, have, had) studied

A **regular verb** forms its past and past participle by adding *-ed* or *-d* to the present form.

- The present and the past forms can be used by themselves as verbs.
- The present participle and the past participle are always used with a helping verb.

Directions Write the form of the underlined verb indicated in ( ).

1. For centuries, people <u>admire</u> the works of Leonardo da Vinci. (past participle)

   _____

2. Today he <u>enjoy</u> the title of greatest genius of the Renaissance. (present participle)

   _____

3. He <u>observe</u> everyday activities as a scientist. (past) _____

4. Leonardo <u>paint</u> with greater skill than any other artist of his time. (past)

   _____

5. He <u>fill</u> notebooks with his observations, illustrations, and original ideas. (past)

   _____

6. Scientists <u>create</u> working models from his instructions and drawings. (past participle)

   _____

7. Leonardo's life <u>inspire</u> me to be more observant. (past participle) _____

Directions Underline the verb in each sentence. Write *present, present participle, past,* or *past participle* to identify the principal part used to form the verb.

8. Leonardo lived in Vinci, Italy, as a boy. _____

9. Soon he had developed a keen eye and an observant nature. _____

10. Most people recognize the name Leonardo da Vinci 500 years after his death.

Home Activity Your child learned about principal parts of regular verbs. Ask your child to write the principal parts of *love, live,* and *dream* and then use each part in a sentence about himself or herself.

Principal Parts of Regular Verbs

Directions Write a complete sentence using the past participle form of the verb in ( ) with *have* or *has*.

1. Ms. Wissing (instruct) this art class for two years.

_____

2. The students (enjoy) her hands-on teaching style.

_____

3. For several weeks our art class (study) how to draw life-forms.

_____

4. Tonya (sketch) the head of a woman.

_____

5. I (complete) my drawing of a horse.

_____

6. The teacher (encourage) my efforts in the past.

_____

Directions Write a paragraph about something you have planned to invent or create. Include past participle forms of verbs where needed.

_____

_____

_____

_____

_____

_____

_____

_____

Home Activity Your child learned how to write principal parts of regular verbs correctly. Ask your child to write about a project he or she has completed recently at school or at home. Remind him or her to use correct verb tenses.

Principal Parts of Regular Verbs

Directions Mark the letter of the item that correctly identifies the form of the underlined word or words in each sentence.

1. Leonardo <u>had planned</u> a new project.
   - **A** present
   - **B** present participle
   - **C** past
   - **D** past participle

2. This <u>surprised</u> no one.
   - **A** present
   - **B** present participle
   - **C** past
   - **D** past participle

3. He <u>pursued</u> a wide range of interests.
   - **A** present
   - **B** present participle
   - **C** past
   - **D** past participle

4. New ideas <u>distracted</u> him from projects.
   - **A** present
   - **B** present participle
   - **C** past
   - **D** past participle

5. Some <u>have observed</u> that he possessed too many abilities.
   - **A** present
   - **B** present participle
   - **C** past
   - **D** past participle

6. One lifetime <u>contains</u> too few hours for such a man.
   - **A** present
   - **B** present participle
   - **C** past
   - **D** past participle

7. The journals of Leonardo <u>have preserved</u> many of his plans and ideas.
   - **A** present
   - **B** present participle
   - **C** past
   - **D** past participle

8. This is how we <u>learn</u> of his great genius today.
   - **A** present
   - **B** present participle
   - **C** past
   - **D** past participle

9. In them he <u>recorded</u> plans for many inventions.
   - **A** present
   - **B** present participle
   - **C** past
   - **D** past participle

10. We <u>are studying</u> his plan for a flying machine.
    - **A** present
    - **B** present participle
    - **C** past
    - **D** past participle

Home Activity Your child prepared for taking tests on principal parts of verbs. Ask your child to name the principal parts of the verbs *paint* and *invent* and then use each part in a sentence.

Principal Parts of Regular Verbs

Directions Write *present, present participle, past,* or *past participle* to identify the form of the underlined verb.

1. Machines <u>existed</u> in Leonardo's day. _____

2. For example, waterwheels <u>turned</u> millstones. _____

3. As a boy, Leonardo <u>had watched</u> machines closely. _____

4. By adulthood, he <u>had analyzed</u> how each part worked. _____

5. Unlike others, Leonardo <u>combined</u> parts in new ways. _____

6. He thought, "Aha! This change <u>improves</u> the machine!" _____

7. He reasoned, "This invention is <u>working</u> better with different parts." _____

8. He <u>explained</u> his analyses in journals. _____

9. Grateful engineers still <u>study</u> his sketches. _____

10. These illustrations <u>are serving</u> as blueprints for us. _____

Directions Write the sentence using the principal part of the underlined verb indicated in ( ).

11. Leonardo <u>refuse</u> all meat. (past)

_____

12. He always <u>love</u> animals. (past participle)

_____

13. Vegetarians still <u>follow</u> his habit. (present).

_____

14. I <u>stop</u> eating meat too. (past participle)

_____

15. Fruits and vegetables <u>provide</u> plenty of nutrition. (present)

_____

Home Activity Your child reviewed principal parts of regular verbs. Have your child identify examples of the use of present, past, and past participle forms in an article or a familiar book.

Grammar and Writing Practice Book

Principal Parts of Irregular Verbs

Usually you add *-ed* to a verb to show past tense. **Irregular verbs** do not follow this rule. Instead of having *-ed* forms to show past tense, irregular verbs usually change to other words.

Present Tense	The king sees the Crystal Palace.
Present Participle	The king is seeing the Crystal Palace.
Past Tense	The king saw the Crystal Palace.
Past Participle	The king has seen the Crystal Palace.

Present Tense	Present Participle	Past Tense	Past Participle
bring	(am, is, are) bringing	brought	(*has, have, had*) brought
build	(am, is, are) building	built	(*has, have, had*) built
choose	(am, is, are) choosing	chose	(*has, have, had*) chosen
come	(am, is, are) coming	came	(*has, have, had*) come
draw	(am, is, are) drawing	drew	(*has, have, had*) drawn
eat	(am, is, are) eating	ate	(*has, have, had*) eaten
find	(am, is, are) finding	found	(*has, have, had*) found
grow	(am, is, are) growing	grew	(*has, have, had*) grown
run	(am, is, are) running	ran	(*has, have, had*) run
set	(am, is, are) setting	set	(*has, have, had*) set
speak	(am, is, are) speaking	spoke	(*has, have, had*) spoken
tell	(am, is, are) telling	told	(*has, have, had*) told

Directions Underline the verb in each sentence. Write *present, present participle, past,* or *past participle* to identify the principal part of the verb.

1. He built a studio in Manhattan. _____

2. Hawkins had chosen Central Park for his display._____

Directions Write the sentence using the principal part of the underlined verb indicated in ( ).

3. Archaeologists <u>find</u> many more dinosaur bones. (past participle)

_____

4. Today dinosaur exhibits <u>draw</u> huge crowds. (present participle)

_____

Home Activity Your child learned about principal parts of irregular verbs. Ask your child to write the principal parts of *tell* and *write* and then use each part in a sentence telling what he or she could communicate about dinosaurs.

Principal Parts of Irregular Verbs

Directions Write a complete sentence using the past participle form of the verb in ( ) with *has* or *have*.

1. Mr. Hancock (run) the museum for five years.

   _____

2. He (choose) May as membership drive month .

   _____

3. He (speak) to many organizations.

   _____

4. The membership list (grow) quite large.

   _____

5. Mr. Hancock (do) it!

   _____

6. The new dinosaur education wing (draw) new members.

   _____

Directions Write a paragraph about dinosaurs. Include some past and past participle forms of such irregular verbs as *be, find, come, know,* and *think.*

   _____

   _____

   _____

   _____

   _____

   _____

   _____

   _____

   _____

Home Activity Your child learned how to write principal parts of irregular verbs correctly. Ask your child to write about a favorite prehistoric animal. Encourage him or her to use forms of *become, is, see, think, go,* and *eat* when writing.

Grammar and Writing Practice Book

Principal Parts of Irregular Verbs

Directions Mark the letter of the item that correctly identifies the form of the underlined word or words in each sentence.

1. A sculptor is <u>building</u> a clay figure.
   A past
   B present
   C past participle
   D present participle

2. She <u>makes</u> a mold of the clay shape.
   A past
   B present
   C past participle
   D present participle

3. She <u>chooses</u> a metal for the mold.
   A past
   B present
   C past participle
   D present participle

4. Many sculptures <u>have begun</u> this way.
   A past
   B present
   C past participle
   D present participle

5. The critics <u>have spoken</u>.
   A past
   B present
   C past participle
   D present participle

6. I <u>saw</u> a wonderful statue.
   A past
   B present
   C past participle
   D present participle

7. He <u>has bought</u> several works by that sculptor.
   A past
   B present
   C past participle
   D present participle

8. I <u>have chosen</u> the artwork I want to buy.
   A past
   B present
   C past participle
   D present participle

9. <u>Set</u> the painting here.
   A past
   B present
   C past participle
   D present participle

10. Who is <u>bringing</u> picture hangers?
    A past
    B present
    C past participle
    D present participle

Home Activity Your child prepared for taking tests on principal parts of irregular verbs. Ask your child to name the principal parts of the verbs *choose* and *find* and then use each part in a sentence.

Principal Parts of Irregular Verbs

Directions Write *present, present participle, past,* or *past participle* to identify the underlined verb form.

1. The diners <u>eat</u> for eight hours. _____

2. Each diner <u>has told</u> at least one story. _____

3. Hawkins <u>chose</u> the iguanodon model. _____

4. He <u>had set</u> a dining table inside it. _____

5. His guests <u>become</u> excited. _____

6. Hawkins <u>thought</u> they would be. _____

7. The guests <u>told</u> about this event for years. _____

8. The dinosaur fad <u>had begun</u>. _____

9. Today we <u>find</u> Hawkins's models odd. _____

10. We <u>are making</u> more discoveries about dinosaurs. _____

Directions Write the sentence using the principal part of the underlined verb indicated in ( ).

11. We <u>know</u> a great deal about the past. (present)

_____

12. In 1850, scientists <u>know</u> much less. (past)

_____

13. They <u>find</u> some fossils of dinosaur bones. (past participle)

_____

14. Sometimes animals <u>freeze</u> in glaciers. (present)

_____

15. Explorers <u>find</u> the remains of these animals. (present participle)

_____

16. A little of Earth's history <u>freeze</u> with them. (past participle)

_____

Home Activity Your child reviewed principal parts of irregular verbs. Have your child identify examples of the use of present, present participle, past, and past participle forms in a cookbook or history book.

Troublesome Verbs

Some pairs of verbs are confusing because they have similar meanings or because they look alike.

	Present	Past	Past Participle
Lay means "put" or "place."	lay	laid	(*has, have, had*) laid
Lie means "rest" or "recline."	lie	lay	(*has, have, had*) lain
Set means "put something somewhere."	set	set	(*has, have, had*) set
Sit means "sit down."	sit	sat	(*has, have, had*) sat
Let means "allow."	let	let	(*has, have, had*) let
Leave means "go away."	leave	left	(*has, have, had*) left

Directions Write the form of the underlined verb indicated in ( ).

1. A teenage girl <u>sit</u> with the choir. (past) _____

2. She has <u>lay</u> her hand over her heart. (past participle) _____

3. The choir director <u>let</u> her join. (past) _____

4. The music never <u>leave</u> her head. (past) _____

5. When she <u>set</u> her suitcases down in Chicago, Mahalia knew she was home. (past) _____

6. Mahalia's father had <u>let</u> her follow her dream. (past participle) _____

Directions Use context to help you decide which verb is needed. Then find the principal part needed on the chart. Underline the verb that correctly completes the sentence.

7. I (set, sit) a CD on the counter.

8. Will you (leave, let) me pay for it?

9. My parents have already (left, let) the store.

10. After dinner we (sat, set) down and listened to the CD.

11. Tom has (laid, lain) down on the floor.

12. Fiona (laid, lied) a log on the fire.

Home Activity Your child learned about troublesome verbs. Ask your child to explain the difference in meaning between *sit/set, lie/lay,* and *leave/let* and then act out the meanings of the verbs in each pair to demonstrate the difference.

Name _____

Troublesome Verbs

Directions Choose the form of the underlined verb indicated in ( ). Use the chart to help you. Write the sentence on the line.

Present	Past	Past Participle
lie ("to rest," "to recline")	lay	(has, have, had) lain
lay ("to put," "to place")	laid	(has, have, had) laid

1. Wes <u>lay</u> the sheet music on the shelf. (past)

_____

2. The twins <u>lie</u> beside the pool relaxing. (past)

_____

3. Their towels <u>lie</u> on the concrete all day. (past participle)

_____

4. We <u>lay</u> the groundwork for next year's concert. (past participle)

_____

5. In this song, <u>lay</u> the heaviest emphasis on long vowels. (present)

_____

6. The secret <u>lie</u> in hours of practice. (present)

_____

Directions Write a paragraph describing a photograph of your family or friends. Use as many principal parts of *sit, set, lie, lay, leave,* and *let* as you can.

_____

_____

_____

_____

_____

_____

Home Activity Your child learned how to write principal parts of troublesome verbs correctly. Ask your child to write sentences about cleaning a room. Encourage him or her to use forms of *lie, lay, sit, set, leave,* and *let.*

Grammar and Writing Practice Book

Troublesome Verbs

Directions Mark the letter of the verb that correctly completes each sentence.

1. I _____ on the couch last night.
   A lie
   B lay
   C laid
   D lain

2. I usually _____ in this chair.
   A sit
   B set
   C has sat
   D setted

3. The bus has _____ already.
   A leave
   B let
   C left
   D leaved

4. The brickmason has _____ stones in concrete.
   A sit
   B set
   C sat
   D sitted

5. The driver has _____ her keys on the seat.
   A lie
   B lay
   C laid
   D lain

6. He doesn't _____ riders get out of their seats.
   A leave
   B let
   C left
   D letted

7. Betty has _____ in bed all week.
   A lay
   B lie
   C laid
   D lain

8. _____ the area at once!
   A Leave
   B Let
   C Left
   D Leaved

9. Who _____ on my hat?
   A sit
   B set
   C sat
   D sitted

10. The cats always _____ in a sunny spot.
    A lied
    B lie
    C laid
    D lain

Home Activity Your child prepared for taking tests on principal parts of troublesome verbs. Ask your child to name the principal parts of the verbs *lie, lay, sit, set, leave,* and *let* and then use each part in a sentence.

Troublesome Verbs

Directions Write the letter of the definition of the underlined verb.

_____ 1. You <u>left</u> without your music.   **A** am seated

_____ 2. She <u>had set</u> it on the piano.   **B** has allowed

_____ 3. <u>Lay</u> the tickets on the counter.   **C** has rested or reclined

_____ 4. I <u>sit</u> and listen to the players.   **D** went away

_____ 5. Joan <u>has lain</u> in the sun too long.   **E** place or put

_____ 6. Tim <u>has</u> not <u>let</u> that bother him.   **F** had put (a thing) somewhere

Directions Choose a verb from the box to complete each sentence. Write the sentence on the line.

lay	leave	let	lain	sit	set

7. _____ the oven at 350° before you leave.

_____

8. Everyone, please _____ at the table.

_____

9. Mom and Dad _____ for their voice lesson at 7:15.

_____

10. They _____ us fix our own dinner.

_____

Directions Underline the verb that correctly completes the sentence.

11. I have (laid, lain) in a hammock.

12. Yesterday you (sat, set) up front.

13. The music teacher (left, let) the room.

14. First she (laid, lain) the chalk on the desk.

Home Activity Your child reviewed principal parts of troublesome verbs. Have your child write a joke using different forms of *sit, set, lie, lay, leave,* and *let* correctly.

Grammar and Writing Practice Book

Name _____

Prepositions and Prepositional Phrases

A **preposition** begins a group of words called a **prepositional phrase**. The noun or pronoun that follows the preposition is called the **object of the preposition**. Prepositional phrases provide details about the rest of the sentence.

People have watched animated movies <u>for</u> a long time. (preposition)
People have watched animated movies <u>for a long time</u>. (prepositional phrase)
People have watched animated movies for a long <u>time</u>. (object of the preposition)

Common Prepositions

about	around	by	into	over	until
above	at	down	near	through	up
across	before	for	of	to	with
after	below	from	on	toward	
against	between	in	onto	under	

Directions Underline the prepositional phrase in each sentence. Write *P* above the preposition. Write *O* above the object of the preposition.

1. The characters in animated films often seem quite real.

2. Young viewers may identify with the superheroes.

3. Ariel was a mermaid who lived under the sea.

4. She wanted a life on dry land.

5. Her father was Neptune, king of the sea.

Directions Underline the prepositional phrases. The number in ( ) tells how many prepositional phrases are in that sentence.

6. Many fairy tales have been made into animated movies for children. (2)

7. Their stories take youngsters from childhood into adulthood. (2)

8. The hero of the tale must pass through trials and adventures. (2)

9. At the end, he or she has shown great strength of character. (2)

Home Activity Your child learned about prepositions and prepositional phrases. Read a favorite story with your child. Ask him or her to point out prepositional phrases and identify the preposition and object of the preposition in each.

Prepositions and Prepositional Phrases

Directions Add a preposition to complete each sentence. Write the sentence on the line.

1. I usually lie _____ the floor when I watch TV.

_____

2. When I get hungry, I get a snack _____ the refrigerator.

_____

3. We have several movies stored _____ the television.

_____

4. I would rather see a movie _____ the theater.

_____

5. The big screen and the smell _____ popcorn create a memorable experience.

_____

Directions Add a prepositional phrase of your own to complete each sentence. Write the sentence.

6. Let's make Dad a cartoon _____ .

_____

7. I'll get the paper and markers _____ .

_____

8. You draw the scenes in pencil, and I'll color them _____ .

_____

9. What colors shall we use _____ ?

_____

10. Dad will hang this cartoon _____ .

_____

Home Activity Your child learned how to use prepositions and prepositional phrases in writing. Ask your child to write about his or her favorite animated film using at least one prepositional phrase in each sentence.

Prepositions and Prepositional Phrases

Directions Mark the letter of the preposition that correctly completes each sentence in the paragraph.

(1) *Pinocchio* was released _____ 1940. (2) It is a tale _____ a puppet who wants to be a real boy. (3) He was carved _____ a woodcarver named Gepetto. (4) A fairy princess turns Pinocchio _____ a wooden boy. (5) _____ his way to school, Pinocchio is lured away by a con artist named Honest John. (6) The con artist sells Pinocchio _____ the puppeteer Stromboli. (7) Next, Pinocchio winds up _____ Pleasure Island. (8) Boys run wild there until they turn _____ donkeys. (9) Then the puppet is swallowed _____ Monstro the whale. (10) Finally, father and son are reunited, and Pinocchio becomes a real boy _____ the end.

1. **A** between
   B with
   C in
   D at

2. **A** about
   B from
   C for
   D into

3. **A** behind
   B before
   C by
   D over

4. **A** from
   B into
   C to
   D down

5. **A** Against
   B Through
   C Across
   D On

6. **A** until
   B to
   C about
   D under

7. **A** on
   B above
   C under
   D after

8. **A** for
   B by
   C around
   D into

9. **A** down
   B by
   C behind
   D toward

10. **A** under
    B around
    C at
    D to

Home Activity Your child prepared for taking tests on prepositions and prepositional phrases. Ask your child to make flash cards for prepositions he or she has learned. Show each card and have him or her use the preposition in a sentence.

Prepositions and Prepositional Phrases

Directions Underline each prepositional phrase. The number in ( ) tells how many prepositional phrases are in that sentence.

1. *Bambi* is an animated movie about a deer. (1)

2. It begins with Bambi's birth in the forest. (2)

3. All the forest creatures are filled with joy at the birth. (2)

4. They welcome the new prince of the forest. (1)

5. Bambi makes two friends of the closest kind. (1)

6. Thumper is a bunny with attitude, who has a sense of fun. (2)

7. Bambi discovers a shy skunk in the flowers and names him Flower. (1)

Directions Write *P* if the underlined word is a preposition. Write *O* if it is the object of the preposition.

8. Today we learned <u>about</u> computer animation. _____

9. We enjoy cartoons thanks <u>to</u> this technique. _____

10. Artists create drawings on the <u>computer</u>. _____

11. With <u>software</u>, they manipulate these drawings. _____

12. <u>Before</u> computers, animation artists drew every frame. _____

13. Now computers move the cartoon <u>for</u> the artist. _____

14. Software also applies colors in the <u>shapes</u>. _____

Directions Underline the prepositional phrase in each sentence. Write *P* above the preposition. Write *O* above the object of the preposition.

15. *Toy Story* is an animated film about a boy's toys.

16. The toys remain loyal to their owner.

17. There is jealousy and competition among the toys.

18. They finally become friends and work together for their own good.

Home Activity Your child reviewed prepositions and prepositional phrases. Have your child see how many prepositional phrases he or she can find on the label of a box or can of food. Have your child identify the prepositions.

Subject and Object Pronouns

A **subject pronoun** is used in the subject of a sentence. Singular subject pronouns are *I, you, he, she,* and *it.* Plural subject pronouns are *we, you,* and *they.* When you use a person's name and a pronoun in a compound subject, be sure to use a subject pronoun.

<u>He</u> has many original ideas. <u>They</u> are exciting and unusual.
Mom and <u>I</u> made bird feeders.

An **object pronoun** is used in the predicate of a sentence after an action verb or with a preposition, such as *for, at, into, with,* or *to.* Singular object pronouns are *me, you, him, her,* and *it.* Plural object pronouns are *us, you,* and *them.* When you use a person's name and a pronoun in a compound object, be sure to use an object pronoun.

The teacher asked <u>him</u> about his project. It seemed brilliant to <u>me</u>.
This project was fun for James and <u>me</u>.

Directions Write *S* if the underlined word is a subject pronoun. Write *O* if the word is an object pronoun.

1. Some kids don't know what to think about <u>him</u>.   _____

2. They can't understand someone who is different from <u>them</u>.   _____

3. <u>She</u> praised his project for its originality.   _____

4. Rainelle and <u>I</u> invited him to sit with us.   _____

5. <u>We</u> were fascinated by his ideas.   _____

6. He has become a valued friend to her and <u>me</u>.   _____

Directions Underline the correct pronoun in ( ) to complete each sentence.

7. Most people choose friends who are like (them, they).

8. (Them, They) feel comfortable with people who agree with them.

9. You and (I, me) have different points of view.

10. A friend with original ideas always surprises (I, me).

11. (Us, We) need to think about what we do and say.

12. (I, Me) prefer independent thinkers.

13. Jose and (her, she) agree with me.

14. We have many exciting conversations with (he, him) and (she, her).

School-Home CONNECTION   **Home Activity** Your child learned about subject and object pronouns. Read a magazine article with your child. Ask him or her to identify several subject pronouns and object pronouns in the article.

Subject and Object Pronouns

Directions Use a pronoun from the box to complete each sentence. Write the sentence.

they	he	I	us
them	she	me	you

1. My mom and _____ plant a garden every summer.

2. _____ lets me pick out the seeds we will plant.

3. Some new flowers surprised _____ both this season.

4. _____ looked very strange among the roses and daisies.

5. As we watched _____ grow, we became more and more amazed.

6. Their enormous leaves and huge white flowers puzzled _____ and Mom.

7. Finally, Dad confessed. _____ had planted moonflower seeds to surprise us!

8. Would _____ have fallen for his joke?

Directions Write a paragraph about a unique person you know. Use subject and object pronouns correctly.

_____

_____

_____

_____

_____

_____

_____

_____

_____

_____

Home Activity Your child learned how to use subject and object pronouns in writing. Ask your child to write a description of something he or she did with a friend or a group. Remind your child to use subject and object pronouns correctly.

Subject and Object Pronouns

Directions Mark the letter of the pronoun that correctly completes each sentence.

1. ____ like to find wild foods.
   A Them
   B I
   C Me
   D She

2. You can make a meal of ____.
   A we
   B they
   C them
   D he

3. Dana and ____ found wild strawberries.
   A he
   B him
   C us
   D them

4. In the fall ____ harvest cattails.
   A me
   B her
   C us
   D they

5. ____ can grind the roots to make flour.
   A Him
   B We
   C Them
   D Her

6. Papa and ____ hunt for mushrooms in the woods.
   A her
   B me
   C she
   D us

7. Have ____ ever picked wild asparagus?
   A you
   B it
   C them
   D him

8. Uncle Dick and ____ found hickory nuts.
   A us
   B her
   C them
   D they

9. Dad asked Phil and ____ to shell the nuts.
   A she
   B he
   C me
   D I

10. He and ____ agreed it is a messy job.
    A them
    B I
    C it
    D her

Home Activity Your child prepared for taking tests on subject and object pronouns. Have your child write subject pronouns and object pronouns on index cards. Then mix the cards and sort them into subject pronoun and object pronoun piles.

Grammar and Writing Practice Book

Subject and Object Pronouns

Directions Write the letter of each pronoun next to the correct category.

_____ 1. Singular subject pronoun   **A** we

_____ 2. Plural object pronoun   **B** she

_____ 3. Singular object pronoun   **C** me

_____ 4. Plural subject pronoun   **D** you

_____ 5. Singular and plural, subject and object pronoun   **E** them

Directions Write *S* if the underlined word is a subject pronoun. Write *O* if the word is an object pronoun.

6. <u>We</u> learned about the Anasazi people.   _____

7. <u>They</u> built a civilization in the Southwest.   _____

8. Like many civilizations, <u>it</u> depended on crops.   _____

9. Maize and pumpkins provided the staple foods for <u>them</u>.   _____

10. Little rain fell, but the Anasazi hoarded <u>it</u> to water crops.   _____

11. The teacher asked Lia and <u>me</u> to report on cliff dwellings.   _____

Directions Underline the correct pronoun in ( ) to complete each sentence.

12. My family and (I, me) visited Chaco Canyon.

13. (Us, We) learned about the pueblos the Anasazi built there.

14. Their skill in building with adobe amazed Sara and (I, me).

15. The people who lived here disappeared 800 years ago and took little with (them, they).

16. Why they left is a mystery to (us, we).

17. Scientists and (they, them) agree that drought may have forced them to migrate.

Home Activity Your child reviewed subject and object pronouns. Challenge your child to write sentences using *you, he, she, it, him, her,* and *them* correctly.

Pronouns and Antecedents

A **pronoun** takes the place of a noun or nouns. An **antecedent**, or referent, is the noun or nouns to which the pronoun refers. A pronoun and its antecedent must agree in number and gender.

Before you use a pronoun, ask yourself whether the antecedent is singular or plural. If the antecedent is singular, decide whether it is masculine, feminine, or neuter. Then choose a pronoun that agrees. In the following sentences, the antecedents are underlined once; the pronouns are underlined twice.

York went with Lewis and Clark on their expedition. He helped them greatly.

Directions Circle the correct pronoun or pronouns in ( ) to complete each sentence. The antecedent of each pronoun is underlined to help you.

1. Lewis and Clark went up the Missouri River so (he, they) could explore the West.

2. York went on the trip because (he, him) was Clark's servant.

3. Lewis and Clark kept journals, and (it, they) tell of many hardships.

4. Sacagawea was helpful because (she, her) spoke the Shoshone language.

5. When York met the Arikara people, the people were awed by (he, him).

6. The explorers lived near Indian tribes and became friends with (they, them).

Directions Underline the antecedent once and the pronoun twice in each sentence.

7. York gave the explorers the greens he found for dinner.

8. Floyd died because the explorers' medicines did not help him.

9. When a torrent of water rushed toward Sacagawea, Clark helped her.

10. The explorers got caught in a storm, and York worried about them.

11. Lewis and Clark built a fort near the Pacific, and it was in a rainy area.

12. Clark appreciated York and named a river for him.

Home Activity Your child learned about pronouns and antecedents. Read a magazine article together and have your child find pronouns that have antecedents and identify both.

Pronouns and Antecedents

Directions Write a sentence or a pair of sentences using the noun or noun phrase and pronoun. Use each noun as an antecedent of each pronoun.

1. Lewis and Clark/they

_____

_____

2. York/him

_____

3. Mandan and Hiditsa people/them

_____

_____

4. Sacagawea/she

_____

_____

5. expedition/it

_____

Directions Write a paragraph about someone who works hard to make a group effort a success. Use at least four pronouns with their antecedents. Underline the antecedent for each pronoun.

_____

_____

_____

_____

_____

_____

Home Activity Your child learned how to use pronouns and antecedents in writing. With your child, write a paragraph about a hard worker you admire. Have your child point out pronouns and underline their antecedents.

Grammar and Writing Practice Book

Pronouns and Antecedents

Directions Read the following paragraph. Mark the letter of the pronoun that correctly completes each sentence.

(1) People admired Lewis and Clark when _____ set off on their expedition. (2) They probably didn't know the others who went with _____. (3) York was strong, and _____ was a hard worker. (4) York met many Indians who were fascinated by _____. (5) The Indians had never seen a black man like _____. (6) The Missouri River was wide, and _____ had a strong current. (7) York helped the explorers overcome hardships _____ encountered on the river. (8) After meeting a young girl, Sacagawea, the explorers took _____ along also. (9) Fortunately _____ spoke an Indian language. (10) Lewis and Clark led the journey, but _____ got much help from others.

1. **A** him
   B she
   C he
   D they

2. **A** him
   B them
   C they
   D he

3. **A** him
   B she
   C they
   D he

4. **A** he
   B she
   C him
   D it

5. **A** he
   B they
   C him
   D them

6. **A** he
   B it
   C they
   D them

7. **A** she
   B we
   C them
   D they

8. **A** it
   B them
   C her
   D him

9. **A** they
   B him
   C she
   D he

10. **A** it
    B he
    C we
    D they

Home Activity Your child prepared for taking tests on pronouns and antecedents. Have your child rewrite a paragraph from a story, replacing each pronoun with its antecedent. Ask him or her to explain why pronouns make the story sound better.

Pronouns and Antecedents

Directions Match the pronoun with the noun or noun phrase that could be its antecedent. Write the letter of the correct antecedent next to the pronoun.

_____ **1.** Lewis and I   **A** he

_____ **2.** Sacagawea   **B** it

_____ **3.** President Jefferson   **C** they

_____ **4.** Fort Clatsop   **D** we

_____ **5.** grizzly bears   **E** she

Directions Circle the antecedent of the underlined pronoun in each sentence.

6. Explorers go to a new place to learn about <u>it</u>.

7. Lewis and Clark went west after Jefferson asked <u>them</u> to.

8. York showed strength and courage as <u>he</u> helped Lewis and Clark.

9. York helped build Fort Clatsop, but the difficult job took a toll on <u>him</u>.

10. Sacagawea took her baby along as <u>she</u> helped Lewis and Clark on their journey.

Directions Write a pronoun to replace each underlined noun or noun phrase.

11. The Mandan tribe befriended Lewis and Clark when <u>Lewis and Clark</u> visited the Mandan village.

_____

12. The hunters went out each day, and everyone depended on <u>the hunters</u> for food.

_____

13. Clark wrote, "<u>Clark</u> gave him a severe trouncing."

_____

14. Clark explored the Yellowstone River, and the explorer took York with <u>Clark</u>.

_____

15. The explorers longed to see the Pacific Ocean, and they finally reached the <u>Pacific Ocean</u>.

_____

Home Activity Your child reviewed pronouns and antecedents. Have your child dictate sentences about what he or she learned about the Lewis and Clark expedition today. Ask your child to underline pronouns and circle any antecedents in the sentences.

Grammar and Writing Practice Book

Possessive Pronouns

Possessive pronouns show who or what owns, or possesses, something. *My, mine, your, yours, her, hers, his, its, our, ours, their,* and *theirs* are possessive pronouns.

- Use *my, your, her, our,* and *their* before nouns.
  Is that <u>your</u> cat? It was <u>her</u> gerbil. They pet <u>our</u> dog.

- Use *mine, yours, hers, ours,* and *theirs* alone.
  The cat is <u>yours</u>. That gerbil is <u>hers</u>. The dog is <u>ours</u>.

- *His* and *its* can be used both before nouns and alone.
  He lost <u>his</u> ferret. The ferret is <u>his</u>.
  The dog lost <u>its</u> collar. The collar is <u>its</u>.

- Do not use an apostrophe with a possessive pronoun.

Directions Replace the underlined words or phrases with possessive pronouns. Rewrite the sentences.

1. An ant colony relies on <u>the ant colony's</u> queen.

   _____

   _____

2. Both males and females have wings on <u>the males' and females'</u> bodies.

   _____

   _____

3. The queen ant flies to a new location to start a colony, then sheds <u>the queen's</u> wings.

   _____

   _____

4. Ants are very strong for <u>ants'</u> size and can carry 25 times <u>ants'</u> weight.

   _____

   _____

5. Most of us think that ants are pests to be swept out of <u>most of us's</u> way.

   _____

   _____

Home Activity Your child learned about possessive pronouns. Ask your child to make up sentences about objects at home that belong to him or her, to the family, and to others. Have your child identify the possessive pronouns he or she uses.

Possessive Pronouns

Directions Underline the error in each sentence. Write the correct possessive pronoun in the space above the error.

(1) Each animal is adapted to it's environment. (2) For example, snakes have temperature-

sensing organs on they're heads. (3) They can use these organs to locate there prey in the dark.

(4) My corn snake Lolamae can take a whole mouse or egg in hers mouth. (5) She can unhinge

her's bottom jaw to fit in a big meal. (6) The aquarium in the corner is her. (7) Lolamae will be

happy to slither up yours arm. (8) It took mine mom a long time to get used to Lolamae too.

Directions Write a paragraph about pets you and your friends have owned. Describe some unique features of the pets. Use at least five possessive pronouns. Underline the possessive pronouns in your paragraph.

_____

_____

_____

_____

_____

_____

_____

_____

_____

_____

_____

_____

_____

Home Activity Your child learned how to use possessive pronouns in writing. Have your child write interview questions to ask you about a prized possession and then write your answers below the questions.

Grammar and Writing Practice Book

Possessive Pronouns

Directions Write the letter of the possessive pronoun that correctly completes each sentence in the paragraph.

(1) Last night I heard a haunting sound outside ____ window. (2) My brother and I ran into ____ yard to find out what it was. (3) He shined ____ flashlight up into a tree. (4) We saw two big eyes, and ____ unblinking stare unnerved me. (5) It was only a screech owl, but ____ hoot sounded eerie. (6) Since that night, owls have become a hobby of ____. (7) Mom loaned me some of ____ biology books. (8) Did you know that owls can turn ____ heads almost completely around? (9) This is an adaptation of ____ that allows them to turn their heads to follow a moving object. (10) Now Mom and I spend ____ free time on weekends bird watching.

1. **A** mine
   B my
   C theirs
   D hers

2. **A** her
   B hers
   C our
   D theirs

3. **A** mine
   B his
   C its
   D their

4. **A** your
   B its
   C their
   D theirs

5. **A** theirs
   B its
   C hers
   D her

6. **A** mine
   B our
   C their
   D it's

7. **A** hers
   B her
   C their
   D theirs

8. **A** our
   B her
   C their
   D my

9. **A** hers
   B his
   C their
   D theirs

10. **A** mine
    B my
    C ours
    D our

Home Activity Your child prepared for taking tests on possessive pronouns. Have your child choose a magazine article and find possessive pronouns in it. Ask him or her to name the person or thing each possessive pronoun stands for.

Possessive Pronouns

Directions Write the letter of the possessive pronoun that can replace the underlined word or words in each phrase.

_____ 1. Aaron's and Mike's question   **A** her

_____ 2. Mr. Shaefer's lesson   **B** their

_____ 3. the book's index   **C** our

_____ 4. Sam's and my interest   **D** its

_____ 5. Mom's degree   **E** his

Directions Underline the pronoun that correctly completes each sentence.

6. We will catch fireflies in (theirs, our) hands.

7. Which of these jars is (your, yours)?

8. Be sure to punch air holes in (it's, its) top.

9. Dusk is (their, theirs) time to glow and flash.

10. I have ten fireflies in (my, mine) jar.

11. The light flashes from (their, it's) abdomen.

12. We let the fireflies go. Our friends released (their, theirs) later.

Directions Write the possessive pronoun that can replace the underlined word or words.

13. A snake sheds a snake's skin when it outgrows it.

_____

14. This bleached-out turtle shell is the one belonging to me.

_____

15. Zara and Ted explained that the rat was Zara's and the hamster was Ted's.

_____

Home Activity Your child reviewed possessive pronouns. Ask your child to list the possessive pronouns on this page, use each one in an example sentence, and tell you what possessive noun the possessive pronoun replaces.

Indefinite and Reflexive Pronouns

Indefinite pronouns may not refer to specific words. They do not have definite antecedents.
  <u>Someone</u> called and left a message.

Some common indefinite pronouns are listed below.

Singular Indefinite Pronouns	**Plural Indefinite Pronouns**
someone, somebody, anyone, anybody, everyone, everybody, something, no one, either, each	few, several, both, others, many all, some

• Use singular verb forms with singular indefinite pronouns and plural verb forms with plural indefinite pronouns: <u>Everyone</u> feels lonely at times. <u>Others</u> offer them friendship.

Reflexive pronouns reflect the action of the verb back on the subject. Reflexive pronouns end in *-self* or *-selves*: Vic wrote a note to <u>himself</u>.

Singular Reflexive Pronouns	**Plural Reflexive Pronouns**
himself, herself, myself, itself, yourself	ourselves, yourselves, themselves

• There are no such words as *hisself, theirself, theirselves,* or *ourself*.

Directions Underline the correct pronoun in ( ) to complete each sentence.

1. (Anyone, Many) benefits by making new friends.

2. (Many, Anyone) treasure old friends too.

3. My friends and I taught (ourself, ourselves) chess.

4. We play in the cafeteria, but (few, no one) know this.

5. (Everyone, Others) is welcome to join us.

6. A new student introduced (himself, hisself).

7. (Some, Someone) calls him Dylan.

8. (Something, Many) tells me Dylan has learned chess from a master.

9. We know the moves, but he knows the game (itself, themselves).

10. (Someone, Others) tell me I'm good at chess, but Dylan beat me.

11. I hope Dylan enjoyed (herself, himself) today.

12. You should learn chess (ourself, yourself).

Indefinite and Reflexive Pronouns

ourselves	everyone	yourself	few
myself	anyone	herself	both

Directions Choose a pronoun from the box to complete each sentence correctly. Be sure indefinite pronouns used as subjects agree in number with their verbs.

1. "Tell us about _____, Tonya," says the teacher.

2. I think to _____, "This is going to be good!"

3. _____ leans forward to listen.

4. Tonya is a cowgirl who taught _____ to ride.

5. _____ of us know anything at all about horses.

6. Tonya says that _____ can ride her gentle horse Bluebonnet.

7. All of us think to _____, "I might not be able to!"

8. My friend Tonya has two horses, and _____ are beautiful.

Directions Write several sentences about a time you made a new friend. Use some indefinite and reflexive pronouns. Underline the indefinite and reflexive pronouns you use.

_____

_____

_____

_____

_____

_____

_____

_____

_____

_____

Home Activity Your child learned how to write indefinite and reflexive pronouns. Have your child write these pronouns on cards. Choose several cards at a time and ask him or her to write sentences using the pronouns.

Indefinite and Reflexive Pronouns

Directions Mark the letter of the pronoun that correctly completes each sentence.

1. This alarm clock turns _____ off.
   A themself
   B itself
   C herself
   D yourself

2. _____ lets the dog out at 3.
   A Someone
   B Many
   C Something
   D Few

3. _____ is welcome to try out.
   A Themselves
   B Others
   C Anyone
   D Many

4. Marla taught _____ to sing.
   A itself
   B themselves
   C himself
   D herself

5. _____ sends us a mystery package every year.
   A Himself
   B Somebody
   C Both
   D Several

6. _____ likes getting a shot.
   A Myself
   B Few
   C No one
   D Many

7. Sam bought _____ a watch.
   A itself
   B themself
   C himself
   D hisself

8. _____ is wrong.
   A Myself
   B Something
   C Itself
   D Others

9. May we help _____?
   A ourself
   B themself
   C hisself
   D ourselves

10. _____ volunteer for safety patrol duty.
    A Many
    B No one
    C Everyone
    D Someone

Home Activity Your child prepared for taking tests on indefinite and reflexive pronouns. Have your child write each indefinite and reflexive pronoun on an index card. Mix the cards and have your child sort them by type and number.

Name _____

Indefinite and Reflexive Pronouns

Directions Underline the pronoun in each sentence. Write *indefinite* or *reflexive* to identify the kind of pronoun it is. Then write *singular* or *plural* to show its number.

1. Everyone wants friends.   _____   _____

2. Anna told herself to smile.   _____   _____

3. A smile multiplies itself.   _____   _____

4. Many begin to smile at Anna.   _____   _____

5. Anybody can give a smile.   _____   _____

Directions Underline the correct pronoun in ( ) to complete each sentence.

6. (Someone, Both) are friendly.

7. (Everyone, Many) agrees they are good friends

8. (No one, Others) are welcome in our club.

9. (Several, Anybody) have inquired about joining.

10. The boys signed (himself, themselves) up for bowling class.

11. (Anybody, Yourself) can try out for the class play.

12. Marcus and I practiced our parts by (himself, ourselves).

Directions Choose a pronoun from the box to complete each sentence correctly. Be sure indefinite pronouns used as subjects agree in number with their verbs.

> ourselves   everybody   themselves   few

13. _____ in class was to choose an after-school activity.

14. A _____ of us are signing up for poetry.

15. Ms. Lonway will let us choose a poet for _____.

16. Humorous poets don't take _____ too seriously.

 Home Activity Your child reviewed indefinite and reflexive pronouns. Have your child reread a favorite story and identify the indefinite and reflexive pronouns in it as singular or plural.

Grammar and Writing Practice Book

Name _____

Using *Who* and *Whom*

People sometimes confuse the pronouns *who* and *whom* when they write. *Who* is a subject form. It is used as a subject of a sentence or a clause.
   Who made this mess?
   I saw a performer *who* could do four back flips. [*Who* is the subject in the dependent clause *who could do four back flips.*]

Whom is an object form. It is used as the object of a preposition or as a direct object.
   To *whom* did you send a letter?
   Whom will you ask?

In the first example, *whom* is the object of the preposition *to*. In the second example, *whom* is a direct object.

• To understand why *whom* is used in the second sentence, change the word order so that the subject comes first. (*Whom will you ask?* becomes *You will ask whom?*) This makes it easier to see that *whom* is a direct object.

Directions How is the underlined word used? Write *subject*, *object of preposition*, or *direct object*.

1. <u>Who</u> wants to learn gymnastics? _____

2. She is a person for <u>whom</u> gymnastics is hard. _____

3. Matt is the person <u>who</u> did a triple somersault. _____

4. <u>Whom</u> did she help the most? _____

5. <u>Who</u> won the Olympic medal last year? _____

Directions Underline *who* or *whom* to complete each sentence correctly.

6. (Who, Whom) should we support?

7. Work with Brenda, (who, whom) has taken gymnastics for years.

8. To (who, whom) should we go for advice?

9. (Who, Whom) remembers the order of events?

10. The gymnast (who, whom) stumbled on the dismount still won a medal.

Home Activity Your child learned about using *who* and *whom*. Ask your child to write sentences about a sport using *whom* as an object and *who* as a subject.

Using *Who* and *Whom*

Directions Choose *who* or *whom* to correctly complete each sentence. Then write this sentence and answer or explain it with another sentence or two.

1. A person who/whom I admire is _____.

_____

_____

_____

2. To who/whom do I go for advice?

_____

_____

_____

3. Who/Whom is my good friend?

_____

_____

_____

4. Who/Whom is a person from history I'd like to meet?

_____

_____

_____

Directions Write two sentences about a sport you would like to learn and the person whom you would like as a coach. Use *who* or *whom* correctly in each sentence.

5. _____

_____

6. _____

_____

Home Activity Your child learned how to use *who* and *whom* correctly in writing. Ask him or her to write a fictional news story about sports and use the pronouns *who* and *whom* in it.

Grammar and Writing Practice Book

Using *Who* and *Whom*

Directions Mark the letter of the answer that tells how the underlined word is used.

1. That is the teacher <u>whom</u> I like best.
   A subject
   B object of preposition
   C direct object
   D noun

2. <u>Whom</u> will you ask to the party?
   A direct object
   B verb
   C subject
   D object of preposition

3. Janelle asked, "<u>Who</u> can help me?"
   A object of preposition
   B adjective
   C direct object
   D subject

4. She is a gymnast <u>who</u> works hard.
   A verb
   B subject
   C direct object
   D object of preposition

5. For <u>whom</u> should we ask?
   A noun
   B subject
   C object of preposition
   D direct object

6. Everyone to <u>whom</u> she spoke smiled.
   A object of preposition
   B subject
   C direct object
   D verb

Directions Mark the letter of the sentence that is correct.

7. A Whom has finished the assignment?
   B By whom was this work done?
   C He is a teacher whom praises students often.
   D Who did he choose?

8. A He helped the students who were having trouble.
   B To who can I turn this in?
   C Who did you help?
   D Whom won the gymnastics award this year?

9. A The winner is the one to who a trophy is given.
   B Chele is the partner with who I worked.
   C He is the judge who gave high marks.
   D She likes the gymnast whom is short and slim.

10. A I like gymnasts whom take chances.
    B Whom was your favorite performer?
    C I choose someone whom has pluck.
    D Whom would you choose?

Home Activity Your child prepared for taking tests on *who* and *whom*. Have your child read newspaper articles to highlight uses of *who* and *whom*. Then ask him or her to tell whether the gwords are used correctly, and why.

Name _____

Using *Who* and *Whom*

Directions Write *subject, object of preposition,* or *direct object* to identify how the underlined word is used.

1. To <u>whom</u> did Rosa speak?   _____

2. <u>Who</u> likes tumbling?   _____

3. A gymnast is someone <u>who</u> is agile and strong.   _____

4. The girl with <u>whom</u> Jordan practices has real talent.   _____

5. People <u>who</u> are flexible are better at somersaults.   _____

6. <u>Whom</u> did you choose as a partner?   _____

Directions Underline *who* or *whom* to complete each sentence correctly.

7. (Who, Whom) said that gymnastics is easy?

8. No one (who, whom) has studied gymnastics would say that.

9. Harry, (who, whom) I have coached for three years, shows promise.

10. To (who, whom) shall we give the "Most Improved" award?

11. Marla is the gymnast with (who, whom) most teammates want to work.

12. Our grandfather, (who, whom) is now 65, competed on his college gymnastics team.

13. (Who, Whom) will win Olympic gold this year?

14. (Who, Whom) made the banner congratulating the team?

Directions Cross out mistakes in the use of *who* and *whom* in the paragraph. Write the correct pronoun above the line.

(15) Kids whom live in the same family often compete with each other. (16) They want

to see who the parents like best. (17) Parents, whom love all their children equally, try not

to play favorites. (18) Although brothers and sisters like to see whom is faster or stronger, they

love each other too.

Home Activity Your child reviewed using *who* and *whom*. Read a story with your child, and then ask him or her to tell about favorite characters, using *who* and *whom* correctly.

Grammar and Writing Practice Book

Name _____

Contractions and Negatives

A **contraction** is a shortened form of two words. An **apostrophe** is used to show where one or more letters have been left out. Some contractions are made by combining pronouns and verbs: *I + have = I've; you + are = you're.* Other contractions are formed by joining a verb and *not: should + not = shouldn't; were + not = weren't.*

- *Won't* and *can't* are formed in special ways (*can + not = can't; will + not = won't*).

Negatives are words that mean "no" or "not": *no, not, never, none, nothing.* Contractions with *n't* are negatives too. To make a negative statement, use only one negative word.

    No: Don't never ask about his leg. There won't be none left.
    Yes: Don't ever ask about his leg. There won't be any left.

- Use positive words instead of the negative in a sentence with *not*:

Negative	Positive	Negative	Positive
nobody	anybody, somebody	nothing	anything, something
no one	anyone, someone	nowhere	anywhere, somewhere
none	any, all, some	never	ever, always

Directions Write the letter of the two words used to form each contraction.

_____	**1.** what's	**A**	has not
_____	**2.** that'll	**B**	that will
_____	**3.** didn't	**C**	they are
_____	**4.** hasn't	**D**	could not
_____	**5.** they're	**E**	did not
_____	**6.** couldn't	**F**	what has

Directions Write the contraction for each pair of words.

7. would + have = _____

9. it + is = _____

8. she + will = _____

10. will + not = _____

Directions Circle the word in ( ) that correctly completes each sentence.

11. You can't (never, ever) tell what those boys will do.

12. There wasn't (nobody, anything) in the hole.

 Home Activity Your child learned about contractions and negatives. With your child, scan articles in the newspaper to find contractions. Ask your child to write the words used to form each contraction.

Name _____

Contractions and Negatives

Directions Use contractions to replace the underlined words. Rewrite the sentence.

1. <u>There is</u> plenty to do on a farm in the summer.

   _____

   _____

2. Those boys <u>will not</u> just swim or fish.

   _____

3. <u>They have</u> thought of some new projects to try.

   _____

4. I <u>do not</u> think the pond is big enough for a submarine.

   _____

   _____

5. Their plane <u>is not</u> ready to take off.

   _____

6. <u>What is</u> that hole for?

   _____

Directions Rewrite the sentences, correcting any double negatives.

7. No one never dug a hole that deep before.

   _____

8. There isn't no better place to dig a hole.

   _____

9. The boys didn't think nothing could get into the hole.

   _____

10. There weren't no animals around when they were digging.

   _____

Home Activity Your child learned how to write negatives and contractions correctly. Ask your child to write a paragraph about what he or she likes to do during the summer, using several contractions and negatives. Have him or her underline these words.

Grammar and Writing Practice Book

Contractions and Negatives

Directions Mark the letter of the contraction that correctly completes each sentence.

1. _____ the skunk come out of the hole?
   A Wont
   B Won't
   C Willn't
   D Don't

2. _____ quite a hole they dug!
   A We've
   B Its
   C That'll
   D That's

3. They _____ believe Dad's reaction.
   A couldnt
   B could'nt
   C couldn't
   D couldnt'

4. They were afraid _____ be mad.
   A he's
   B he'd
   C he'ill
   D hed

5. _____ been a while since the skunk jumped in.
   A Its
   B Its'
   C It's
   D Thats'

6. _____ be all right.
   A He'l
   B He'll
   C Hel'l
   D He'ill

Directions Mark the letter of the words that correctly complete the sentence.

7. _____ gotten the skunk out yet?
   A Hasn't no one
   B Has no one not
   C Hasn't anyone
   D Hasn't anyone never

8. There _____ use for the hole.
   A wasn't any
   B wasn't no
   C isn't no
   D was'nt any

9. The cow _____ go near the hole.
   A didn't never
   B didn't ever
   C didn't not ever
   D didnt' ever

10. Dad said, "Don't _____ else."
    A build nothing
    B never build nothing
    C never build anything
    D build anything

Home Activity Your child prepared for taking tests on contractions and negatives. Ask your child to write contractions on one side of index cards and the words used to form them on the other side. Help your child practice identifying them.

Contractions and Negatives

Directions Underline the contraction in each sentence. Write the words that make up the contraction.

1. What's our next project going to be? _____

2. I've got a great idea. _____

3. We'll build a bridge across the creek. _____

4. It'll be made out of firewood. _____

5. I am the best engineer you've ever seen. _____

Directions Draw a line to connect each contraction with the words used to form it.

6. could've   you are

7. they'll   it is

8. who'd   could have

9. you're   who would

10. it's   they will

Directions Circle the word in ( ) that correctly completes each sentence.

11. Crazy Eddie didn't (ever, never) run out of ideas.

12. There hasn't ever been (anybody, nobody) as creative as he was.

13. His dad found out there was (anything, nothing) Eddie wouldn't try.

14. Of course, his projects didn't (ever, never) turn out perfect.

15. I bet Eddie's chemistry experiments aren't (ever, never) boring.

Home Activity Your child reviewed contractions and negatives. Ask him or her to write a story that uses at least five contractions and five negatives correctly. Have your child highlight these words and read you the story.

Grammar and Writing Practice Book

Name _____

Adjectives and Articles

An **adjective** describes a noun or pronoun. It tells what kind, how many, or which one.

What Kind	a gigantic white iceberg
How Many	numerous icebergs; several chances
Which One	this lifeboat

The **articles** *a, an,* and *the* appear before nouns or other adjectives.

- Use **a** before words that begin with a consonant sound: a disaster, a rapid speed.
- Use **an** before words that begin with a vowel sound or a silent *h*: an ending, an eerie noise.
- Use **the** before words beginning with any letter: the site, the passengers.

An adjective formed from a proper noun is a **proper adjective**. Proper adjectives are capitalized: American newspapers.

Directions Underline the articles and circle the adjectives in each sentence.

1. An iceberg is a huge mass of ice that has broken off from a glacier.

2. A large iceberg can weigh a million tons and stretch many miles.

3. In the Atlantic Ocean, most icebergs come from the island of Greenland.

4. Icebergs are made of frozen fresh water.

5. For travelers, they are beautiful and deadly.

6. As they float south, icebergs melt in the warm sun.

Directions Write *a, an,* or *the* to complete each sentence. Use the article that makes sense.

7. Some icebergs are carried by wind into _____ Atlantic Ocean.

8. Only _____ small part of an iceberg is visible above the water.

9. _____ iceberg is quite impressive to behold.

Directions Complete each sentence with an adjective or adjectives of your own.

10. The wreck of the _____ ship lies in _____ pieces on the ocean floor.

11. A litter of belongings tells the _____ tale of lost life.

12. The once _____ ship is now a _____ heap on the ocean floor.

Home Activity Your child learned about adjectives and articles. Ask your child to expand sentences such as the following by adding adjectives and articles: *The ship sank. It struck an iceberg. People died. Today it's a legend.*

Adjectives and Articles

Directions Choose an adjective from the box to complete each sentence.

> | hollow | Greek | strange | deep-sea |
> |--------|-------|---------|----------|
> | several | five | 4,500 | |

1. *Bathys* is a _____ word meaning "deep," and a *sphere* is a globe or ball.

2. The bathysphere was the first _____ machine that took people far beneath the waves.

3. This _____ steel ball, which weighed _____ pounds, was raised and lowered by a cable.

4. It was about _____ feet in diameter and was fitted inside with oxygen tanks.

5. Divers reported news of the _____ animals they saw via a telephone cable to a ship on the surface.

6. _____ creatures had never been seen by humans before!

Directions Think about what you would like to see on a visit to the ocean floor. Write a sentence to answer each question below. Use adjectives and articles and underline them.

7. How far down would you travel?

_____

_____

8. What equipment would you take?

_____

_____

9. What would you look for?

_____

_____

10. What do you think it would look like?

_____

_____

Home Activity Your child learned how to write adjectives and articles correctly. Ask your child to write a paragraph describing what it is like to move under water. Have him or her circle adjectives and articles used.

Grammar and Writing Practice Book

Adjectives and Articles

Directions Mark the letter of the adjective in each sentence.

1. *Alvin* is a small American submarine used to explore the ocean.
   A Alvin
   B American
   C submarine
   D ocean

2. Go for an eight-hour dive in *Alvin*.
   A Go
   B for
   C eight-hour
   D dive

3. Three people can fit inside.
   A Three
   B people
   C fit
   D inside

4. You can travel up to 4,500 meters below the surface.
   A travel
   B up
   C 4,500
   D below

5. On the bottom, you can conduct scientific experiments.
   A bottom
   B you
   C conduct
   D scientific

6. In the basket on the front of *Alvin*, you can load many instruments.
   A basket
   B front
   C load
   D many

7. Robotic arms help you move the equipment.
   A Robotic
   B help
   C move
   D equipment

8. *Alvin* carries lights to the dark ocean floor.
   A lights
   B to
   C dark
   D floor

9. *Alvin* has traveled to the bottom 4,000 times!
   A has
   B traveled
   C bottom
   D 4,000

10. The discovery of the *Titanic* was a famous adventure.
    A discovery
    B *Titanic*
    C famous
    D adventure

Home Activity Your child prepared for taking tests on adjectives and articles. Copy a page from a storybook. Have your child highlight the adjectives in red and the articles in blue.

Adjectives and Articles

Directions Underline the articles and circle the adjectives in each sentence.

1. Huge icebergs break off the vast ice near Greenland.

2. One iceberg can be a dangerous object for ships at sea.

3. They look like beautiful islands, but they hide treacherous ice beneath the surface.

4. Most pilots keep a sharp lookout for icebergs.

Directions Write *what kind, how many,* or *which one* to tell what question each underlined adjective answers about a noun.

5. Many people enjoy going on cruises.   _____

6. In 1912, trans-Atlantic travel required a ship.   _____

7. Cruising was not the main reason for getting on board.   _____

8. Those passengers were entertained royally.   _____

9. There was plenty of rich food and drink.   _____

Directions Write *a, an,* or *the* in the blank to complete each sentence. Choose the article that makes sense and follows the rules for articles.

10. They dressed for dinner almost _____ hour before it was served.

11. Mrs. Astor was escorted to her table by _____ captain.

12. _____ elegant glass dome rose over the grand staircase.

13. Fine linen, china, and silver gleamed upon _____ tables.

14. This glamour would all be gone in _____ few short hours.

15. But for now, the room was _____ magical place.

16. It was _____ most special spot in the world.

Home Activity Your child reviewed adjectives and articles. With your child, read an encyclopedia article about the *Titanic*. Ask your child to point out adjectives and articles in at least one paragraph.

Name _____

This, That, These, and *Those*

The adjectives *this, that, these,* and *those* tell which one or which ones. *This* and *that* modify singular nouns. *These* and *those* modify plural nouns. *This* and *these* refer to objects that are close by. *That* and *those* refer to objects farther away.

<u>This</u> shirt I have on is like <u>that</u> one in the store window.

<u>These</u> pencils just fit in the pocket, but <u>those</u> pens on the desk did not fit.

- Do not use *here* or *there* after *this, that, these,* or *those.*
  No: <u>This here</u> article is about NASA. <u>That there</u> one is about new computers.
  Yes: <u>This</u> article is about NASA. <u>That</u> one is about new computers.

- Do not use *them* in place of *these* or *those.*
  No: She wrote <u>them</u> articles for *Newsweek.*
  Yes: She wrote <u>those</u> articles for *Newsweek.*

Directions Write the letter of the sentence in which the underlined part is correct.

_____ 1. A <u>That there</u> space capsule is smaller than I realized.
B <u>That</u> space capsule is smaller than I realized.

_____ 2. A I think <u>them</u> astronauts were brave to travel in it.
B I think <u>those</u> astronauts were brave to travel in it.

_____ 3. A Is <u>that</u> spacesuit the one worn by John Glenn?
B Is <u>those</u> spacesuit the one worn by John Glenn?

_____ 4. A <u>This here</u> time line shows the history of space flight.
B <u>This</u> time line shows the history of space flight.

_____ 5. A Robert Goddard helped design <u>these</u> early rockets.
B Robert Goddard helped design <u>them</u> early rockets.

Directions Write each sentence. Use the correct adjective in ( ).

6. Will (that, those) storm reach Florida today?

_____

7. If it does, NASA will postpone (this, these) shuttle launch.

_____

8. Use (them, those) binoculars to view the launch.

_____

 Home Activity Your child learned about *this, that, these,* and *those.* Write the words on four index cards. Ask your child to match each word with the appropriate category: singular near, singular far, plural near, plural far.

Name _____

This, That, These, and Those

Directions Think of an exciting new product that might come from the space program. Complete the following ad for this product. Use the adjectives *this, that, these,* or *those* and underline them.

These _____ are what America has been waiting for!

_____

_____

_____

_____

_____

_____ This ad has been brought to you by

_____

Directions Think about an object that you treasure. Tell what makes it special. Use the adjectives *this, that, these,* and *those* correctly.

_____

_____

_____

_____

_____

_____

_____

_____

_____

_____

Home Activity Your child learned how to use *this, that, these,* and *those* in writing. Ask your child to write sentences about things near and far, using each of the four adjectives correctly.

This, That, These, and Those

Directions Mark the letter of the adjective that completes each sentence correctly.

1. _____ orange I'm eating is delicious.
   A This
   B That
   C These
   D Those

2. It is better than _____ apples from last week.
   A this
   B that
   C these
   D those

3. Astronauts don't get fresh fruit like _____ peaches we are eating.
   A this
   B that
   C these
   D those

4. _____ meals they take into space are freeze-dried.
   A This
   B That
   C These
   D Those

5. _____ fact means they must add water to them.
   A This here
   B That
   C These
   D Those there

6. Let's exchange _____ bread for these crackers.
   A this
   B that
   C these
   D those

7. Let's try some of _____ freeze-dried steak.
   A this here
   B them
   C those there
   D this

8. Is _____ water boiling yet?
   A this here
   B that
   C these here
   D that there

9. _____ granola bars are tasty too.
   A Them
   B This here
   C These here
   D These

10. Don't sign me up for _____ next shuttle flight.
    A that there
    B that
    C these here
    D these

Home Activity Your child prepared for taking tests on *this, that, these,* and *those.* Ask your child to use these adjectives with the names of objects you point out in a room to describe their number and location.

Grammar and Writing Practice Book   Unit 5 Week 3 **91**

This, That, These, and *Those*

Directions Match each adjective with the phrase that describes it.

_____ **1.** this
_____ **2.** that
_____ **3.** these
_____ **4.** those

A modifies plural nouns that are close by

B modifies singular nouns that are close by

C modifies singular nouns that are far away

D modifies plural nouns that are far away

Directions Underline the word in ( ) that completes each sentence correctly.

5. (This, Those) summer I am going to space camp.

6. At (that, these) camp we will train like astronauts.

7. Astronauts must take many tests, and one of (them, those) tests involves gravity.

8. Gravity pulls us to Earth. (This, These) force becomes very great when we try to leave Earth's atmosphere.

9. Takeoff pushes the spacecraft into space. During (this, those) minutes, the body has to withstand strong G-forces.

10. In space the body floats because it is weightless. I want to imitate (this, these) experience at camp.

Directions Write the sentences correctly.

11. Ellen Ochoa invented an optical system. That there system "sees" flaws in a repeating pattern.

_____

_____

_____

12. Ochoa holds three patents for inventions. Them inventions all involve optical systems or robotics.

_____

_____

_____

Home Activity Your child reviewed *this, that, these,* and *those.* Have your child read an encyclopedia or Internet biography about Ellen Ochoa and then summarize it using *this, that, these,* and *those.*

Grammar and Writing Practice Book

Comparative and Superlative Adjectives

Comparative adjectives are used to compare two people, places, things, or groups. Add *-er* to most short adjectives to make their comparative forms. Use *more* with longer adjectives. **Superlative adjectives** are used to compare three or more people, places, things, or groups. Add *-est* to most short adjectives to make their superlative forms. Use *most* with longer adjectives.

Adjective	Comparative	Superlative
great	great<u>er</u>	great<u>est</u>
enormous	<u>more</u> enormous	<u>most</u> enormous

- Adjectives such as *good* and *bad* have irregular comparative and superlative forms: *good, better, best; bad, worse, worst.*

- Never use *more* or *most* with *-er* and *-est.*
  No: more sillier, most ancientest
  Yes: sillier, most ancient

Directions Complete the table. Add *-er, -est, more,* or *most* as needed.

Adjective	Comparative	Superlative
primitive	1. _____	2. _____
great	3. _____	4. _____
calm	5. _____	6. _____
wet	7. _____	8. _____
frightening	9. _____	10. _____
exciting	11. _____	12. _____

Directions Write the correct forms of the adjectives in ( ) to complete the sentences.

13. Is Ray Bradbury _____ (famous) than Jules Verne was?

14. Readers might think Jules Verne was the _____ (lucky) science fiction writer of all.

15. Did Verne write _____ (good) fiction than Lewis Carroll?

16. His _____ (important) legacy of all was his influence on twentieth-century scientists, inventors, and explorers.

Home Activity Your child learned about comparative and superlative adjectives. Ask your child to use these forms to expand these sentences: *Science fiction is <u>fascinating</u>. Reading is <u>fun</u>. ____ is a <u>good</u> book.*

Name _____

Comparative and Superlative Adjectives

Directions Write a comparative or superlative form of the adjective in ( ) to make each sentence precise.

1. I think Jules Verne was a _____ writer than Philip K. Dick. (inventive)

2. From childhood, he had been _____ of all when observing how things worked. (happy)

3. He always researched the very _____ scientific ideas. (new)

4. I like his books _____ than those of Charles Dickens. (good)

5. Verne included the _____ details possible in his novels. (realistic)

6. The submarine, motorcar, and navigable airship are just three inventions he anticipated from a

_____ age. (late)

Directions Write a paragraph to persuade a classmate to read one of your favorite books. Include comparative and superlative adjectives.

_____

_____

_____

_____

_____

_____

_____

_____

_____

_____

_____

_____

Home Activity Your child learned how to use comparative and superlative adjectives in writing. Ask your child to compare two of his or her favorite book characters using comparative and superlative adjectives.

Grammar and Writing Practice Book

Comparative and Superlative Adjectives

Directions Mark the letter of the adjective form that correctly completes each sentence.

1. Most dinosaurs were ____ than today's reptiles.
   A most big
   B bigger
   C biggest
   D more big

2. *Tyrannosaurus rex* was the ____ dinosaur of all.
   A scary
   B more scary
   C scarier
   D scariest

3. Today, scientists have a ____ idea of what dinosaurs looked like than they used to.
   A good
   B best
   C better
   D more better

4. Sue is the ____ *T. rex* yet discovered.
   A more large
   B most large
   C larger
   D largest

5. She stands in one of the country's ____ natural history museums.
   A finest
   B most finest
   C finer
   D more finer

6. The Field Museum has the ____ dinosaur collection I have ever seen.
   A bestest
   B best
   C good
   D most best

7. The museum has many dinosaurs that are ____ than *T. rex*.
   A smaller
   B smallest
   C more small
   D most small

8. To many kids, dinosaurs are the ____ creatures in the world.
   A fascinatingest
   B fascinatinger
   C most fascinating
   D more fascinating

9. Dinosaurs appear ____ in science fiction than in romance novels.
   A more often
   B most often
   C more oftener
   D most oftenest

10. Which of these two books do you think is ____?
    A excitingest
    B excitinger
    C most exciting
    D more exciting

Home Activity Your child prepared for taking tests on comparative and superlative adjectives. Ask your child to use the correct adjective forms on this page in sentences to compare sets of two objects, then sets of three objects.

Comparative and Superlative Adjectives

Directions If the adjective forms are correct, write *Correct* on the line. If they are not correct, write the comparative and superlative forms correctly on the line.

Adjective	Comparative	Superlative	
1. happy	more happier	most happiest	_____
2. hungry	hungrier	hungriest	_____
3. beloved	beloveder	belovedest	_____
4. sad	more sadder	most saddest	_____

Directions Underline the adjective form in ( ) to complete each sentence correctly.

5. Jules Verne was (most unhappy, most unhappiest) as a stockbroker.

6. He was (happier, more happier) writing plays.

7. However, he was a much (more better, better) novelist than a playwright.

8. He left business and went on to become the (more successful, most successful) writer of his time.

9. He wrote more books than other authors, and they were of (higher, most highest) quality.

10. They were scientifically accurate, but readers found them (entertaininger, more entertaining) than educational.

Directions Write the correct forms of the adjectives in ( ) to complete the sentences.

11. The Earth has three layers. Which layer is _____? (thin)

12. The outer layer, called the crust, is the _____ layer of the three. (rigid)

13. The middle layer, called the mantle, contains melted rock and is much _____ than the crust. (hot)

14. The core, in the Earth's center, is under the _____ pressure of all. (intense)

15. Jules Verne's idea for a journey to the core is _____ than realistic. (fantastic)

Home Activity Your child reviewed comparative and superlative adjectives. Reread the selection with your child. Have him or her describe the fighting monsters using comparative and superlative adjectives.

Grammar and Writing Practice Book

Adverbs

Adverbs tell more about verbs. They explain *how, when,* or *where* actions happen. Many adverbs that tell *how* end in *-ly*. Adverbs can appear before or after the verbs they describe.

How	Cowboys rode <u>expertly</u>. They worked <u>hard</u>.
When	They <u>seldom</u> slept past daybreak. They <u>always</u> took care of their horses.
Where	A cowtown existed <u>here</u>. Cowboys visited <u>there</u> for entertainment.

Some adverbs tell more about an adjective or another adverb:

A ghost town seems <u>rather</u> spooky to me. I <u>very</u> rarely go to such places.

Comparative adverbs compare two actions. Add *-er* to form a comparative adverb. **Superlative adverbs** compare three or more actions. Add *-est* to form a superlative adverb. If an adverb ends in *-ly*, use *more* or *most* instead of *-er* or *-est*.

Comparative Adverb	The stagecoach rolled <u>more slowly</u> going up the mountain than going down.
Superlative Adverb	When they were fresh, the horses pulled <u>most quickly</u> of all.

• The adverbs *well* and *badly* use special forms to show comparison.

Adverb	Comparative	Superlative
well	better	best
badly	worse	worst

Directions Underline the adverb or adverbs in each sentence. Circle the word that each adverb tells more about.

1. Pioneer women bravely risked their lives.

2. They worked tirelessly to feed and clothe their families.

3. They seldom shopped at a store.

4. They were often lonely in their isolated homes.

5. They toiled outdoors in gardens and indoors at wood stoves.

Directions Underline the correct adverb in ( ) to complete each sentence.

6. We can point (proudly, more proudly) at the staying power of pioneers.

7. They lived with hardship (better, more better) than I would have.

8. If crops failed, they faced a (terrible, terribly) hard winter.

9. Towns needed railroads (more desperately, most desperately) than they needed settlers.

10. Railroads connected settlers (direct, directly) to supplies and goods.

School-Home
CONNECTION

Home Activity Your child learned about adverbs. Ask your child to expand these sentences using adverbs to tell how, when, and where: *Settlers traveled. They built homes and towns. They raised food.*

Adverbs

Directions Write an adverb on the line to make each sentence more lively and colorful.

1. The prospector whispered _____, "Can it be?"

2. Then he began to leap and dance _____ around the campsite.

3. The large lump in the pan gleamed _____ in the sunlight.

4. The assayer's report erased his joy _____.

5. The old man limped _____ back to camp.

6. He said _____, "It was only fool's gold."

Directions Imagine you are touring a ghost town in the Old West. Write a paragraph describing how the town looks and what is happening there. Use adverbs to help make your description vivid and colorful.

_____

_____

_____

_____

_____

_____

_____

_____

_____

_____

_____

_____

_____

_____

Home Activity Your child learned how to use adverbs in writing. With your child, make up a story about a cowboy's trip to town. Encourage your child to include adverbs to make actions vivid and precise.

Adverbs

Directions Mark the letter of the word that is an adverb in each sentence.

1. Pete sometimes pretends he is a strong, silent cowboy.
   A sometimes
   B pretends
   C strong
   D silent

2. He practices lassoing fenceposts faithfully.
   A he
   B lassoing
   C fenceposts
   D faithfully

3. He wears a very old ten-gallon hat.
   A ten-gallon
   B a
   C very
   D hat

4. Pete is anxiously waiting for his birthday.
   A Pete
   B anxiously
   C waiting
   D his

5. He has always dreamed of having a horse.
   A always
   B dreamed
   C having
   D horse

Directions Write the letter of the correct answer to each question.

6. Which word or phrase is the comparative form of the adverb *quickly*?
   A quicklier
   B quickliest
   C more quickly
   D most quickly

7. Which word or phrase is the superlative form of the adverb *badly*?
   A worse
   B worst
   C more badly
   D most badly

8. Which word is an adverb that tells when an action occurred?
   A downtown
   B slowly
   C easily
   D never

Home Activity Your child prepared for taking tests on adverbs. Have your child read a favorite story aloud, point out the adverbs, and tell what words they describe. Encourage your child to add adverbs to the story.

Adverbs

Directions Write the comparative and superlative forms of each adverb.

Adverb	Comparative Adverb	Superlative Adverb
fast	1. _____	2. _____
hard	3. _____	4. _____
eagerly	5. _____	6. _____
badly	7. _____	8. _____

Directions Underline the adverb in each sentence. Circle the word or words that each adverb tells more about.

9. The man looked extremely nervous.

10. He waited impatiently for the stage.

11. It seemed as though it would never arrive.

12. Finally, he heard a storm of hooves.

13. The dusty stage rolled westward toward town.

14. The man greeted his bride warmly.

Directions Underline the correct adverb in ( ) to complete each sentence.

15. California was settled (sooner, more sooner) than many Western states.

16. The promise of gold (first, firstly) drew miners and settlers.

17. Good climate and fertile land held them there (more successfully, most successfully) though.

18. Nevada treated its settlers (harshlier, more harshly) than California.

19. When the silver ran out, miners (quickly, most quickly) left Nevada's hot, dry territory.

Home Activity Your child reviewed adverbs. Have your child clip adjectives from magazine advertisements, change them into adverbs, write the comparative and superlative form of each adverb, and use both forms in sentences.

100 Unit 5 Week 5

Grammar and Writing Practice Book

Modifiers

Adjectives, adverbs, and prepositional phrases are **modifiers**, words or groups of words that tell more about, or modify, other words in a sentence. Adjectives modify nouns and pronouns. Adverbs modify verbs, adjectives, or other adverbs. Prepositional phrases can act as adjectives or adverbs.

As Adjective   The caterpillar with yellow stripes is beautiful.
As Adverb   It crawls across the branch.

To avoid confusion, place modifiers close to the words they modify. Adjective phrases usually come right after the word they modify. Adverb phrases may appear right after a verb or at the beginning of a sentence.

The meaning of a sentence can be unclear if the modifier is misplaced.

  No: The butterflies flew by the girls with bright orange wings.
  Yes: The butterflies with bright orange wings flew by the girls.

The position of *only* in a sentence can affect the sentence's entire meaning. Place *only* directly before the word or words it modifies.

Example: Only he watches the caterpillar. (Nobody else watches it.)
He only watches the caterpillar. (He doesn't do anything except watch.)
He watches only the caterpillar. (He doesn't watch anything else.)

Directions Write *adverb, adjective,* or *prepositional phrase* to identify each underlined modifier. Write *adjective* or *adverb* to identify how a prepositional phrase is used.

 1. This caterpillar stays in a jar. _____

 2. The fuzzy caterpillar will soon become a butterfly. _____

 3. The butterfly will fly outside in the fresh air. _____

Directions Each sentence has a misplaced modifier. Rewrite the sentence and put the phrase where it belongs.

 4. A caterpillar caught the boy's eye with bright red spots.

 _____

 _____

 5. He took the caterpillar off the tree with a smile.

 _____

 _____

Home Activity Your child learned about modifiers. With your child, read a newspaper article. Ask your child to identify several modifiers, including adjectives, adverbs, and prepositional phrases.

Modifiers

Directions Add adjectives, adverbs, and prepositional phrases to these sentences. Use modifiers to create a more specific, interesting picture.

1. The branches held insects.

_____

_____

2. A caterpillar crawled.

_____

_____

3. The creature changed.

_____

_____

4. The butterfly flew.

_____

_____

Directions Imagine you find something interesting in a tree. Write a description of what you find and how you find it. Use modifiers to create a vivid word picture.

_____

_____

_____

_____

_____

_____

_____

Home Activity Your child learned how to use modifiers in writing. Give your child simple sentences such as those in items 1–4 on this page and have him or her add modifiers to make interesting story starters.

Grammar and Writing Practice Book

Modifiers

Directions Mark the letter of the item that correctly identifies the underlined word or words in each sentence.

1. Dad found caterpillars <u>in his rose bush</u>.
   - **A** adjective
   - **B** adverb
   - **C** prepositional phrase/adjective
   - **D** prepositional phrase/adverb

2. The <u>soft</u> caterpillars interested me.
   - **A** adjective
   - **B** adverb
   - **C** prepositional phrase/adjective
   - **D** prepositional phrase/adverb

3. I <u>quickly</u> gathered leaves and twigs.
   - **A** adjective
   - **B** adverb
   - **C** prepositional phrase/adjective
   - **D** prepositional phrase/adverb

4. I put a lid <u>with several holes</u> on a jar.
   - **A** adjective
   - **B** adverb
   - **C** prepositional phrase/adjective
   - **D** prepositional phrase/adverb

5. Soon, butterflies flew <u>out of the jar</u>.
   - **A** adjective
   - **B** adverb
   - **C** prepositional phrase/adjective
   - **D** prepositional phrase/adverb

6. They had wings <u>with brilliant colors</u>.
   - **A** adjective
   - **B** adverb
   - **C** prepositional phrase/adjective
   - **D** prepositional phrase/adverb

Directions Mark the letter of the sentence that has a misplaced modifier.

7. **A** One morning I looked at an oak tree.
   B I saw a creature on a leaf with many legs.
   C Its colors blended with the brown leaf.
   D I studied the caterpillar for only a minute.

8. **A** We saw trees full of butterflies.
   B The butterflies went from tree to tree.
   C They migrated to the trees from Canada.
   D The butterflies have marks on their wings.

Home Activity Your child practiced for taking tests on modifiers. Copy a paragraph from one of your child's favorite stories, leaving blanks where modifiers go. Ask your child to suggest possible modifiers for the blanks. Compare with the original.

Modifiers

Directions Underline the prepositional phrase in each sentence. Write *adverb* or *adjective* to identify how the prepositional phrase is used.

1. We observed some insects with red eyes. _____

2. Up the glass crept a graceful brown spider. _____

3. A firefly flashed its light across the dim room. _____

4. The ladybug had four black spots on its back. _____

5. We saw a bee with a long stinger. _____

6. A black fly buzzed around the jar. _____

Directions Underline the adjectives, adverbs, and prepositional phrases in each sentence. The number in ( ) tells how many modifiers a sentence contains. (Do not underline the articles *a* and *the*.)

7. The scientist has several unusual butterflies in her collection. (3)

8. There is a huge black swallowtail from Africa. (3)

9. In the spring, she found a bright blue butterfly on a flower. (4)

10. She carefully preserves the rare insects. (2)

11. Delicate butterflies add beauty and color to the world. (2)

Directions Underline the misplaced modifier in each sentence. Rewrite the sentence, and put the modifier where it belongs.

12. He only collects Monarch butterflies—nothing else.

_____

_____

13. She saw a rare copper butterfly resting with her binoculars.

_____

_____

14. The butterflies amazed the students with their intricately patterned wings.

_____

_____

Home Activity Your child reviewed modifiers. Have your child use a magazine article or story to show you good examples of adjectives, adverbs, and prepositional phrases that make the writing specific and interesting.

Conjunctions

A conjunction is a word such as *and, but,* or *or* that joins words, phrases, and sentences.

- Use *and* to join related ideas: The snowy owl <u>and</u> snow bunting are arctic birds.
- Use *but* to join contrasting ideas: I like the snow <u>but</u> not the cold.
- Use *or* to suggest a choice: Is that a ringed seal <u>or</u> a hooded seal?

You can use conjunctions to make compound subjects, compound predicates, and compound sentences. Place a comma before the conjunction in a compound sentence.

Compound Subject   Frigid cold <u>and</u> deep snow make arctic life difficult.
Compound Predicate   Arctic foxes do not hibernate <u>but</u> withstand the cold.
Compound Sentence   They feed on live prey, <u>or</u> they can eat remains of a polar bear's meal.

Directions Underline the conjunction(s) in each sentence.

1. The arctic fox makes a burrow in a hill or cliff, but it does not hibernate.

2. It is well adapted for the cold with its furry feet and small, rounded ears.

3. A polar bear is huge but surprisingly fast and can outrun a caribou.

Directions Underline the conjunction in ( ) that completes each sentence.

4. The tundra has very little moisture (or, and) a short growing season.

5. The climate is harsh, (or, but) more than 1,700 kinds of plants live in the Arctic.

Directions Use the conjunction *and, but,* or *or* to join each pair of sentences. Write the new sentences. Remember to add a comma.

6. The Arctic is frigid in winter. It is much warmer in summer.

_____

_____

7. Arctic plants must grow quickly. They won't have time to reproduce.

_____

_____

Home Activity Your child learned about conjunctions. Have your child write *and, but,* and *or* on index cards and then read a short article, making a tally mark on the appropriate card each time he or she sees that conjunction.

Conjunctions

Directions Write a conjunction on each line to complete the paragraph.

(1) The island features spectacular cliffs _____ volcanic mountains. (2) That odd seabird you observed might be a petrel _____ a fulmar. (3) The climate is extremely cold, _____ many birds are able to live here. (4) They build their nests in the cliffs _____ raise their young. (5) Birds can breed on the island, _____ they need not stay all year. (6) Some birds migrate to warmer winter headquarters, _____ others build up an insulating layer of fat. (7) One bird you are sure to see is McKay's bunting, which breeds here _____ nowhere else.

Directions Combine the short sentences to make one longer, smoother sentence. Use conjunctions. Write the new sentence.

8. In 1944, voles lived on St. Matthew Island. So did arctic foxes.

_____

_____

_____

_____

9. The Coast Guard introduced 24 female reindeer to the island. They also introduced 5 males.

_____

_____

_____

_____

10. Years before there were reindeer everywhere. Now only a few remained.

_____

_____

_____

_____

Home Activity Your child learned how to use conjunctions in writing. Have your child read about reindeer and write simple sentences about them. Ask your child to find ways to combine some of the related sentences.

Conjunctions

Directions Mark the letter of the word that best completes each sentence.

1. Which is bigger: a reindeer _____ an elk?
   A however
   B also
   C but
   D or

2. Reptiles _____ amphibians do not live in the Arctic.
   A and
   B if
   C because
   D but

3. It is too cold _____ dry for them there.
   A but
   B and
   C or
   D however

4. Female reindeer do have antlers, _____ males have much larger ones.
   A anyway
   B if
   C but
   D or

5. Did the reindeer die of disease _____ hunger?
   A because
   B also
   C but
   D or

6. Some of the deer survived, _____ most of them starved.
   A but
   B or
   C and
   D because

7. Forty-one females _____ one male were alive.
   A so
   B and
   C but
   D when

8. They did not produce young, _____ the herd soon died out.
   A and
   B or
   C until
   D but

9. This is an unfortunate _____ predictable story.
   A for
   B or
   C but
   D because

10. The island had too little space _____ not enough predators.
    A until
    B and
    C when
    D but

Home Activity Your child prepared for taking tests on conjunctions. Have your child find and circle *and, but,* and *or* in ads. Ask your child to explain why each word is used.

Conjunctions

Directions Underline the conjunction in each sentence.

1. Birds and small mammals live on the island.

2. Did a fox or a rabbit make that nest?

3. Count the animals on the island, and we will make a chart.

4. You can count them but cannot determine their sex.

5. We will find out what happened or guess the cause of the die-off.

Directions Underline the conjunction in ( ) that completes each sentence.

6. Nature holds many mysteries, (and, or) scientists want to solve them.

7. Scientists use logic and scientific method, (or, but) imagination is also important.

8. Dr. David Klein had to count (and, or) also weigh reindeer on St. Matthew Island.

9. He knew the reindeer were not killed by diseases (but, or) parasites.

10. Low weight (or, and) missing bone marrow suggested the deer had starved.

Directions Use the conjunction *and, but,* or *or* to join each pair of sentences. Write the new sentences. Remember to add a comma.

11. Polar mammals have fur and fat to keep them warm. People have to dress warmly.

_____

_____

_____

_____

12. Layers of clothing trap warm air next to the skin. This keeps people warm in cold weather.

_____

_____

_____

_____

Home Activity Your child reviewed conjunctions. With your child, make a favorite food. Ask your child to talk about the process, using the conjunctions *and, but,* and *or* to describe actions and choices in the process.

Grammar and Writing Practice Book

Commas

Commas can clarify meaning and tell readers when to pause.

- Put a comma after every item in a *series* but the last.
  Poets pay attention to the sounds, meanings, and emotions of words.
  The audience applauded, cheered, and stood up.

- When you speak or write to someone, you may use the person's name or title. This noun of *direct address* is set off with a comma, or two commas if it is in the middle of a sentence.
  Will you read some more, Mr. Berry?
  I'd love to, children, if you aren't tired of sitting.

- *Appositives* are noun phrases that describe another noun. They are set off by commas.
  Ted Kooser, a wonderful poet, lives in Nebraska.

- Put a comma after an *introductory word or phrase,* such as *yes, no, well, of course,* or *in fact.*
  No, I haven't read the new book. As usual, I'm too busy.

Directions Add commas to each sentence where they are needed.

1. Harry enjoys writing stories poems and articles.

2. Voni do you prefer reading fairy tales tall tales or myths?

3. *King Midas* a myth about values features a greedy king.

4. Were you surprised Kaela when the glowing young man appeared?

5. No I expect magical things to happen in tales.

6. King Midas's gift is deadly because he cannot eat drink or touch people.

Directions Rewrite each sentence. Add commas where they are needed.

7. By the way King Midas what did you learn about gold?

_____

_____

8. I learned that gold is cold hard and meaningless by itself.

_____

_____

Home Activity Your child learned about commas. Record a short conversation with your child about his or her favorite foods or activities. Ask your child to write the conversation adding commas where they are needed.

Commas

Directions Add commas in the sentences to make the meaning clear. Rewrite the paragraph.

(1) Some things are necessities items we could not live without. (2) Food water and shelter fit in this category. (3) What more do we need dear reader to live and be happy? (4) Many people believe they would be happy if only they had lots of money possessions and free time. (5) In fact people's real needs are quite different. (6) The happiest people are those who have good health loving relationships and useful work.

_____

_____

_____

_____

_____

_____

_____

_____

Directions Write sentences to answer each question. Use commas to set off words in a series, appositives, words of direct address, and introductory words.

7. What are three possessions that are precious to you?

_____

_____

8. Explain why one of these objects is important to you. Address your sentences to a friend.

_____

_____

_____

Home Activity Your child learned how to use commas in writing. With your child, read a story or article. Have your child point out commas that are used to set off series, appositives, introductory words, and nouns of direct address.

Commas

Directions Mark the letter of the choice that tells why commas are used in each sentence.

1. The king ate porridge, toast, and jam.
   A series
   B appositive
   C introductory word
   D direct address

2. Dad, do you know this story?
   A series
   B appositive
   C introductory word
   D direct address

3. This story is a myth, a kind of story.
   A series
   B appositive
   C introductory word
   D direct address

4. Yes, it has a happy ending.
   A series
   B appositive
   C introductory word
   D direct address

Directions Mark the letter of the choice that shows the word or words and punctuation needed to complete each sentence correctly.

5. A king's castle had a drawbridge, ____ lookout towers.
   A a moat and
   B a moat and,
   C a moat, and
   D a moat, and,

6. Look at this picture ____ Cate.
   A of, a castle,
   B of a castle,
   C of a castle
   D of a castle;

7. Medieval castles were ____ homes.
   A fortresses gathering places and
   B fortresses, gathering places and,
   C fortresses, gathering places and
   D fortresses, gathering places, and

8. ____ have you ever seen a castle?
   A Henry,
   B Henry
   C Henry;
   D , Henry

9. ____ castles sat on a hilltop and had high stone walls.
   A Usually,
   B Usually
   C Usually;
   D Usually.

10. Castles were designed as ____ attack.
    A fortresses; strongholds against
    B fortresses. Strongholds against
    C fortresses, strongholds against
    D fortresses strongholds against

11. A castle usually had a ____ around it.
    A moat; a water-filled ditch;
    B moat, a water-filled ditch,
    C moat. A water-filled ditch
    D moat a water -filled ditch

12. ____ a moat did not always have water in it.
    A No,
    B No;
    C No
    D No.

Home Activity Your child prepared for taking tests on commas. Ask your child to give example sentences to teach you about the four uses of commas he or she learned.

Name _____

Commas

Directions Add commas to each sentence where they are needed.

1. Many tales involve kingdoms magic creatures and wishes.

2. Have you noticed Danny that humans always seem to use these wishes foolishly?

3. Yes tales also often have a young person as the hero.

4. Tales usually have a talking animal stone or tree.

5. One tale featured Excalibur a sword with a mind of its own.

6. Mr. Wickness our reading teacher said we could write a tale a mystery or a poem.

Directions Rewrite each sentence. Add commas where they are needed.

7. Gold has been used for centuries to make coins jewelry and accessories.

_____

_____

8. Can you tell me Mr. Liakos if the king's crown is made of gold?

_____

_____

9. Yes it is made of gold and inset with precious gems.

_____

_____

10. Both crown and scepter a staff symbolizing the king's power were made of valuable materials.

_____

_____

11. In fact the scepter has more diamonds on it than the crown does.

_____

_____

Home Activity Your child reviewed commas. Ask your child to write an imaginary conversation between two friends about their favorite things. Have your child highlight the commas in another color.

Grammar and Writing Practice Book

Quotations and Quotation Marks

A **direct quotation** gives a person's exact words and is enclosed in **quotation marks** (" "). Direct quotations begin with capital letters and end with proper punctuation. End punctuation is inside the closing quotation marks. Words that tell who is speaking are set off from the quotation by punctuation.

- When the quotation comes last in a sentence, set it off with a comma.
    Jamie asked**,** "What was the *Hindenburg?*"

- When the quotation comes first in a sentence, a comma, question mark, or exclamation mark sets off the quotation.
    "It was a dirigible**,**" replied May. "It was enormous!" she added.

- When the quotation is interrupted by words that tell who is speaking, use two sets of quotation marks. Notice that words telling who is speaking are followed by punctuation. Use a comma if the second part of the quotation does not begin a new sentence.
    "Dirigibles were lighter than air**,**" he added**,** "because they were filled with hydrogen."

- Use end punctuation and a capital letter if the second part of the quotation does begin a new sentence.
    "Isn't hydrogen flammable?" asked Jamie. "What kept it from exploding?"

Directions Rewrite each sentence. Add quotation marks where they are needed.

1. Are the blimps dirigibles? asked Max.

_____

2. No, they aren't, explained Vi, because they aren't rigid.

_____

_____

Directions Write each sentence correctly. Add capital letters, quotation marks, and other punctuation as needed.

3. Vi said the framework is like a skeleton

_____

4. fabric covers it she added like skin

_____

Home Activity Your child learned about quotations and quotation marks. With your child, find quotations in a newspaper or magazine article. Have your child highlight the quotation marks and other punctuation and explain why they are used.

Quotations and Quotation Marks

Directions Choose a sentence from the box that supports the ideas in each paragraph. Write the sentence, adding quotation marks and correct punctuation.

> A radio announcer moaned over the airwaves Oh, the humanity!
>
> Modern airships are generally known only as flying billboards one expert says.
>
> As airship historian R. D. Layman explains A balloon cannot be piloted in any sense of the word.

1. The hot air balloon and airship differ in important ways. An airship is powered by a motor and propellers, but a balloon is not. An airship's horizontal path can be controlled, but a balloon's cannot. A balloon can be raised or lowered by adjusting the propane burner that heats the air inside it. However, it goes wherever the wind takes it.

_____

_____

2. The burning of the *Hindenburg* on May 6, 1937, is the most famous airship disaster. The spectacular accident was witnessed by many and actually covered on the air. It turned the public away from airships. They watched as the enormous fireball plummeted from the sky and people lost their lives. One cry in particular spoke for the American public.

_____

_____

Directions Do you think airship travel should have been abandoned or continued? On another sheet of paper, write a paragraph to persuade readers that your opinion is correct. Use quotations from *The Hindenburg* to support your argument. Use quotation marks and punctuation to set off your quotations correctly.

_____

_____

_____

_____

_____

_____

Home Activity Your child learned how to use quotations and quotation marks in writing. With your child, write dialogue for characters in a story about flying. Have your child punctuate the dialogue correctly.

Grammar and Writing Practice Book

Quotations and Quotation Marks

Directions Mark the letter of the item that completes each sentence correctly.

1. "I'm going on a hot-air balloon ____ said Sherry.
   A ride"
   B ride."
   C ride,"
   D ride?"

2. "Wow! That's so ____ exclaimed Phil.
   A cool"
   B cool!"
   C cool."
   D cool?"

3. He asked ____ you think I could come too?"
   A earnestly, "Do
   B earnestly "Do
   C earnestly "do
   D earnestly. "Do

4. "I'll ask my ____ Sherry said.
   A dad."
   B dad,"
   C dad"
   D dad?"

5. "What is it ____ inquired Phil.
   A like,"
   B like."
   C like?,"
   D like?"

6. She replied ____ like floating on a cloud."
   A dreamily, "it's
   B dreamily. "It's
   C dreamily, "It's
   D dreamily "It's

7. "The buildings and cars below look like ____ continued.
   A toys," she
   B toys," She
   C toys" she
   D toys." She

8. "How do you make it go up and ____ Phil.
   A down? asked
   B down," asked
   C down?" asked
   D down?" Asked

9. "A burner heats the ____ Sherry.
   A air, explained
   B air," Explained
   C air" explained
   D air," explained

10. "More hot air takes you ____ less takes you down."
    A up," she said. "and"
    B up," She said, "And
    C up," she said, "and
    D up." she said. "And

Home Activity Your child prepared for taking tests on quotations and quotation marks. Have your child interview you about your day and write your reply as a quotation, beginning with *He/She said* and using quotation marks correctly.

Quotations and Quotation Marks

Directions Rewrite each sentence. Add quotation marks where they are needed.

1. Tell us about blimps, requested Sean.

_____

2. What do you want to know? asked the museum guide.

_____

_____

3. Sean asked Do they have a framework inside to give them shape?

_____

_____

4. They do not, replied the guide. They get their shape from the gas inside them.

_____

_____

Directions Write each sentence correctly. Add capital letters, quotation marks, and other punctuation as needed.

5. Blimps are filled with helium he continued

_____

6. how are they used asked Sean

_____

7. the military has used blimps he replied to learn where land mines are located

_____

_____

8. some companies use them for advertising he continued and for aerial views of sports events

_____

_____

Home Activity Your child reviewed quotations and quotation marks. Ask your child to write sentences about the *Hindenburg* and include dialogue. Remind your child to use quotation marks and other punctuation correctly.

Punctuation

You have already learned about punctuation such as commas, quotation marks, and end marks. Here are some other kinds of punctuation.

- A **colon** (:) is used to introduce a list of items. It is also used to separate hours and minutes in expressions of time. In addition, it is used after the salutation in a business letter.
    Use these ingredients: two eggs, one cup of flour, and a stick of butter.
    10:30 A.M.   9:15 P.M.   Dear Ms. Glover: Sir:

- A **hyphen** (-) is used in some compound words. Two common uses are numbers from twenty-one to ninety-nine and compound words that are thought of as one word.
    old-time music   best-known book   forty-nine   five-year-old boy

- A **semicolon** (;) can be used to join two independent clauses instead of a comma and a conjunction.
    Jazz is a mixture of different types of music; New Orleans was its birthplace.

- **Italics** or **underlining** is used for titles of books, newspapers, magazines, and works of art. Because you cannot write italics, underline titles in your writing.
    the *Chicago Tribune* (newspaper)   *Time for Kids* (magazine)
    or   the Chicago Tribune   Time for Kids

- A **dash** (—) sets off information or a comment that interrupts the flow of a sentence.
    Jazz had developed many styles—bebop and Dixieland, for example—by the 1940s.

Directions Rewrite each sentence on the lines. Add punctuation where it is needed.

1. Jinny is writing a how to book titled You Can Do Most Anything.

_____

_____

2. The first show is at 800 P.M. the second is at 1030 P.M.

_____

_____

3. Cuthbert we call him Chip is my best friend.

_____

4. Mae made a last minute effort to learn twenty two songs.

_____

Home Activity Your child learned about punctuation. Have your child explain and model a use for colons and semicolons.

Punctuation

Directions Add the punctuation named in ( ) to make the meaning of the sentence clear. Write the sentence.

1. These woodwind instruments are reed instruments clarinet, saxophone, bassoon, English horn, and oboe. (colon)

   _____

   _____

2. Woodwinds were once made of wood now they are also made of other materials. (semicolon)

   _____

   _____

3. The after school program will show the movie The Music Man at 300 P.M. (hyphen, underlining, colon)

   _____

   _____

Directions Add punctuation to the following paragraph to make it clear. Rewrite the paragraph.

   The clarinet is a single reed woodwind instrument. Its thin, flat reed is attached to the mouthpiece. The clarinet player takes the mouthpiece in her mouth and blows then the reed vibrates against the mouthpiece. Vibrating air is pushed through the straight, tube shaped instrument. Fingers press keys to open and close holes. A good clarinet player that's not me yet can make a wide range of smooth sounds.

   _____

   _____

   _____

   _____

   _____

   _____

   _____

Home Activity Your child learned how to use punctuation in writing. With your child, write a letter to a music store asking about a special CD. Be sure your child includes appropriate punctuation marks.

Grammar and Writing Practice Book

Punctuation

Directions Mark the name of the punctuation mark that matches the definition.

1. Used to join two independent clauses
   A colon
   B dash
   C semicolon
   D hyphen

2. Used to set off information that interrupts a sentence
   A italics or underlining
   B dash
   C colon
   D semicolon

3. Used in some compound words
   A italics or underlining
   B colon
   C semicolon
   D hyphen

4. Used to separate hours and minutes in expressions of time
   A colon
   B semicolon
   C dash
   D hyphen

Directions Mark the choice that correctly completes each sentence.

5. The letter began "Dear Mr. _____ I have been a fan of yours for years."
   A Benny:
   B Benny,
   C Benny!
   D Benny—

6. "I read an article about you in _____ magazine."
   A Fanfare
   B *Fanfare*
   C —Fanfare—
   D : Fanfare:

7. The band played from _____.
   A 715 to 800 P.M.
   B 715: to 800: P.M.
   C 7:15 to 8:00 P.M.
   D 715—800 P.M.

8. Kids can sign up for band in sixth _____ wait to join!
   A grade? I can't
   B grade, I can't
   C grade; I can't
   D grade-I can't

9. Thursday _____ is sign-up day.
   A , that's today,
   B ; that's today;
   C -that's today-
   D —that's today—

10. The band has _____ members.
    A fiftyone
    B fifty-one
    C fifty:one
    D fifty one

Home Activity Your child prepared for taking tests on punctuation. Have your child make index cards for the colon, semicolon, dash, hyphen, and italics and then search books and magazines for examples of the use of each mark.

Punctuation

Directions Match the punctuation mark with the correct description.

_____ **1.** colon (:) **A** used to set off material that interrupts

_____ **2.** semicolon (;) **B** used in some compound words

_____ **3.** dash (—) **C** used after the salutation of a business letter

_____ **4.** italics (*Big*) **D** used to join two independent clauses

_____ **5.** hyphen (-) **E** used to indicate titles

Directions Rewrite each sentence. Add the missing punctuation marks.

6. Troy doesn't like the old fashioned music that WDQB plays from 1030 to midnight.

_____

_____

7. I began my letter, "Dear Sir Please cancel my subscription to Music Classics."

_____

_____

8. Aunt Kay plays guitar have you heard her? like a pro.

_____

_____

9. She owns several instruments a guitar, a banjo, and a piano.

_____

_____

10. She thought I was mature for a ten year old kid she even taught me to play some chords.

_____

_____

Home Activity Your child reviewed punctuation. Have your child make a list of favorite books and magazines with correct underlining.

Grammar
Cumulative Review

Four Kinds of Sentences and Interjections

Directions Write *D* if the sentence is declarative. Write *IN* if the sentence is interrogative. Write *IM* if the sentence is imperative. Write *E* if the sentence is exclamatory.

1. Keesha's family took a kayak trip in Alaska. _____

2. How do you make a kayak go? _____

3. A kayaker uses a long paddle. _____

4. Please find out who invented kayaks. _____

5. Eskimos used kayaks thousands of years ago. _____

6. Eskimo kayaks were made of sealskins. _____

7. A kayak weighs as little as 32 pounds. _____

8. Wow, that is really light! _____

9. Can you ride a kayak in rapids? _____

10. Kayaking is so much fun! _____

Directions Complete each sentence with words from the box. Then write *D, IN, IM,* or *E* to identify the kind of sentence.

can participate in races.   kayaking can be dangerous?

include kayak races.   me how to kayak.

exciting the rapids are!

11. Don't you think _____

_____

12. Good kayakers _____

_____

13. How _____

_____

14. Please teach _____

_____

15. The Olympic Games _____

_____

Simple and Complete Subjects and Predicates

Directions Draw a line between the complete subject and the complete predicate in each sentence. Circle the simple subject and the simple predicate.

1. Many useful tools are made from metal.

2. Steel is an important metal for buildings and tools.

3. This alloy contains a mixture of iron and carbon.

4. An iron bar will rust over time.

5. Oxygen from the air mixes with the metal.

6. That orange deposit on the outside surface is called rust.

7. Many ranchers mend fences regularly.

Directions Underline each simple subject once. Underline each simple predicate twice.

8. The shiny thin wires are stretched from post to post.

9. Someone hammers the wire to the post.

10. The wooden posts stretch off in a straight line.

11. This job is certainly hard work.

12. A work crew will repair the old fence today.

Directions Write *F* after a fragment. Write *R* after a run-on. Write *S* after a complete sentence.

13. Has been replaced by plastic in many products. _____

14. Plastic is hard and durable at the same time, it is lighter than metal. _____

15. Many parts of today's trucks and automobiles. _____

16. Plastic is not only lighter than metal it is cheaper too. _____

17. Just think about all the uses for plastic! _____

18. Many new materials from recycled products. _____

Independent and Dependent Clauses

Direction Write *I* if the underlined group of words is an independent clause. Write *D* if it is a dependent clause.

1. <u>We visited the seashore</u> when we went to California. _____

2. <u>After we walked on the beach,</u> we swam in the ocean. _____

3. Although the sun was warm, <u>I shivered with cold.</u> _____

4. The water seemed even colder <u>because our skin was hot.</u> _____

5. <u>If you look far out,</u> you can see dolphins swimming. _____

6. <u>They leap out of the water</u> as if they are playing. _____

7. While I was resting on the sand, <u>I spied something.</u> _____

8. <u>When I looked through binoculars,</u> I saw they were seals. _____

9. As I watched, <u>some of them slid into the water.</u> _____

10. <u>Since I saw them,</u> I have read more about seals. _____

Directions Complete each sentence by adding a clause from the box. Underline the dependent clause in each sentence.

> it is the exception to the rule   while a seal has none   it can weigh up to 8,800 pounds
> because walruses are usually much bigger   you will remember it

11. You can tell a walrus and a seal apart _____

    _____

12. In addition, a walrus has two large ivory tusks _____

    _____

13. Because an elephant seal can grow very large, _____

    _____

14. If you run into an elephant seal, _____

    _____

15. When a male elephant seal is full grown, _____

    _____

Grammar and Writing Practice Book

Compound and Complex Sentences

Directions Write *compound* if the sentence is a compound sentence. Write *complex* if the sentence is a complex sentence.

1. Great athletes seem superhuman, but they often begin humbly. _____

2. After they learned the basics, they practiced hard.   _____

3. If they had failures, they did not give up.   _____

4. They kept at it for years, and they improved.   _____

Directions Combine the pairs of simple sentences using the conjunction in ( ). Write the compound sentence on the line.

5. I like swimming. My dad coaches track. (but)

_____

6. I can jump like a rabbit. I can run like a racehorse. (and)

_____

7. I could choose one sport. I could do both. (or)

_____

8. According to Mom, I should decide. She is usually right. (and)

_____

Directions Write the word in ( ) that best connects the clauses. Underline the dependent clause in the complex sentence.

9. The players are tired _____ they have played two games. (because, if)

10. _____ they finish their games, they sleep on the bus. (Although, After)

11. They may travel for hours _____ they reach the next town. (before, since)

12. The driver will not wake them _____ the bus gets to the hotel. (after, until)

Common and Proper Nouns

Directions Write the proper noun from the box that matches each common noun. Add capital letters where they are needed.

> empire state building   mount everest   aunt lucinda
> *the dark is rising*   ms. simpson

Common Noun	Proper Noun
1. teacher	_____
2. building	_____
3. mountain	_____
4. book	_____
5. relative	_____

Directions Rewrite each sentence. Capitalize all proper nouns.

6. Americans in new york and pennsylvania had good train service.

_____

_____

7. People in san francisco and other parts of california needed better transportation.

_____

_____

8. Some workers from china were led by mr. charles crocker.

_____

_____

9. The eastern and western tracks were joined in promontory, utah, on may 10, 1869.

_____

_____

10. The tracks met near aunt joan's house: 491 e. 1st st., ogden, ut 84404.

_____

_____

Regular and Irregular Plural Nouns

Directions Write the plural form of each noun.

1. guess _____

2. cocoon _____

3. ax _____

4. branch _____

5. boy _____

6. story _____

7. life _____

8. mouse _____

9. foot _____

10. jacket _____

Directions Underline the plural nouns in each sentence.

11. There are many kinds of beaches in our fifty states.

12. Some shores are packed with shops, restaurants, and hotels.

13. Some are friendly spaces, popular among families with children.

14. In other areas, fishermen catch trout, salmon, and other fish.

15. People can swim in the waves or collect seashells at the beach.

Directions Cross out each incorrectly spelled plural noun. Write the correct spelling above the word you crossed out.

16. In autumn, bushes with red leafs and berrys grow near the sand dunes.

17. Foxs, deers, and wolves are spotted on the sand.

18. Several men and woman relax on benchs near the water.

Possessive Nouns

Directions Write the possessive form of each underlined noun.

1. <u>mother</u> advice   _____

2. <u>survivor</u> story   _____

3. <u>child</u> toy   _____

4. <u>man</u> overcoat   _____

5. <u>monument</u> history   _____

6. <u>mothers</u> lessons   _____

7. <u>survivors</u> groups   _____

8. <u>children</u> books   _____

9. <u>men</u> clothing   _____

10. <u>monuments</u> construction _____

Directions Rewrite each sentence. Write the possessive form of the underlined noun.

11. A box is tucked away in my <u>grandfather</u> closet.

_____

12. It contains a <u>soldier</u> memories of service.

_____

13. Several <u>pictures</u> edges are worn and crumpled.

_____

14. In those pictures, the young <u>men</u> faces are handsome and smiling.

_____

_____

15. Grandpa treasures his war <u>friends</u> letters and visits.

_____

_____

Action and Linking Verbs

Directions Underline the verb in each sentence. Write *A* if it is an action verb. Write *L* if it is a linking verb.

1. Myths and tales often seem true. _____

2. They are important to each civilization. _____

3. Myths address basic human questions. _____

4. Myths are part of every culture. _____

5. Animals often play a role in myths and tales. _____

6. These animals speak like people. _____

7. Their actions are clever. _____

8. Early civilizations understood the value of myths. _____

9. They sought answers around them. _____

10. Today science, not stories, explains the world. _____

Directions Write a verb from the box to complete each sentence. On the line after the sentence, write *A* if the verb is an action verb. Write *L* if it is a linking verb.

brought	tells	was	cause
seems	honored	frightened	were

11. Early people _____ spirits. _____

12. Good and evil spirits _____ all around them. _____

13. Offerings _____ the goodwill of spirits. _____

14. Scary masks _____ away evil spirits. _____

15. Sickness _____ a sign of evil spirits. _____

16. Now this idea _____ quaint to us. _____

17. Germs, not spirits, _____ sickness. _____

18. Science _____ us this fact. _____

Main and Helping Verbs

Directions Find the verb phrase in each sentence. Underline the helping verb. Circle the main verb.

1. A new animal shelter has opened in our town.

2. It will provide a temporary home for lost animals.

3. Many pets are abandoned by their owners.

4. The lucky ones are taken to the shelter.

5. They will be fed.

6. They will be treated by a veterinarian.

7. However, these animals should have homes.

8. They have done nothing wrong.

9. Pet owners should take responsibility.

10. Your pets are depending on you.

Directions Underline the verb phrase in each sentence. Write *Present* or *Past* to tell the time of the action.

11. American bison have lived in North America for thousands of years. _____

12. These huge animals are also known as buffalo. _____

13. Millions of them had long roamed on the Great Plains. _____

14. In the 1800s, they were hunted mercilessly. _____

15. Almost all of the buffalo were killed for sport. _____

16. Cattle ranchers also were invading their grazing land. _____

17. The last few hundred bison were protected by law in 1905. _____

18. Today thousands are roaming in parks and refuges. _____

19. You can see these amazing animals. _____

20. With people's help, the buffalo has survived. _____

Subject-Verb Agreement

Directions Underline the verb in ( ) that agrees with the subject of each sentence.

1. Today horses (is, are) no longer needed for transportation.

2. We (use, uses) them to ride for pleasure.

3. Some horse lovers (buy, buys) horses of their own.

4. Food and equipment (become, becomes) expensive.

5. Martin (take, takes) riding lessons at a stable.

6. He (enjoy, enjoys) a horse without the responsibilities of ownership.

7. A saddle and bridle (cost, costs) quite a bit.

8. Our family (do, does) not have the land to keep a horse.

9. A dude ranch (offer, offers) accommodations with horse riding privileges.

10. Guests (stay, stays) in a bunkhouse.

Directions Add a verb to complete each sentence. Be sure the verb agrees with the subject.

11. Paul Revere's horse _____ the ground impatiently.

12. Redcoats _____ the river under cover of night.

13. Two lights _____ from the church tower.

14. The man and horse _____ away on their journey.

15. A little moonlight _____ through the clouds.

16. A warning cry _____ out in the night.

17. As the sun rises, farmers _____ their muskets.

18. They _____ for independence.

19. The fighting _____ fierce.

20. The colonial militia _____ the redcoats.

Past, Present, and Future Tenses

Directions Write the correct present, past, and future tense of each verb.

Verb	Present	Past	Future
1. spy	He _____.	He _____.	He _____.
2. have	I _____.	I _____.	I _____.
3. trap	You _____.	You _____.	You _____.
4. think	She _____.	She _____.	She _____.
5. eat	They _____.	They _____.	They _____.

Directions Identify the tense of each underlined verb. Write *present, past,* or *future.*

6. Many people <u>dreamed</u> of a perpetual motion machine. _____

7. This machine <u>runs</u> forever. _____

8. It <u>will make</u> its own energy. _____

9. The machine <u>will save</u> tons of money! _____

10. The Perez twins <u>created</u> a version of the machine. _____

11. But the machine <u>borrows</u> energy from other machines. _____

12. Sadly, the perpetual motion machine <u>will remain</u> a dream. _____

Directions Rewrite each sentence. Change the underlined verb to the tense in ( ).

13. Once, the idea of a computer <u>seems</u> impossible. (past)

_____

14. Now, people constantly <u>use</u> computers for work and enjoyment. (present)

_____

_____

15. Someday, perhaps a perpetual motion machine <u>is</u> a reality. (future)

_____

_____

Principal Parts of Regular Verbs

Directions Write *present, present participle, past,* or *past participle* to identity the principal part of the underlined verb.

1. What <u>defines</u> genius? _____

2. A genius <u>offers</u> a fresh view. _____

3. Often, the public <u>has rejected</u> ideas of genius at first. _____

4. After time <u>has passed</u>, we understand what was offered. _____

5. People <u>recognized</u> Leonardo's genius at once. _____

6. He <u>concealed</u> many of his ideas in journals. _____

7. Today we <u>are studying</u> them. _____

8. Many of his ideas <u>have appeared</u> as inventions. _____

9. His ideas <u>waited</u> for the right time and place. _____

10. We <u>acknowledge</u> his genius gratefully. _____

Directions Write the sentence using the principal part of the underlined verb indicated in ( ).

11. Brilliant ideas <u>change</u> the world. (present participle)

_____

12. Sir Isaac Newton <u>discover</u> universal laws of motion. (past)

_____

13. An object in motion <u>tend</u> to stay in motion. (present)

_____

14. This concept <u>form</u> the basis for the first of his laws of motion. (present)

_____

15. Newton's laws <u>help</u> us understand how the world works. (past participle)

_____

Principal Parts of Irregular Verbs

Directions Write *present, present participle, past,* or *past participle* to identify the principal part used to form the underlined verb.

1. Dinosaurs <u>have been</u> extinct for millions of years. _____

2. The iguanodon <u>was</u> a plant eater. _____

3. An iguanodon <u>stood</u> about 16 feet tall. _____

4. It <u>ran</u> on two legs or walked on four. _____

5. Gideon Mantell <u>had found</u> a few bones in 1822. _____

6. He <u>had seen</u> the similarity to an iguana. _____

7. Mantell <u>gave</u> the dinosaur its name. _____

8. Even today, archaeologists <u>are finding</u> dinosaur bones. _____

9. Bones and fossils <u>tell</u> us much about extinct animals. _____

10. We <u>draw</u> conclusions about their size and shape. _____

Directions Write the sentence using the principal part of the underlined verb indicated in ( ).

11. Once all of Earth's land <u>be</u> one big mass. (past)

_____

12. Over time, it <u>break</u> into pieces. (past)

_____

13. We now <u>know</u> these pieces moved. (present)

_____

14. They <u>become</u> the seven continents. (past participle)

_____

15. Forces inside the Earth <u>make</u> the landmasses move. (past)

_____

Troublesome Verbs

Directions Write the form of the underlined verb indicated in ( ).

1. Mahalia <u>leave</u> listeners dazzled by her talent. (past)   _____

2. They <u>lay</u> down their troubles for a while. (past)   _____

3. Her success <u>lets</u> other women dream of a career in music. (past)   _____

4. Young Aretha Franklin <u>sit</u> with Mahalia's fans. (past participle)   _____

5. Aretha <u>set</u> goals and achieved them. (past)   _____

Directions Underline the verb that correctly completes the sentence.

6. They have (sat, set) in this pew for years.

7. The choir (sat, set) their hymnals on the bench.

8. A bell (lays, lies) on its side.

9. Someone (lay, laid) it there.

10. She has (left, let) a cup of water on the stand.

11. (Leave, Let) us ask for her autograph.

12. The piano (sets, sits) on a platform.

Directions Complete each sentence with the correct form of the verb in ( ).

13. Please _____ with us at the concert. (sit)

14. The singers have _____ their music down. (set)

15. Yesterday we _____ our friends at school. (leave)

16. Did you _____ your guitar at home? (leave)

17. Ms. Guthrie _____ me pick my recital piece. (let)

18. Yesterday afternoon he _____ the horn on the table. (lay)

19. The horn has _____ there ever since. (lay)

20. She will _____ down and rest before the performance. (lie)

Prepositions and Prepositional Phrases

Directions Underline the prepositional phrase in each sentence. Circle the preposition.

1. Over the holidays, we had a movie marathon.

2. The family watched a series of animated films.

3. We have quite a few in our film library.

4. I have watched *Dumbo* about 20 times.

5. Dumbo is a baby elephant with enormous ears.

6. Dumbo stays near his mother.

7. She feels protective toward her baby.

8. Dumbo finds a great use for his ears.

9. Dumbo can fly through the sky.

10. He is the biggest hit at the circus.

Directions Write *P* if the underlined word is a preposition. Write *O* if it is the object of the preposition.

11. Heckle and Jeckle are two crows <u>in</u> *Dumbo*. _____

12. They make fun <u>of</u> the baby elephant. _____

13. They are amazed when Dumbo soars into the <u>air</u>. _____

14. Some encouragement <u>from</u> a little mouse helps Dumbo. _____

15. I think the moral is "Believe in <u>yourself</u>." _____

Directions Underline the prepositional phrases. The number in ( ) tells how many prepositional phrases are in that sentence.

16. The theater is down this street and around a corner. (2)

17. Buy four tickets at the booth and two bags of popcorn from the concession stand. (3)

18. We always sit toward the back under the balcony. (2)

19. At the beginning, it seems very dark in the theater. (2)

20. The ads before the show make me hungry for a snack. (2)

Subject and Object Pronouns

Directions Write *S* if the underlined word is a subject pronoun. Write *O* if the word is an object pronoun.

1. In *Weslandia*, Wesley is the main character. <u>He</u> has problems. _____

2. Wesley doesn't act like the other kids, and they pick on <u>him</u>. _____

3. His parents worry that <u>they</u> have raised an odd son. _____

4. Wesley creates a new civilization, and <u>it</u> fascinates everyone. _____

5. <u>I</u> really enjoyed reading this story. _____

6. Wesley's ingenious uses for his crop amused <u>me</u>. _____

7. My friend Winnie said the suntan oil was funniest to <u>her</u>. _____

8. <u>You</u> should read this story too! _____

9. Our teacher, Mr. Su, asked <u>us</u> about civilizations. _____

10. Native peoples create <u>them</u> based on climate and crops in their region. _____

Directions Underline the correct pronoun in ( ) to complete each sentence.

11. Corn has many uses. Many farmers plant (it, they).

12. (They, Them) can sell the grain as a food or as a raw material for fuel.

13. The stalks can be ground up. There are several uses for (it, them) as well.

14. John and (I, me) have learned about soybeans.

15. (We, Us) get nutritious foods from them.

16. Do you like tofu? (It, Them) is a curd made from soybeans.

17. Mom served tofu to Karl and (I, me).

18. She didn't tell (us, we) what we were eating.

19. When (he, him) found out it was bean curd, Karl laughed.

20. Mom had disguised it in pudding. That was clever of (her, she)!

Pronouns and Antecedents

Directions Match the pronoun with the noun or noun phrase that could be its antecedent. Write the letter of the correct antecedent next to the pronoun.

_____ **1.** her   **A** William Clark

_____ **2.** it   **B** explorers

_____ **3.** them   **C** York and I

_____ **4.** us   **D** Missouri River

_____ **5.** he   **E** Shoshone woman

Directions Circle the antecedent of the underlined pronoun in each sentence.

6. Lewis observed the plants and animals around <u>him</u>.

7. Sacagawea came from the region, so <u>she</u> guided the explorers.

8. York did many jobs; sometimes <u>he</u> picked greens for dinner.

9. The men ate much meat, so eating greens was a treat for <u>them</u>.

10. The men gathered materials for a fort and then built <u>it</u>.

11. The boatmen were strong, so <u>they</u> could row for many hours.

12. Modern Americans have cars and airplanes, so <u>we</u> can barely imagine the expedition's difficulties.

Directions Write a pronoun to replace each underlined noun or noun phrase.

13. Americans sometimes forget how important the Louisiana Purchase was for <u>Americans</u>. _____

14. Our country ended at the Mississippi River; after the purchase, <u>our country</u> went to the Rocky Mountains. _____

15. Jefferson bought the land from France, but <u>Jefferson</u> didn't know much about the land. _____

16. Jefferson chose Lewis and Clark to explore the area, and <u>Lewis and Clark</u> soon set off. _____

17. Jefferson was interested in botany, so Lewis sent many plant specimens to <u>Jefferson</u>. _____

18. Americans didn't know about some Indian tribes; Lewis and Clark learned about <u>the Indian tribes</u>. _____

Possessive Pronouns

Directions Write the letter of the possessive pronoun that can replace the underlined word or words in each phrase.

_____ **1.** Lori's idea   **A** her

_____ **2.** Nate's paper   **B** their

_____ **3.** the twins' pet   **C** our

_____ **4.** an owl's eyes   **D** its

_____ **5.** Ti's and my cat   **E** his

Directions Underline the pronoun that correctly completes each sentence.

6. Each ant colony has (its, their) own smell.

7. The ants can recognize an intruder in (theirs, their) nest.

8. They also know which eggs are not (theirs, we).

9. A female worker will help defend (her, she) home.

10. I know some ants can sting because an ant stung (mine, my) foot!

Directions Write the possessive pronoun that can replace the underlined word or words.

11. Dad and I love to have honey on Dad's and my toast.   _____

12. Mom likes honey on Mom's oatmeal.   _____

13. Sam puts honey on Sam's peanut butter sandwiches.   _____

14. Bees make honey for the bees' food.   _____

15. A bee can always fly back to a bee's hive.   _____

16. I washed my plate, and now you can wash the plate belonging to you.   _____

17. Paul put his glass in the dishwasher, and then I added the glass belonging to me. _____

18. He found his fork, but she couldn't find the fork belonging to her.   _____

Name _____

Indefinite and Reflexive Pronouns

Directions Underline the pronoun in each sentence. Write *indefinite* or *reflexive* to identify the kind of pronoun it is. Then write *singular* or *plural* to show its number.

1. Everybody eats lunch in the cafeteria.   _____   _____

2. Many of the students bring a sack lunch.   _____   _____

3. Others eat a hot lunch.   _____   _____

4. Students help themselves to milk.   _____   _____

5. Mom says, "Give yourself time to eat."   _____   _____

Directions Underline the correct pronoun in ( ) to complete each sentence.

6. I chose a special place for (myself, myselves).

7. (Everybody, Many) needs a place to be alone and think.

8. (Few, No one) is immune to stress.

9. The teacher said, "Do your work by (theirself, yourself)."

10. (Several, Someone) of my friends have private places.

Directions Choose a pronoun from the box to complete each sentence correctly. Be sure indefinite pronouns used as subjects agree in number with their verbs.

> herself   many   myself   something   everybody

11. If I see someone new, I introduce _____.

12. I tell the new person _____ about the school.

13. The new girl said to _____, "I won't make any friends."

14. _____ appreciates a friendly welcome.

15. _____ try to make newcomers feel at home.

Grammar and Writing Practice Book

Using *Who* and *Whom*

Directions Write *subject, object of preposition,* or *direct object* to identify how the underlined word is used.

1. <u>Who</u> likes cheerleading? _____

2. Jim is the one for <u>whom</u> the crowd is applauding. _____

3. Everyone <u>who</u> is watching was impressed. _____

4. <u>Whom</u> will the judges select? _____

5. To <u>whom</u> were you speaking? _____

Directions Underline *who* or *whom* to complete each sentence correctly.

6. (Who, Whom) would like something to drink?

7. Stu is the person to (who, whom) you should give your money.

8. He is the fellow with (who, whom) I went to the concession stand.

9. Anyone (who, whom) watches a gymnastics meet gets thirsty.

10. The judges, (who, whom) are volunteers, do a fantastic job.

11. (Who, Whom) shall we invite next time?

12. It should be someone with (who, whom) you can spend hours.

13. Spectators (who, whom) are veterans bring seat cushions for the bleachers.

14. Everybody (who, whom) sits through the entire gymnastics meet gets sore.

15. For (who, whom) is the meet the most fun?

Directions Cross out mistakes in the use of *who* and *whom* in the paragraph. Write the correct pronoun above the line. One sentence is correct.

(16) The girl watched her older brother, whom was turning cartwheels. (17) He wondered

whom else might be looking. (18) He fell, and the dog with who the girl had been playing ran to

lick his face. (19) The girl shrieked with laughter, and the mother, whom had been doing laundry,

rushed into the yard. (20) "Who is ready for a snack?" asked the mother.

Name _____

Contractions and Negatives

Directions Write the words used to form the contractions.

1. wouldn't _____

2. she'll _____

3. he's _____

4. we're _____

5. isn't _____

6. can't _____

Directions Write the contraction for each pair of words.

7. will + not _____

8. I + am _____

9. he + had _____

10. you + are _____

Directions Write the contraction for the underlined words.

11. What is the craziest project <u>you have</u> ever done? _____

12. Ashley says <u>she has</u> started a zoo. _____

13. <u>She had</u> collected a turtle, a mouse, and a snake. _____

14. Ashley says <u>she will</u> make another zoo in the future. _____

Directions Circle the word in ( ) that correctly completes each sentence.

15. My friend and I aren't (ever, never) without a new plan.

16. We don't ever do (anything, nothing) without our parents' permission.

17. They wouldn't (ever, never) let us do anything dangerous.

18. We don't want (anybody, nobody) to get hurt.

Adjectives and Articles

Directions Underline the articles and circle the adjectives in each sentence.

1. A few brave adventurers are searching for shipwrecks.

2. They dive deep beneath the surface in search of an exciting find.

3. One group of divers found the treasure of a Spanish galleon.

4. The jewels, coins, and other artifacts are priceless.

5. Five hundred years ago, these ships sailed from Mexico loaded with silver and gold.

Directions Write *what kind, how many,* or *which one* to tell what question each underlined adjective answers about a noun.

6. That sunken ship is scary. _____

7. All tour boats pass by it. _____

8. The captain explains its tragic wreck. _____

9. A million tourists have seen it. _____

10. Some sad songs have been written about it. _____

11. This song tells about a sailor's wife. _____

12. She looked for her husband for ten years. _____

Directions Write *a, an,* or *the* to complete each sentence. Choose the article that makes sense and follows the rules for articles.

13. Have you ever found _____ real treasure?

14. Once I found _____ old box.

15. It was buried in _____ bushes behind my house.

16. Inside _____ box were some rocks.

17. It was _____ disappointing moment.

18. Later, I found out _____ rocks were valuable.

19. One rock was _____ rare geode.

20. It was _____ amazing experience.

This, That, These, and Those

Directions Write *this, that, these,* or *those* to describe each object.

1. a book in your hands   _____ book

2. a store a mile away   _____ store

3. dogs in a neighbor's yard   _____ dogs

4. shoes on your feet   _____ shoes

Directions Underline the word in ( ) that completes each sentence correctly.

5. (That there, That) constellation is called Orion.

6. (This, This here) observatory will give us a good view.

7. (Them, Those) astronauts who have gone into space have not reached the stars.

8. (These, Them) articles tell about their trips to the moon.

9. I have reached (this, those) conclusion: Astronauts must be brave.

10. Can someone tell me if (this, these) facts are accurate?

Directions Write each sentence correctly.

11. That there telescope is called the Hubble Telescope.

_____

_____

12. These here photographs I'm showing you were made by that telescope.

_____

_____

13. Can you believe that this here photograph shows the birth of a galaxy?

_____

_____

14. A telescope on Earth could not take them photographs.

_____

_____

Comparative and Superlative Adjectives

Directions Complete the table. Add *-er, -est, more,* or *most* as needed.

Adjective	Comparative	Superlative
fierce	1. _____	6. _____
small	2. _____	7. _____
ridiculous	3. _____	8. _____
icy	4. _____	9. _____
hot	5. _____	10. _____

Directions Underline the adjective form in ( ) to complete each sentence correctly.

11. Which dinosaur was the (stronger, strongest) of all?

12. *Triceratops* had a (more dangerous, most dangerous) horn and tail than *Tyrannosaurus*.

13. However, *Tyrannosaurus* probably had the (greater, greatest) speed and strength of all the dinosaurs.

14. Bill has a (larger, largest) collection of dinosaur figures than I do.

15. He has the (more complete, most complete) collection of anyone I know.

Directions Write the correct forms of the adjectives in ( ) to complete the sentences.

16. Do you think description is _____ than plot in a story? (important)

17. I think stories with good characters are _____ than stories with good plots. (memorable)

18. The _____ characters of all are the villains. (interesting)

19. A _____ book may not be better than a shorter one. (long)

20. The _____ books of all are the ones that make you think. (good)

Adverbs

Directions Write the comparative and superlative forms of each adverb.

Adverb	Comparative	Superlative
sadly	1. _____	5. _____
wildly	2. _____	6. _____
late	3. _____	7. _____
well	4. _____	8. _____

Directions Underline the adverb in each sentence. Circle the word or words that each adverb tells more about.

  9. Settlers waited impatiently for the mail.

10. Mail traveled slowly by stagecoach.

11. The Pony Express was a very welcome change.

12. Riders on horseback raced westward day and night.

13. The mail had never moved faster.

14. Soon railroads replaced the Pony Express.

Directions Underline the correct word in ( ) to complete each sentence.

15. The Pony Express moved the mail (most quickly, more quickly) than stagecoaches did.

16. The daring riders (certain, certainly) appealed to the public.

17. Of all western heroes, these young men lived (more dangerously, most dangerously).

18. The Pony Express worked (better, best) for some than for others.

19. It cost more to send a letter than most people could (possible, possibly) afford.

20. Today, airplanes serve the public (better, best) of all.

Name _____

Modifiers

Directions Underline the adjectives, adverbs, and prepositional phrases in each sentence. (Do not underline the articles *a* and *the*.)

1. A tiny caterpillar came slowly out of the egg.

2. It quickly ate some nearby green leaves.

3. The plump caterpillar later became a motionless pupa.

4. In spring, a tiny head emerged from its hard shell.

5. At last, the homely caterpillar will become a pretty butterfly.

Directions Write *adverb, adjective,* or *prepositional phrase* to identify each underlined modifier. Write *adjective* or *adverb* to identify how a prepositional phrase is used.

6. Our science class studied <u>different</u> insects.   _____

7. Insects live <u>everywhere</u>.   _____

8. Some insects blend <u>perfectly</u> with their environments.   _____

9. Some insects are harmful because they feed <u>on our crops</u>.   _____

10. The bee is a very <u>useful</u> insect.   _____

11. Many fruits and vegetables are fertilized <u>by bees</u>.   _____

12. The ladybug, <u>with its cheerful colors</u>, is my favorite insect.   _____

Directions Underline the misplaced modifier in each sentence. Rewrite the sentence, and put the modifier where it belongs.

13. Farmers fight harmful insects in airplanes called crop dusters.

_____

_____

14. They only want to kill harmful insects and not useful ones.

_____

_____

15. Campers battle mosquitoes with big bottles of insect repellent.

_____

_____

Conjunctions

Directions Underline the conjunction in each sentence.

1. Scientists look for facts and solve problems.

2. All problems are different, but each problem takes time to solve.

3. Scientists search for answers in an orderly and exact way.

4. They use scientific method, or a systematic approach to problem solving.

5. Eventually, they form a hypothesis, but this is not the end.

6. They must analyze the data and draw a conclusion.

Directions Underline the conjunction in ( ) that completes each sentence.

7. Is a scientific truth a theory (and, or) a law?

8. A theory may be logical, (or, but) a law is widely accepted.

9. Newton's ideas about motion are called laws, (and, but) Einstein's idea about relativity is called a theory.

10. Both Newton (and, or) Einstein used scientific method.

Directions Use the conjunction *and, but,* or *or* to join each pair of sentences. Write the new sentences. Remember to add a comma.

11. The reindeer population grew large. Then most of the reindeer died suddenly.

_____

_____

12. Were the reindeer diseased? Did they starve?

_____

_____

13. The animals had lost weight. Their bone marrow contained no fat.

_____

_____

14. The reindeer had eaten all the island's food. Then disaster struck.

_____

_____

Grammar and Writing Practice Book

Commas

Directions Add commas to each sentence where they are needed.

1. Rafael has joined the Fleet Feet a traveling soccer team.

2. He will have to buy shoes a uniform and a ball.

3. Dad how can I earn money?

4. Well son you could do more chores around the house.

5. Rafael washed the car walked the dog and watered the garden.

6. He also received money as gifts from his aunt grandparents and parents.

Directions Rewrite each sentence. Add commas where they are needed.

7. "Anna are you a good money manager?"

_____

_____

8. In general people are better at spending than saving.

_____

_____

9. Most people need a budget a plan for keeping track of their income and expenses.

_____

_____

10. I spend my money on lunches books and supplies.

_____

_____

11. George a friend who does not have a budget is always short of money.

_____

_____

12. "By the way George you owe me fifty cents."

_____

_____

Quotations and Quotation Marks

Directions Write *C* if the sentence uses quotation marks and other punctuation correctly. Write *NC* if it is not correct.

1. "Are you going to take a vacation," asked Aaron? _____

2. "I usually fly to my grandparents' home in Michigan," said Pat. _____

3. "Do you like to fly," asked Aaron, "or would you rather take a train?" _____

4. "Pat replied, I like different things about both." _____

5. "A train lets you see more things," she explained. "However, an airplane is quicker." _____

Directions Write each sentence correctly. Add capital letters, quotation marks, and other punctuation as needed.

6. when does our flight take off asked Nina

_____

7. it is scheduled to leave at 8:00 A.M. said Mom

_____

8. she added that means we should be at the airport by 6:00 A.M.

_____

_____

9. no way cried Nina that's too early

_____

10. it is early agreed Mom however, we have to allow plenty of time

_____

_____

11. after we check our bags she suggested we can have breakfast

_____

_____

12. that sounds good said Nina can I buy a magazine to read

_____

_____

Punctuation

Directions Match the punctuation with a description of its use.

_____ **1.** italics (underlining)   **A** join clauses without a conjunction

_____ **2.** colons (:)   **B** introduce a list, express hours and minutes, and appear after the salutation in a business letter

_____ **3.** dashes (—)   **C** join some compound words

_____ **4.** semicolons (;)   **D** set off titles of books, magazines, and works of art

_____ **5.** hyphens (-)   **E** set off words that interrupt the sentence

Directions Rewrite each sentence. Add the missing punctuation marks.

6. I'm always losing things I can usually find them in a few minutes.

_____

_____

7. I have lost several things this week six notebooks, twenty one pencils, and my America Sings book.

_____

_____

8. Now my jacket it's the one with the gold buttons is missing.

_____

_____

9. It could be in the car it might be in my locker.

_____

_____

10. There's one thing this ten year old will never forget. School ends at 345 P.M.!

_____

_____

Standardized Test Practice

Language Test

Read the passage and decide which type of mistake, if any, appears in each underlined section. Mark the letter of your answer.

> *The Swiss Family Robinson,* by Johann david Wyss, is an adventure story
> (1)
> for all ages. When these six people are shipwrecked on a tropical island
> (2)
> they must meet the challenge to survive. In fact, they succeed in creating
> a new life for themselfs. The family's active imagination helps it figure
> (3) (4)
> out ways to farm, build, and tame wild animals. Would love to live in their
> (5)
> treehouse. Action and adventures waits on every page.
> (6)

1. **A** Spelling
   B Capitalization
   C Punctuation
   D No mistake

2. **F** Spelling
   G Capitalization
   H Punctuation
   J No mistake

3. **A** Spelling
   B Capitalization
   C Punctuation
   D No mistake

4. **F** Spelling
   G Capitalization
   H Punctuation
   J No mistake

5. **A** Missing sentence part
   B Verb tense
   C Subject-verb agreement
   D No mistake

6. **F** Missing sentence part
   G Verb tense
   H Subject-verb agreement
   J No mistake

Writing Test

Read the paragraph and answer questions 1–4.

> (1) Tie a string around an apple, as though cutting it in half from top to bottom. (2) Then wrap the string around the apple at right angles to the first string and tie it at the top. (3) Do you know how to make a square knot? (4) Next, spread peanut butter over the outside of the apple. (5) Now roll the delicious fruit in a bowl that you previously filled with birdseed until you can no longer see peanut butter through the birdseed. (6) Hang your feeder by its string to a nail hammered into a tree trunk.

1. Which sentence should be left out of this paragraph?

  A Sentence 1

  B Sentence 3

  C Sentence 4

  D Sentence 6

2. Which sentence is the best revision of sentence 5?

  F Now roll it in birdseed until you can no longer see the peanut butter through the birdseed.

  G Now roll the apple in a bowl of birdseed until it is covered.

  H Cover the apple with birdseed.

  J Take the apple and put it in birdseed and cover it with birdseed.

3. Which transition would be a good addition to sentence 6?

  A Before going farther,

  B However,

  C Finally,

  D As a third step,

4. Which sentence has the best voice and mood to end this paragraph?

  F We must do our best to assist our dear feathered friends.

  G Your difficult task has come to an end.

  H I hope you enjoy watching the birds as much as I do.

  J The birds will polish off every bit of this feeder, except the string!

Language Test

Read the passage and decide which type of mistake, if any, appears in each underlined section. Mark the letter of your answer.

Many people consider Thomas Alva Edison to be the greatest <u>inventer of</u>
<u>(1)</u>
<u>all time.</u> Not only did he perfect the light bulb, <u>but he also sit up</u> the first
<u>(2)</u>
electrical power company. What is more, he <u>invents the phonograph and</u>
<u>(3)</u>
improved the telegraph, the telephone, and motion picture technology. He

established a research laboratory and produced most <u>of him inventions</u> from
<u>(4)</u>
that laboratory. Amazingly, Edison obtained 1,093 United States patents—

about one every two weeks <u>of his working life.</u> <u>This record surprised even</u>
<u>(5)</u>   <u>(6)</u>
<u>Edison hisself.</u>

1. **A** Spelling
   B Capitalization
   C Punctuation
   D No mistake

2. **F** Prepositional phrase error
   G Pronoun-antecedent error
   H Verb error
   J No mistake

3. **A** Prepositional phrase error
   B Verb error
   C Pronoun-antecedent error
   D No mistake

4. **F** Prepositional phrase error
   G Verb error
   H Possessive pronoun error
   J No mistake

5. **A** Prepositional phrase error
   B Pronoun-antecedent error
   C Possessive pronoun error
   D No mistake

6. **F** Subject-verb agreement error
   G Reflexive pronoun error
   H Possessive pronoun error
   J No mistake

Writing Test

Read the paragraph and answer questions 1–4.

> (1) *Dinosaur* means "terrible lizard," but how do dinosaurs compare to today's lizards? (2) The body covering of both animals is similar—a tough, dry skin covered in scales. (3) Nonetheless, while the dinosaur was a sort of first cousin to the ancient reptiles, dinosaurs differed in several ways. (4) Dinosaurs had powerful legs that moved directly under the body, but reptiles' legs extend out to the sides. (5) Think about how a lizard moves, slowly, with side-to-side motion; compare this to the strong-legged, swift *Tyrannosaurus rex*. (6) Some scientists think that dinosaurs were related to birds. (7) In addition, dinosaurs had skulls designed for strength, for grasping and tearing prey.

1. Which sentence does not stick to the topic?

   A Sentence 1

   B Sentence 3

   C Sentence 4

   D Sentence 6

2. Which sentence is the best choice for topic sentence?

   F Sentence 7

   G Sentence 4

   H Sentence 2

   J Sentence 1

3. Which sentence elaborates on the idea of differences between dinosaurs and lizards?

   A Sentence 2

   B Sentence 3

   C Sentence 5

   D Sentence 6

4. Which of the following sentences would be a good conclusion for this paragraph?

   F Strong, swift dinosaurs were better suited to prehistoric life than lizards, their modern cousins.

   G Dinosaurs and lizards were as different as night and day.

   H Both lizards and dinosaurs seem creepy and scary to me.

   J It seems odd that scientists think dinosaurs are similar to birds, since they had no feathers.

Language Test

Read the passage and decide which type of mistake, if any, appears in each underlined section. Mark the letter of your answer.

> It took ten years and six tries, but Steve Fossett <u>wouldnt give up.</u> On July
> (1)
> 2, 2002, he became the first person <u>around the world</u> to pilot a balloon solo.
> (2)
> This remarkable feat took 13 days, 8 hours, 33 <u>minutes and it involved</u>
> (3)
> moving in the jet stream at speeds up to 200 miles per hour. Imagine doing
> this task all <u>alone and being able to sleep only</u> for short periods. In all his
> (4)
> attempts to circumnavigate, or travel around the world, Fossett <u>faced the</u>
>
> <u>most terrifyingest storms</u> and other problems. Describing his feelings about
> (5)
> his success, Fossett <u>said, It's enormous</u> relief and satisfaction."
> (6)

1. **A** Spelling
   B Capitalization
   C Punctuation
   D No mistake

2. **F** Double negative
   G Misplaced modifier
   H Conjunction error
   J No mistake

3. **A** Conjunction error
   B Misplaced modifier
   C Comma error
   D No mistake

4. **F** Comma error
   G Conjunction error
   H Misplaced modifier
   J No mistake

5. **A** Quotation error
   B Comparative adjective error
   C Conjunction error
   D No mistake

6. **F** Quotation error
   G Comma error
   H Conjunction error
   J No mistake

Writing Test

Read the paragraph and answer questions 1–4.

> (1) The 1883 eruption of the volcano on Krakatoa affected the world profoundly. (2) It released four times the energy of the biggest human-made bomb. (3) Scientists think that Krakatoa had another major eruption in A.D. 416. (4) The 1883 explosions were heard over a third of the Earth's surface. (5) Shock waves from the explosions circled the Earth seven times, and darkness fell on the area. (6) The most lasting effects resulted from volcanic ash. (7) It encircled the globe. (8) For years, Earth's temperatures were lowered as much as 1.2° Centigrade, and people observed spectacular red sunsets and blue and green suns.

1. Which sentence is the paragraph's topic sentence?

   A Sentence 1

   B Sentence 3

   C Sentence 4

   D Sentence 6

2. Which is the best way to combine sentences 6 and 7?

   F The most lasting effects encircled the globe.

   G The most lasting effects resulted from the volcanic ash but encircled the globe.

   H The most lasting effects resulted from the volcanic ash who encircled the globe.

   J The most lasting effects resulted from volcanic ash that encircled the globe.

3. Which of the following sentences is the best paraphrase of sentences 6, 7, and 8?

   A Volcanoes can lower Earth's temperature and change climates.

   B Krakatoa's volcanic ash lowered temperatures and colored the view of the sun worldwide.

   C Volcanic ash from the Krakatoa explosion drifted around the world.

   D The colors we see can be changed by adding dust to Earth's atmosphere.

4. Which sentence could be deleted?

   F Sentence 2

   G Sentence 3

   H Sentence 5

   J Sentence 7

Unit Writing Lessons

Name _____

Notes for a Personal Narrative

Directions Fill in the graphic organizer with information about the event or experience that you plan to write about.

Summary

What happened? _____

When? _____

Where? _____

Who was there? _____

Details

Beginning

Middle

End

Name _____

Words That Tell About *You*

Directions How did you feel about the challenge facing you at the beginning, middle, and end of your experience? Choose one or two words from the word bank to describe each part of your experience. Then add details that *show* readers each feeling.

anxious	thrilled	proud	inspired
disappointed	excited	contented	determined
dismayed	fearful	delighted	upset

Beginning _____

_____

_____

_____

Middle _____

_____

_____

_____

End _____

_____

_____

_____

Name _____

Elaboration

Combine Sentences

> You can improve your writing by combining short simple sentences to make compound or complex sentences. This will create a smoother flow of ideas in your writing. The two sentences you combine must make sense together. You can create compound sentences by combining short sentences using the words *and*, *but*, or *or*. You can create complex sentences by combining short sentences with *if*, *because*, *before*, *after*, *since*, or *when*.

Directions Use the word in ( ) to combine the two sentences. Remember to capitalize the first word of the new sentence and to replace the first period with a comma.

1. (but) My big sister could climb the pine tree in the pasture. I had not tried.

   _____

   _____

2. (because) The first limbs were so high. I thought it was too hard.

   _____

   _____

3. (when) She boosted me up. I could just reach the lowest limb.

   _____

   _____

4. (and) The rough bark scratched my skin. Sticky pine resin oozed onto my hands.

   _____

   _____

5. (but) I was scared. I climbed to the very top of that pine.

   _____

   _____

Name _____

Self-Evaluation Guide
Personal Narrative

Directions Think about the final draft of your personal narrative. Then rate yourself on a scale from 4 to 1 (4 is the highest) on each writing trait. After you fill out the chart, answer the questions.

Writing Traits	4	3	2	1
Focus/Ideas				
Organization/Paragraphs				
Voice				
Word Choice				
Sentences				
Conventions				

1. What is the best part of your personal narrative? Why?

_____

_____

_____

_____

2. Write one thing you would change about this personal narrative if you had the chance to write it again. Why?

_____

_____

_____

_____

Name _____

How-to Chart

Directions Fill in the graphic organizer with information about your project.

Explain Task _____

_____

_____

Materials _____

_____

_____

Introduction _____

_____

_____

_____

Steps _____

_____

_____

_____

_____

_____

Conclusion _____

_____

_____

Name _____

Time-Order Words

Directions Add a time-order word to each of the five steps below. Write each sentence. Then add a final sentence using a time-order word. Tell what would happen in the last step.

1. Grab a soccer ball and head to the field.

_____

_____

2. Stand about five feet in front of the goal posts.

_____

_____

3. Take five steps back and two large steps to the left.

_____

_____

4. Drop the ball to the ground in front of you.

_____

_____

5. Wind up and kick that soccer ball as hard as you can toward the goal.

_____

_____

6. _____

_____

Name _____

Elaboration

Strong Action Verbs

You can improve your writing by using strong action verbs. The right action verbs make your writing more vivid and interesting to readers.

Vague   Last night snow <u>fell in</u> our city.
Specific   Last night snow <u>blanketed</u> our city.

Directions Replace each underlined word with an action verb. Write each sentence.

1. After a heavy snowfall I love to <u>make</u> a snowman.

_____

_____

2. Begin by <u>getting</u> the largest snowball you can.

_____

_____

3. Then <u>move</u> the snowball through the snow.

_____

_____

4. Next, <u>put</u> three of these giant snowballs one on top of the other.

_____

_____

5. Finally, <u>put</u> your snowman in clothes, a scarf, or a hat.

_____

_____

Name _____

Self-Evaluation Guide

How-to Report

Directions Think about the final draft of your how-to report. Then rate yourself on a scale from 4 to 1 (4 is the highest) on each writing trait. After you fill out the chart, answer the questions.

Writing Traits	4	3	2	1
Focus/Ideas				
Organization/Paragraphs				
Voice				
Word Choice				
Sentences				
Conventions				

1. What is the best part of your how-to report?

   _____

   _____

   _____

   _____

   _____

2. Write one thing you would change about this how-to report if you had the chance to write it again.

   _____

   _____

   _____

   _____

   _____

Name _____

Venn Diagram

Directions Fill in the Venn diagram with similarities and differences about the two things you are comparing.

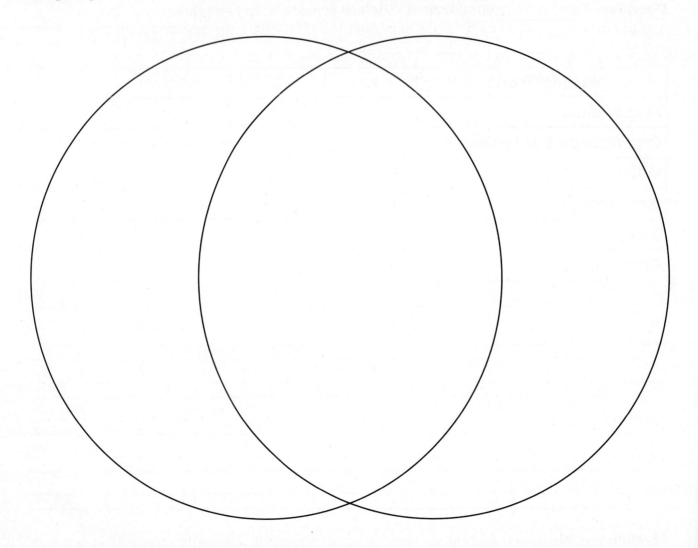

Name _____

Words That Compare and Contrast

Directions The words in the box signal that two things are alike or different. Write two sentences that explain how your two inventions are alike, using words from the box. Then write two sentences that explain how your two inventions are different, using words from the box.

Words That Signal Similarity	Words That Signal Difference
and	but
also	however
too	unlike
as well	on the other hand
like	

How the two things are alike

1. _____

_____

_____

2. _____

_____

_____

How the two things are different

1. _____

_____

_____

2. _____

_____

_____

Name _____

Elaboration

Parallelism

> If a sentence has parts that are alike, those parts should have the same form or pattern. **Parallelism,** or **parallel structure,** refers to the pattern, or organization, of similar sentence parts, such as verbs or adjectives.
>
> **Not Parallel** Riders were expected to ride a horse, facing dangers, and go for hours without sleep.
>
> **Parallel** Riders were expected to ride a horse, face dangers, and go for hours without sleep.

Directions Rewrite the sentences to make them parallel.

1. The Pony Express carried mail, rode long distances, and they travel at 10 miles per hour.

   _____

   _____

2. Today, e-mail makes modern communication much quicker, cheaper, and easy to use.

   _____

   _____

3. Riders for the Pony Express rode 75–100 miles at a time, changed horses every 10–15 miles, and are earning $100 a month.

   _____

   _____

4. Unlike the Pony Express, you can send an e-mail, are receiving a reply, and respond in just minutes!

   _____

   _____

5. Do you communicate by e-mail, letters, or talking on the telephone?

   _____

Grammar and Writing Practice Book

Name _____

Self-Evaluation Guide
Compare and Contrast Essay

Directions Think about the final draft of your compare and contrast essay. Then rate yourself on a scale from 4 to 1 (4 is the highest) on each writing trait. After you fill out the chart, answer the questions.

Writing Traits	4	3	2	1
Focus/Ideas				
Organization/Paragraphs				
Voice				
Word Choice				
Sentences				
Conventions				

1. What is the best part of your compare and contrast essay?

_____

_____

_____

_____

2. Write one thing you would change about this compare and contrast essay if you had the chance to write it again.

_____

_____

_____

_____

Name _____

Story Chart

Directions Fill in the story chart with the characters, setting, events, and solution for your story.

Title

Characters

Setting

Events

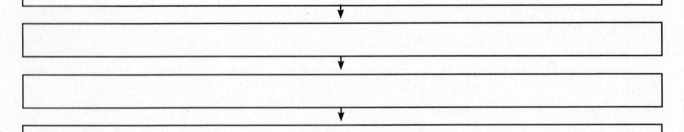

Solution

Name _____

Good Beginnings

Directions Practice writing sentences that will grab your reader's attention. Using your story idea as the topic, write one sentence for each strategy. You can use one of the sentences to start your first draft.

1. Ask a question.

_____

_____

2. Use an exclamation.

_____

_____

3. Use a sound word.

_____

_____

4. Hint at the ending.

_____

_____

5. Use a simile.

_____

_____

6. Make a list.

_____

_____

7. Set the scene.

_____

_____

Name _____

Elaboration

Pronouns

Directions The sentences below need a pronoun or an antecedent. Replace the underlined word or words with an appropriate pronoun or antecedent.

1. <u>It</u> is so useful. Did you ever wonder who invented it?

   _____

   _____

2. I've had my skateboard for so long, <u>my skateboard</u> is covered in stickers.

   _____

   _____

3. Beth is such a great singer because <u>Beth</u> has been taking lessons since <u>Beth</u> was five years old.

   _____

   _____

4. <u>She</u> is the best runner in class. No one can beat her in the 50-yard dash.

   _____

   _____

5. Dan left for school without <u>it</u>, and he had to call home and ask his mom to bring it to him.

   _____

   _____

6. John asked if <u>John</u> could go to the movies Friday night.

   _____

   _____

Name _____

Self-Evaluation Guide
Story

Directions Think about the final draft of your story. Then rate yourself on a scale from 4 to 1 (4 is the highest) on each writing trait. After you fill out the chart, answer the questions.

Writing Traits	4	3	2	1
Focus/Ideas				
Organization/Paragraphs				
Voice				
Word Choice				
Sentences				
Conventions				

1. What is the best part of your story?

_____

_____

_____

_____

_____

2. Write one thing you would change about this story if you had the chance to write it again.

_____

_____

_____

_____

_____

© Pearson Education, Inc. 5

Name _____

Persuasive Argument Chart

Directions Fill in the graphic organizer with ideas for the introduction, supporting reasons, and conclusion in your persuasive essay.

Introduction: State your opinion or goals

↓

First reason

↓

Second reason

↓

Third reason (most important)

↓

Conclusion

Name _____

Persuasive Words

Directions Add a persuasive word from the box or a word of your own to each sentence. Rewrite the sentence.

Persuasive Words				
better	worse	should	never	most important
best	worst	must	necessary	effective

1. A camping trip in the Alaskan wilderness is the _____ excursion for our class.

   _____

   _____

2. It is _____ to set up camp away from any bear habitats.

   _____

   _____

3. Plenty of protective gear is _____ for survival.

   _____

   _____

4. While camping in Alaska, we'll learn that teamwork is _____ than working alone in the wilderness.

   _____

   _____

5. You _____ experience the wide-open spaces on our adventure in Alaska.

   _____

   _____

Name _____

Elaboration

Descriptive Words

Directions Rewrite each sentence using the correct form of the adjective in parentheses.

1. What could be (good) than exploring a deserted island in the Pacific?

   _____

   _____

   _____

2. Traveling by plane is the (memorable) way to get to the island because you land on the beach!

   _____

   _____

   _____

3. Going by boat is (popular) than flying, but it is much slower, and some students may get seasick.

   _____

   _____

   _____

4. There are many activities we can do on the island, some (easy) and others (challenging).

   _____

   _____

   _____

5. I chose the (spectacular) destination I could think of because I want this trip to be the adventure of a lifetime!

   _____

   _____

   _____

Name _____

Self-Evaluation Guide
Persuasive Essay

Directions Think about the final draft of your persuasive essay. Then rate yourself on a scale from 4 to 1 (4 is the highest) on each writing trait. After you fill out the chart, answer the questions.

Writing Traits	4	3	2	1
Focus/Ideas				
Organization/Paragraphs				
Voice				
Word Choice				
Sentences				
Conventions				

1. What is the best part of your persuasive essay?

_____

_____

_____

_____

2. Write one thing you would change about this persuasive essay if you had the chance to write it again.

_____

_____

_____

_____

Name _____

K-W-L Chart

Directions Fill out this K-W-L chart to help you organize your ideas.

Topic _____

What I **K**now	What I **W**ant to Know	What I **L**earned

Controlling Question _____

Name _____

Topic and Detail Sentences

Directions Decide how you will organize your paragraphs. Then write a topic sentence and supporting details for each paragraph.

Paragraph 1
Topic Sentence _____

_____

Detail Sentences _____

_____

_____

Paragraph 2
Topic Sentence _____

_____

Detail Sentences _____

_____

_____

Paragraph 3
Topic Sentence _____

_____

Detail Sentences _____

_____

_____

Paragraph 4
Topic Sentence _____

_____

Detail Sentences _____

_____

Name _____

Elaboration

Combine Sentences

Directions Use the word in parentheses to combine each pair of sentences. Remember to capitalize the first word of each new sentence and to add a comma when necessary.

1. (because) You can't see faults. They are far below the surface of the Earth.

_____

_____

2. (when) An earthquake occurs. Parts of the Earth's crust suddenly break and shift.

_____

_____

_____

3. (or) Are all earthquake waves the same? Are there different kinds of earthquake waves?

_____

_____

_____

4. (and) The Richter scale measures energy released. The Mercali scale measures the results of an earthquake.

_____

_____

_____

5. (but) Today geologists can neither predict nor prevent earthquakes. One day they hope to do both.

_____

_____

_____

Grammar and Writing Practice Book

Name _____

Self-Evaluation Guide

Research Report

Directions Think about the final draft of your research report. Then rate yourself on a scale from 4 to 1 (4 is the highest) on each writing trait. After you fill out the chart, answer the questions.

Writing Traits	4	3	2	1
Focus/Ideas				
Organization/Paragraphs				
Voice				
Word Choice				
Sentences				
Conventions				

1. What is the best part of your research report?

_____

_____

_____

_____

2. Write one thing you would change about this research report if you had the chance to write it again.

_____

_____

_____

_____

_____